INTERNATIONAL SOCIETY FOR
SOIL MECHANICS AND
FOUNDATION ENGINEERING

GEOSYNTHETICS CASE HISTORIES

Edited

by

Gerald P. Raymond
Professor of Civil Engineering
Queen's University at Kingston

Jean-Pierre Giroud
Senior Principal and Chairman
GeoSyntec Consultants

on behalf of
ISSMFE TECHNICAL COMMITTEE TC9
GEOTEXTILES AND GEOSYNTHETICS
© March 1993

ABSTRACT

Geosynthetics Case Histories, edited by G.P. Raymond and J.P. Giroud on behalf of the International Society for Soil Mechanics and Foundation Engineering's Technical Committee TC9 on Geotextiles and Geosynthetics, March 1993, p. 277, hard cover. The book contains 127 case histories involving geosynthetic materials used in geotechnical engineering applications reported from 24 countries. The case histories are organized into 11 chapters based on type of application. These cover most of the applications of geosynthetics in geotechnical engineering. The chapters are as follows:- 1. Dams (12 case histories); 2. Containment ponds, irrigation and reservoirs (14 case histories); 3. Scour erosion control (10 case histories); 4. Slope, bank and pipeline erosion control (15 case histories); 5. Tunnel and hydroelectric applications (4 case histories); 6. Railways and asphalt pavements (13 case histories); 7. Deep foundation improvement (11 case histories); 8. Pavement subgrade and base reinforcement (16 case histories); 9. Fill and embankment reinforcement (12 case histories); 10. Reinforced soil slopes (9 case histories); 11. Reinforced soil walls (11 case histories).

KEY WORDS

Synthetic materials, Geosynthetics, Case histories, Geotechnical engineering, Soil mechanics.

DISCLAIMER

COPYRIGHT

DISTRIBUTOR

Geosynthetics Case Histories may be obtained by writing to BiTech Publishers Ltd, 173 - 11860 Hammersmith Way, Richmond, British Columbia, V7A 5G1, Canada.

ISBN No. 0-9696924-0-4

FOREWORD

The use of geosynthetic materials in geotechnical structures is still relatively new and unfamiliar to many practising engineers. It is nevertheless a rapidly expanding area of geotechnical technology with numerous new products and applications being introduced within any one year. In 1986, under the then President of ISSMFE Professor B.B. Broms, the Technical Committee TC9 entitled Geotextiles and Geosynthetics was established under the Chair of Dr. J.P. Giroud, USA, with Professor A. Arman, USA, as its Secretary.

At the suggestion of Dr. Giroud one of the objectives assigned to the Committee was to provide geotechnical engineers with information on case histories related to the use of geosynthetic materials. With this in mind the Committee agreed to organize, under the guidance of Dr. Giroud, a collection of case histories with the members acting as agents within their own countries. This turned out to be a much more ambitious task than first envisioned. Extensive selection reviews of all papers were carried out by various persons, notably Dr. A. Arman and Professor J.R. Bell of the USA, and Dr. Daniele Cazzuffi of Italy who travelled twice to the USA to work with Dr. Giroud on an extensive screening and classification of all papers received.

In 1990 the Chair was passed to myself with Professor P.M. Jarrett, Canada, as Secretary. Professor N.R. Morgenstern, the new President of ISSMFE, confirmed the commitment of the society to the collection of case histories. In 1991 all retained case history files were passed to Professor G.P. Raymond, Canada, who agreed to undertake the task of editorship with Dr. Giroud. His first task was to divide the collection into chapters. He had all case histories edited, typeset to a common format and re-reviewed. He had many of the figures redrawn to establish a good readability prior to assembly in camera ready form for publication. Both editors must be given our most grateful thanks for carrying out their task with such a high degree of skill which is evidenced by the quality of this book.

It must be emphasized that the case histories represent the opinions and experience of their author(s) with the use of various types of geosynthetics in a wide variety of applications. Many describe first time applications and, as such, expand our knowledge of geosynthetic applications. The Editors, any member of the Technical Committee, and of the ISSMFE do not accept any responsibility for the statements made or for the opinions expressed in the following pages. Nevertheless, I hope they will prove to be a valuable source of information for users and, more importantly, potential users of geosynthetic materials.

Professor Alan McGown,
Chair, Technical Committee TC9,
University of Strathclyde,
Glasgow, United Kingdom.
March 1993.

MEMBERSHIP OF ISSMFE TECHNICAL COMMITTEE TC9, on GEOTEXTILES AND GEOSYNTHETICS.

J.P. Giroud	*(Chair*	*1986-90)*
A. Arman	*(Secretary*	*1986-90)*
A. McGown	*(Chair*	*1990-present)*
P.M. Jarrett	*(Secretary*	*1990-present)*

P. R. Aguiar	*(Brazil)*
S. Andrei	*(Romania)*
J.R. Bell	*(USA)*
H. Brandl	*(Austria)*
I. Brorsson	*(Sweden)*
D. Cazzuffi	*(Italy)*
C. Cleaver	*(South Africa)*
P. Delmas	*(France)*
A. Engelaan	*(The Netherlands)*
R. Floss	*(Germany)*
J.P. Gourc	*(France)*
T. De Groot	*(The Netherlands)*
M.R. Hausmann	*(Australia)*
V.D. Kazarnovksy	*(Russia)*
R.M. Koerner	*(USA)*
H. Larsen	*(Denmark)*
T. Laszlo	*(Hungary)*
K.R. Legge	*(South Africa)*
C. Legrand	*(Belgium)*
E. Leflaive	*(France)*
Z.Y. Liu	*(China)*
J.N. Mandal	*(India)*
F.De Meerleer	*(Belgium)*
J.A. Minojosa	*(Spain)*
S. Mortensen	*(Denmark)*
A.G. Mouw	*(The Netherlands)*
J. Pachowski	*(Poland)*
P.De Porcellinis	*(Spain)*
G.V. Rao	*(India)*
H. Rathmayer	*(Finland)*
G.P. Raymond	*(Canada)*
H. Schneider	*(Austria)*
J.B. Sellmeijer	*(The Netherlands)*
J. Wales	*(South Africa)*
P.J. Van der Walt	*(South Africa)*
T. Yamanouchi	*(Japan)*
F.F. Zitscher	*(Germany)*

INTRODUCTION

by

G.P. Raymond and J.P. Giroud

THE NEED

Many engineering disciplines have developed in great part by virtue of example, and the use of geosynthetics in geotechnical engineering has been no exception: a number of original applications developed by a few have served as examples to many.

Manufacturers of geosynthetics and their sales representatives have played a key role in spreading the knowledge of new concepts and applications as they were developed. This has not always been fully effective, because geotechnical engineers due to the nature of the materials they deal with are often sceptical of received information — however excellent it may be — provided for them by manufacturers or salespeople. It is reasonable therefore that the information provided by manufacturers be supplemented by information generated by engineers and made available through the usual channels of technical literature. In the past decade, the technical literature on geosynthetics has been remarkably abundant. However, there is a shortage of case histories because many publications deal with theoretical or experimental subjects, as they are often considered more glamorous. Also, potential authors are often hesitant to publish case histories, due to concerns over professional liability.

THE BOOK

The above considerations dictated the concept of this book of case histories. Placing it under the ISSMFE banner was a way to ensure that the book would be prepared by geotechnical engineers for geotechnical engineers. Members of the ISSMFE Technical Committee on Geotextiles and Geosynthetics should be commended for having encouraged and organized the preparation and submission of case histories in their respective countries. This was a remarkable example of international cooperation. In particular this book brings to the reader some case histories that so far were not available in English.

As announced when the case histories were collected, each contribution is restricted to two pages in order to keep the book to a reasonable length. This has been achieved, in some cases, by editing. We hope the affected authors are not in disagreement with our reductions. All contributors were requested to provide at least one photograph. This has been achieved with one exception. No restriction was placed on case histories that were not a first time publication provided they were accompanied by references to allow further study. In quite a number of cases no references are included since it is a first time contribution. We welcome this kind of contribution and thank the authors for making these available to the reader.

Most of the case histories which were collected were actually used in the book. In those cases when the histories were incomplete or not consistent with the requested format, we collected more information from the authors and/or helped them to complete the paper. This took time. We take this opportunity to thank the authors for their cooperation and patience.

The book contains 127 case histories from 24 countries. The case histories have been organized into 11 chapters, covering all applications of geosynthetics. The order of the chapters results from two considerations. First, we wanted to start on a strong note, hence we start with the contributions on dams, an application where geosynthetics may play a critical role and where design engineers are often hesitant to use innovative solutions. Second, we wanted a logical organization; to that end the applications mostly devoted to liquid control were grouped in several contiguous chapters and the applications mostly devoted to soil reinforcement in another series of contiguous chapters. We elected to organise the book by type of application rather than according to the functions played by the geosynthetics since we feel the latter would have been too abstract.

The materials used in the projects presented in the case histories encompass all types of geosynthetic materials including geotextiles, geomembranes, geomats, geonets, geogrids, geocomposites, and related products (some of them made from natural fibres, but included into the geosynthetic category according to the prevailing usage). Also, a number of case histories deal with geosynthetics systems: soil-yarn and soil-mesh mixtures, geotextile-concrete erosion control mattresses, and concrete blocks or panels associated with geosynthetic reinforcement, to name a few.

THE PRESENTATION

All case histories are presented in a consistent manner. The left-right two-page format gives quick access to all the information provided for each case history. All case histories contain the same type of information presented, as much as possible, in the same order. The titles of all case histories start with a geoword that identifies the geosynthetic(s) used, and all titles end with the name of the location where the project is sited. As a result, valuable information can be found just by scanning the Table of Contents.

To achieve consistent presentation of the case

histories, various degrees of editing were required depending on the case history. A few of the case histories were in quasi-final form when they reached us, many required substantial editing, and several had to be entirely rewritten after communication with the authors to get the missing information. All case histories were reviewed several times by both editors. In spite of all the care taken, it is difficult to avoid all mistakes. We apologize for any mistake we may have made in the editing process.

Through editing, we eliminated commercialism and excessive or unjustified claims. We believe we did it in an equitable manner. However, misjudgments are possible.

Another important aspect of editing was terminology. Since one of the goals of this book is to educate those who desire to become more familiar with geosynthetics, it was essential to make sure the same terminology is used throughout the book, quite a challenge considering that 181 authors were involved in the preparation of the case histories. In particular, we strove to use the geowords consistently throughout the book.

Since most technical journals now require publication with SI units, these are used in the book, and it is believed that readers who are not familiar with these units have access to conversion tables. Despite the common usage of the SI system of units in many technical journals, deviations from correct practice in the expression of multiples are common. For example, with coefficients of permeability (hydraulic conductivities), multiplying factors such as 10^{-6} are often used instead of prefixes such as μ (micro). Herein, prefixes have been used. Since some readers may be unfamiliar with these prefixes, a table is provided below.

The editing process has been much longer than expected, which delayed the publication of the valuable information that was collected. The positive aspect of the delay is that a number of authors took advantage of the situation to add to their case histories the latest available data on the performance of the described projects. Thus, the value of a number of case histories has been significantly increased.

We acknowledge the input of many colleagues involved in early stages of the editing process. In particular, we would like to express our gratitude to A. Arman and J.R. Bell who participated in a first review of the case histories and to D. Cazzuffi who devoted a significant amount of time to organizing the papers and reviewing a number of them.

THE EXAMPLE

The 127 case histories presented in this book demonstrate the feasibility of using geosynthetics in a wide spectrum of geotechnical applications. Many of the projects described have been in use for ten or more years and their excellent performance since construction provides a valuable indication of the durability of geosynthetics. Some case histories describe projects more than twenty years old. The geosynthetics used in these projects are still performing well. In one of the projects, for example, the geosynthetic performance was established through an extensive investigation — which should encourage those potential users of geosynthetics who may still have doubts regarding the durability of these materials. One case history describes the construction of a temporary structure more than thirty-five years before the publication of this book. This temporary structure does not give any information on geosynthetic durability, but the difficult conditions of the construction and the elegance of the "geosynthetic" solution that was adopted illustrate the power of innovative techniques. To the best of our knowledge, this was the first use of a synthetic fabric in civil engineering — the word geotextile did not exist at that time — and it is not surprising that the structure described in this case history was constructed in a part of the world where the ground exists only because it was conquered and where innovation is a requirement for survival.

It is hoped this book will not only provide useful examples to designers and constructors, but will also encourage users of geosynthetics to write about their projects and provide their peers with more case histories. We hope this book will be regarded as an example of a collective effort of many transferring knowledge to many, thereby contributing to the progress of our discipline.

Table. Prefixes for the SI system of units.		
MULTIPLYING FACTOR	PREFIX	SYMBOL
$1\,000\,000\,000\,000 = 10^{12}$	tera	T
$1\,000\,000\,000 = 10^{9}$	giga	G
$1\,000\,000 = 10^{6}$	mega	M
$1\,000 = 10^{3}$	kilo	k
$100 = 10^{2}$	hecto	h
$10 = 10^{1}$	deca	da
$0.1 = 10^{-1}$	deci	d
$0.01 = 10^{-2}$	centi	c
$0.001 = 10^{-3}$	milli	m
$0.000\,001 = 10^{-6}$	micro	μ
$0.000\,000\,001 = 10^{-9}$	nano	n
$0.000\,000\,000\,001 = 10^{-12}$	pico	p

TABLE OF CONTENTS

CHAPTER 7 - DEEP FOUNDATION IMPROVEMENT

CHAPTER 8 - PAVEMENT SUBGRADE AND BASE REINFORCEMENT

Blank page.

CHAPTER 1

DAMS

GEOTEXTILE FILTERS FOR DOWNSTREAM DRAIN AND UPSTREAM SLOPE VALCROS DAM, FRANCE

J.P. Giroud and B.A. Gross
GeoSyntec Consultants
Boca Raton, Florida, USA

In 1970, for the first time, geotextiles were used in an earth dam, Valcros Dam, located in southeast France. Geotextile filters were used around the downstream gravel drain and under the rip-rap protecting the upstream slope. The geotextile performance has been documented through extensive investigation.

DESCRIPTION

The Dam

The dam is 135 m long and 17 m high, with 3H:1V slopes. It is constructed with silty sand containing 28% by weight of particles smaller than 0.075 mm and 85% by weight of particles smaller than 7 mm.

Downstream Drain

Installation of downstream drains to collect water seeping through earth dams is standard practice. In Valcros Dam, the original feature is the use of a geotextile in place of a sand filter (Photo 1). The senior author decided during construction to use a geotextile because it was difficult to obtain the specified sand. A nonwoven geotextile with a mass per unit area of 300 g/m² was used.

Upstream Slope Protection

The upstream slope was divided into three zones (Figure 1, Photo 2). Zone A was protected in the conventional manner by a 400 mm thick layer of 250 mm rounded rocks resting on a 150 mm thick layer of 6 to 40 mm gravel. Zone B was covered with only a sheet of nonwoven geotextile with a mass per unit area of 400 g/m² formed by sewing together geotextile strips which were fixed to the ground by metal pins. Zone C was protected by a 400 mm thick layer of rocks, identical to those used in Zone A, resting on the same geotextile as in Zone B.

GEOTEXTILE SELECTION

In 1970, only one type of geotextile was available in France: a polyester, needlepunched, nonwoven geotextile with continuous filaments (Bidim). Little was known about geotextile filter criteria. The only design consideration was that the geotextile opening size should be smaller than the d_{85} of the soil (7 mm). This simplistic criterion would have authorized the use of a geotextile with 7 mm openings, i.e., larger than the openings of the gravel drain. A number of years later, the use of a filter criterion [Giroud, 1982] which takes into account the soil coefficient of uniformity (very large in this case) has shown that the geotextile opening size should be less than 0.17 mm. The actual geotextile openig size was 0.15 mm.

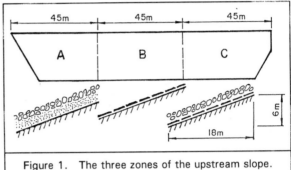

Figure 1. The three zones of the upstream slope.

PERFORMANCE

Downstream Drain

Since the construction of the dam in 1970, water flowing from the drain has always been clean, except during the filling of the reservoir when suspended particles were noticed. No seepage from the downstream slope of the dam has ever been observed. This indicates that the drain has functioned correctly.

Upstream Slope Protection

Zones A and C have functioned as intended since construction. In Zone B, by 1972, the bank was eroded underneath the geotextile at two levels, at the water level by wave action and above the water level by rain. This incident, which did not endanger the safety of the dam, shows that a geotextile alone cannot prevent erosion. Furthermore, the geotextile in Zone B deteriorated as a result of exposure to sunlight.

To repair Zone B, the geotextile was cut to conform to the shape of the bank and was covered. The cover consisted of another geotextile of the same type and rocks identical to those in the other zones. Since then, the entire slope protection has been functioning satisfactorily.

GEOTEXTILE CONDITION

In 1976, geotextile samples were taken from the dam: (a) geotextile located at the outlet of the downstream drain and exposed to sunlight for six years; (b) geotextile from the downstream drain, buried in the dam for six years; (c) geotextile from Zone B of the upstream slope protection, which was exposed to sunlight for two years (1970-1972) and then covered with a new geotextile and rocks; and (d) geotextile from Zone C of the upstream slope protection, at the water level.

Photo 1. Downstream drain during geotextile filter placement.

Photo 2. Upstream slope protection during geotextile placement in Zone C. (The rocks stockpiled in the foreground were placed in Zone C).

Observations made in 1976 showed that samples (b) and (d), which had been protected from sunlight by either earth or rock, appeared to be in good condition, while samples (a) and (c), which were exposed to sunlight, exhibited a colour change and were weak: filaments were broken or could be pulled out by hand. Laboratory tests conducted in 1976 have been reported by Giroud et al. [1977] and are summarized below.

Tensile tests conducted in 1976 showed the following strength losses compared to control samples: 10 to 20% for samples (b) and (d), which had not been exposed to sunlight; 50% for sample (c), which had been exposed two years; and 80% for sample (a), which had been exposed six years.

Permeability tests were conducted in 1976 on samples (b) and (d). Sample (b) was clean, while sample (d) was dirty, except in areas where it was in contact with the rocks. In those areas, sample (d) was clean on both sides, because the pressure exerted by the rocks prevented soil movement and minimized flow of water. The following values were obtained for the geotextile coefficient of permeability: 1 mm/s for sample (b) prior to washing; 1.5 mm/s for sample (b) after thorough washing; 0.165 mm/s for the dirty portion of sample (d) after light brushing to remove the soil adhering to the sample so as to retain only those particles that had actually lodged between the filaments; and 1.75 mm/s for sample (d) after thorough washing. It therefore appears that the change in permeability was negligible for sample (b), taken from the downstream drain, and was of approximately an order of magnitude for sample (d), taken from the upstream slope protection. Sample (d), however, was still much more permeable than the adjacent silty sand.

Additional samples were taken in 1992 at locations (b) and (d) where samples had been taken in 1976 [Delmas et al., 1992]. Tests conducted on the 1992 samples did not show any measurable change in tensile characteristics and permeability between 1976 and 1992.

Microstructural tests on filaments from samples taken from Valcros Dam in 1976 have been published by Leclercq and Sotton [1981, 1982, 1984], and more testing is in progress on samples taken in 1992.

The performance of the dam and the extensive testing of geotextile samples taken from the dam by several independent teams clearly demonstrate the viability of geotextile filters in dams and other applications.

CONCLUSIONS

The extensive investigation of the performance of the geotextiles used in Valcros Dam leads to the following conclusions:

1. Simplistic filter criteria may lead to severe problems with soils having a large coefficient of uniformity.

2. A geotextile filter may exhibit a decrease in permeability due to soil particle intrusion if it is not maintained in contact with the soil by a uniform pressure.

3. Exposure to sunlight rapidly deteriorates a geotextile, even one made from polyester.

4. A geotextile made with an adequate polymer may be buried in the ground for decades without significant deterioration.

5. A properly selected and installed geotextile may function as a filter for decades.

REFERENCES

Delmas, P., Nancey, A., Faure, Y. and Farkouh, B., "Long Term Behaviour of a Nonwoven Geotextile in a 21 year-old Dam", Proc. of Geo-Filters '92, Karlsruhe, Germany, Oct 1992.

Giroud, J.P., Gourc, J.P., Bally, P. and Delmas, P., "Comportement d'un textile non tissé dans un barrage en terre", Coll. Int. Sols et Textiles, Session 6, Paris, Avril 1977, 213-218.

Giroud, J.P., "Filter Criteria for Geotextiles", Proc. of the 2nd. Int. Conf. on Geotextiles, Vol. 1, Las Vegas, Aug. 1982, pp. 103-108.

Leclercq, B. and Sotton, M., "La durabilité des géotextiles", Proc. of Index 84, Session 11, EDANA, Brussels, Belgium, 1984, pp. 1-10.

Sotton, M. and Leclercq, B., "Les géotextiles et les tests de vieillissement accéléré", Proc. of the 2nd. Int. Conf. on Geotextiles, Vol. 2, Las Vegas, Aug. 1982, pp. 559-564.

Sotton, M., "Le vieillissement et la durabilité des géotextiles", Proc. of Index 81, Session 7, EDANA, Brussels, Belgium, 1981, pp. 1-18.

GEOMEMBRANE UPSTREAM EMBANKMENT DAM BARRIER
OSPEDALE AND CODOLE DAMS, CORSICA, FRANCE

C. Tisserand
Somivac
Corsica, France

J.P. Gourc
Irigm-UJF
Grenoble, France

To the authors' knowledge, the Ospedale dam is the first dam more than 20 m high ever built with a waterproofing system consisting of a geomembrane. Construction work on this dam was completed in 1978. This was then followed by construction of the Codole dam. The Codole dam was completed in 1983. It is also located in Corsica and designed according to the same model.

GENERAL CONTEXT

Owing to its relief, Corsica is at a disadvantage concerning its natural water supply. This is principally due to the short distance between the central mountain range and the coastline. The water supply problem has become more acute as tourism and agricultural development has led to greater demands for drinking and irrigation water.

DESCRIPTION OF THE TWO DAMS

The two dams are of the rockfill type sealed by a thin upstream lining. The main component of this lining is its geomembrane. The main features of these dams are given in Table 1.

CHOICE OF A GEOMEMBRANE UPSTREAM FACING

The initial design of the Ospedale dam provided for a 0.24 m thick asphaltic concrete upstream facing. This

Table 1. Details of dams.		
	Ospedale	Codole
Reservoir level (m)	950	115
Reservoir capacity (m³)	3,000,000	6,500,000
Dam height (m)	25	28
Crest length (m)	135	460
Base width (m)	90	95
Upstream slope	1.7H:1V	1.7H:1V

solution was estimated to be extremely costly due to three main factors (1) the small surface area of the facing (3,800 m²), (2) the limited height of the dam and, (3) the geographical location of the site (1,000 m altitude). It was for this reason that the "geomembrane" choice was selected (it was estimated to cost 30% less). This solution was favourably received by the Comité Technique Permanent des Barrages (Permanent Technical Committee on Dams). This Committee was set up by the French authorities, following the collapse of the Malpasset dam in 1962. Their task is to approve the design and proposed construction methods of all French dams exceeding 20 m in height.

In view of the excellent results obtained on the Ospedale dam, and considering its great similarity to

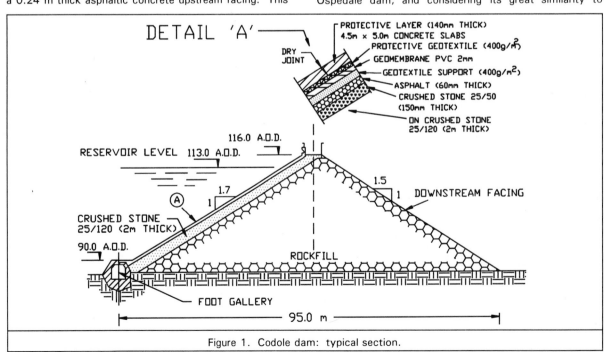

Figure 1. Codole dam: typical section.

Photo 1. Codole dam: nearing completion.

Photo 2. Codole dam: placing of upstream geomembrane.

Codole dam, the "geomembrane" solution was also chosen for Codole dam.

Geomembrane waterproofing involves three main components: the support layer, the waterproof lining and the protective layer.

Support Layer for Waterproof Lining

In order to obtain a satisfactory transition between the waterproofing material and the body of the rockfill dam, a layer of 25/120 mm crushed stone was first placed for both dams to a thickness of 2 m. This base layer was then covered with 150 mm of 25/50 mm crushed stone impregnated with bitumen. To eliminate any surface defects a top-surface course (60 mm thick) of 3/5 mm asphalt was then applied.

Waterproof Lining

The geomembrane is separated from the support by a layer of nonwoven polyester geotextile (270 g/m² Bidim at Ospedale and 400 g/m² Geosom at Codole). The geotextile's purpose was to prevent any holes being punched in the geomembrane. The geomembrane used at Ospedale is a bituminous membrane reinforced with polyester felt, while at Codole, a non reinforced PVC was used. The main features are shown in Table 2.

The strips of bituminous geomembrane at Ospedale were heat-welded together by a special hot-air machine, with 300 mm overlap of adjacent strips. These heat-welded geomembrane seams were inspected by an ultrasonic tester.

The PVC geomembranes at Codole dam were heat-welded manually by means of welding torches, with a 50 mm overlap of adjacent strips. Then the seam welds were inspected by electronic scanning, although visual inspection was found more efficient.

Protective Layer

The outer layer was necessary so as to weight the geomembrane in place (i.e. to prevent it being torn away be wind, waves, etc.) and to protect it from external agents (heat, ultraviolet rays, impacts, etc.)

At Ospedale, this protective layer consisted of 80 mm thick interlocking concrete paving blocks. These blocks were laid by hand on a nonwoven geotextile. At Codole, this protective layer consisted of 140 mm thick, 4.5 m x 5 m concrete slabs.

Table 2. Main features of geomembranes.		
	Ospedale	Codole
Geomembrane	Coletanche NTP3	TERSOM V20/10
Thickness (mm)	4.8	2
Tensile strength (kN/m)	14 to 21	17
Strain (%)	59	170
Bursting pressure (kPa)	800	> 1200

PERFORMANCE

Since their completion, the waterproofing systems has proved satisfactory. A total leakage rate measured is about 1 litre/s at Ospedale, and 2 litres/s at Codole.

The only problem raised by this new technique was the stability of the interlocking paving blocks. At Ospedale dam, an area of 350 m² of this protecting facing was disrupted during severe storms over the reservoir. The two major factors responsible for this deterioration were wave action and the relatively steep slope of the facing (1.7H:1V). Scale model tests (1:5) carried out at Cemagref laboratories showed uplift pressures under the blocks during wave backwash. This resulted in a new design for the repair work.

CONCLUSION

The first major dam constructed with a geomembrane waterproof upstream facing has, after ten years of service, given ample proof of high performance. The technique was easy to install, inspect and repair. There were significant savings over the more conventional methods.

REFERENCES

Bianchi, C., Rocca-Serra, C., and Girollet, J., "Utilisation d'un revêtement mince pour l'étanchéité d'un barrage de plus de 20 m de hauteur" Proc. of the 13th. Congress on Large Dams, C11, New Delhi, 1979, pp. 173-186.

Grossmann, A., "Le Barrage de Codole: une seconde expérience d'étanchéité par membrane mince sur un grand barrage" Proc. of Colloquium on surface waterproofing of basins, dams and canals, Session 4, Cemagref, Paris, Feb. 1983, pp. 171-174.

Labre, J. and Loudière, D., "Design of fill dams including a geomembrane" Proc. of Int. Conf. on Geomembranes, Denver 1984.

GEOMEMBRANE BARRIER FOR RAISING EMBANKMENT DAM
PACTOLA DAM ON RAPID CREEK, SOUTH DAKOTA, USA

G.G. Hammer
Colorado Division of Water Resources
Greeley, Colorado, USA

T.L. Lippert
U.S. Bureau of Reclamation
Denver, Colorado, USA

Pactola Dam is a U.S. Bureau of Reclamation earth and rockfill dam located on Rapid Creek above Rapid City, South Dakota. New hydrologic data resulting from the June 9th, 1972 flood, necessitated raising the dam crest and enlarging the rock-cut spillway to safely route the Probable Maximum Flood (PMF). U.S. Highway 385 passes over the crest of the dam and carries heavy tourist traffic through the scenic Black Hills. A geomembrane was selected as the impervious barrier for the raised embankment to ease handling of the high traffic volume, reduce the number of construction seasons, and avoid unsightly borrow area construction.

DESCRIPTION

The original dam was a 67 m earth core rockfill structure with a crest length of 381 m. In addition to the dam, two dikes (32 m high 242 m long, and 20 m high 379 m long) completed the impoundment of the 122,000,000 m^3 reservoir. The spillway was a 73 m wide rock channel cut into a knoll at the left abutment of the dam, between the dam and dikes.

The zone 1 core of the original dam is a sandy clay excavated from borrow areas in the Rapid Creek flood-plain. The rockfill shell consists of metamorphic amphibolites, schists and slates from the spillway excavation and a right abutment rock source. To modify the dam for the PMF, the spillway was widened by 56 m, and the dam and dike crests were raised 4.5 m (total crest length of 1575 m). Materials from the required spillway excavation were used in the raised embankment.

TECHNICAL CONSIDERATIONS

Design constraints included those imposed by abutment topography, the dam crest highway geometry, and a requirement that the seasonal tourist traffic routing be maintained. The original idea called for a clay core with a graded sand filter. A review late in the design schedule found that a geomembrane could effectively serve as the impervious barrier for the top of the flood surcharge pool. A geomembrane would also mitigate the impacts from the design constraints. It significantly reduced the graded sand filter zone, for which a 96 km haul was anticipated. Deleting the clay core negated the need for borrow area development in the scenic Black Hills National Forest. Construction cost savings were estimated at $0.5 million with additional savings of $1 million anticipated from a shorter construction period and reduced personnel and office expenses.

An initial selection to use a 2.5 mm high density polyethylene (HDPE) was subjectively based on value judgments by the designers. The durability of this material addressed the designers' concern that the geomembrane would be placed against sharp angular rock.

To evaluate the likelihood of puncturing, a testing program was developed at the U.S. Bureau of Reclamation Engineering & Research Center Laboratories [USBR, 1981]. Four geomembranes were tested: 0.8 mm PVC (polyvinyl chloride), 0.9 mm CSPE(R) (reinforced chloro-sulfanated polyethylene), and 1 mm and 2 mm HDPE (high density polyethylene). Testing, conducted over three subgrade conditions, included use of various geotextile backings to determine if a geotextile would increase puncture resistance [Morrison, 1984]. Based on the results, the design was modified to use either 1 mm HDPE or 1.1 mm CSPE(R) with a nonwoven geotextile placed under the geomembrane. A 1 mm HDPE geomembrane was used on a geotextile with a mass per unit area of 400 g/m^2.

To mitigate concerns of possible failure occurring if the geomembrane was punctured, the embankment was designed to remain stable in the absence of the geomembrane. Flood routing studies showed that spillway releases started at the 200-year storm level. Before modification, embankment overtopping would begin at the 500-year flood level. Routing of the PMF through the enlarged spillway resulted in the water surface rising above the original dam crest for only six hours, with a maximum head on the geomembrane of 4.8 m. To ensure embankment stability, a 300 mm graded sand zone was to be placed upstream of the geomembrane. This would serve as a filter for the rock fines upstream of the sand. The sand and geotextile backing would act as cushions between the rock fines and geomembrane as the fill was compacted. Under these conditions, the designers reasoned that a puncture of the geomembrane would not result in failure of the embankment.

Design of the anchorage for the top of the geomembrane used a standard technique. This consisted of a 300 by 600 mm deep anchor trench excavated behind the face of the supporting fill. The geomembrane would be laid in the excavation and the trench backfilled.

Anchoring the toe required measures to ensure that an impermeable seal be achieved to both a rock abutment and the original zone 1 core of the dam and dikes. Connection to the zone 1 clay core was made by excavating a 900 mm deep trench into which the geomembrane was inserted. A lean concrete backfill provided adhesion to the surrounding soil and the geomembrane.

The dam and dike abutments are metamorphic

Photo 1. View of downstream slope after completion of the modification.	Photo 2. Upstream view of installed geomembrane prior to placement of embankment.

bedrock. Connecting the geomembrane to the rock entailed trenching the rock and placing lean concrete into the trench. A standard concrete connection, using bolts and neoprene, attached the geomembrane to this concrete anchor wall.

CONSTRUCTION

Construction of the dam modification occurred over the period of 1985-1987. While the construction was expected to be completed in one or two years, some difficulty developed in obtaining the needed rock sizes for the rockfill zones. Due to these complications, installation of the geomembrane occurred over two seasons. During the winter shutdown, installed sections were covered with soil for protection. Some damage to the geomembrane occurred during removal of the cover material. Repair was made using standard welded patch techniques.

As installation progressed, field personnel modified the construction techniques to adjust to problems as they developed. While some difficulties were anticipated, the problems were primarily the result of using a new and unfamiliar material. Placement and compaction operations on the slope created extreme tension in the geomembrane which, in one instance, resulted in splitting of the geomembrane. This was remedied by only loosely anchoring the top of the geomembrane. Other minor changes eased handling of material in the toe anchor trench.

Anticipated difficulties also arose concerning field seam construction. The original design did not allow horizontal field seams, and specified minimal vertical seaming. For ease of construction, a horizontal seam was later permitted. Elimination of buckling, resulting from the severely curved alignment, required special trimming and seaming.

Following completion, several test pits were excavated to determine if damage may have occurred during construction. The geomembrane observed in the test pits was in good condition and showed no signs of distress.

CONCLUSIONS

This use of a geomembrane as the impervious barrier for a storage reservoir is believed to be the first such application by the USBR. In this particular case, the loading conditions are not severe, and may never be imposed due to the low probability of a major flood event occurring. Nevertheless, the use of a geomembrane was the right decision as it did significantly reduce construction impacts as expected. Cost savings were substantial and would have been greater if the construction time had not been extended due to difficulty in obtaining suitable rockfill materials.

From the experience gained in this project, the following general recommendations can be made regarding the use of geomembranes in large dams:

- Geomembrane thickness less than 1.5 mm should be avoided in a rocky environment, even when geotextile cushioning is used, because damage to a thin geomembrane can occur during transportation, handling, and placement.

- The number of seams on steep or curved slopes should be minimized. If seams cannot be avoided in such areas they should be placed along the direction of maximum slope.

- On steep, rough slopes, the geomembrane should be anchored loosely prior to placement of the backfill against the geomembrane. This allows the geomembrane material to adjust and conform to the slope with less stress.

- To the extent possible, construction activities on slopes above the geomembrane should be keep to a minimum.

- A contractor with experience in construction involving geosynthetic materials should be selected.

REFERENCES

Morrison, W.R., "Pressure Cell Testing of Flexible Membrane Linings for Pactola Dam", Applied Sciences Referral Memorandum No. 84-1-11, USBR, Dec. 17, 1984.

USBR, Design and Development of an Automated Hydrostatic Flexible Membrane Test Facility, Laboratory Report No. REC-ERC-80-9, January 1981.

Lippert, T.L. and Hammer, G.G., "The use of a geomembrane in heightening the Pactola dam", Water Power and Dam Construction, Vol. 41, No. 2, Feb. 1989, pp. 15-17.

GEOCOMPOSITE SLIDING LAYER FOR CONCRETE CORE DAM
BOCKHARTSEE DAM, AUSTRIA

J. Henzinger
Höhere Techn.
Lehranstalt Imst, Austria

G. Werner
Polyfelt Ges. m.b.H.
Linz, Austria

In 1982, the world's first large rockfill dam with a concrete core diaphragm wall, the Bockhartsee dam, was constructed near Salzburg, Austria. A geosynthetic was used as a sliding layer to reduce wall friction between the upstream rockfill material and the concrete core. The geosynthetic consisted of a geotextile combined with a glass fibre reinforced bitumen layer. The sliding layer allowed the construction of a thin concrete core as the sealing element for this rockfill dam (Figure 1).

DESCRIPTION

The dam is 239.5 m long and 31 m high, with slopes 1.55H:1V (upstream) and 1.5H:1V (downstream). The 600 mm thick concrete core was founded on granite-gneiss. The supporting shells consist of quarry-material on the upstream side and morainal fill on the downstream side.

CONCEPT

The main objective for the sliding layer was to reduce the wall friction and the resulting compressive stresses in the concrete due to the differential settlement between the core and the rockfill. As the less rigid rockfill slides downwards along the core it induces great forces into the core. This makes the construction of thin cores difficult. However, slender cores are a prerequisite to maintaining the concrete as crack free as possible. This is even more true when high curvature stresses and strains develop in the core due to any horizontal displacements of the dam.

Preliminary tests in different shear apparatuses showed that the major problem in the practical application of the reinforced bitumen layer is the penetration of soil particles into the thin bitumen layer. This makes the shear stress in the slip layer normal-stress dependent and therefore ineffective.

GEOCOMPOSITE REQUIREMENTS

The protection of the reinforced bitumen layer by an appropriate geotextile is a condition for the adequate performance of the bitumen layer over several decades. The primary function of the geotextile is to prevent the penetration of soil particles into the bitumen layer. The geotextile must resist excessive penetration of bitumen into itself. It should also minimize stress concentrations at the interface between bitumen and support fill (Figure 2). Other important aspects for the use of bitumen layer-geotextile combination were the ease of application and economic manufacture. An industrial manufactured laminated geocomposite offered an adequate solution: it is composed of a 700 g/m² polypropylene needlepunched nonwoven geotextile (Polyfelt TS 008), and a 4 mm thick bitumen layer (B 85/25), reinforced with a 60 g/m² glass fleece and laminated with a thin polyethylene separation foil of 0.01 mm (Figure 3). The separation foil prevents the bitumen layer and the geotextile from sticking together when rolled for storage and transport purposes. The foil is burnt off by a propane gas torch during installation.

LABORATORY TESTS

Numerous experiments with direct shear apparatus, ring shear apparatus, large scale direct shear apparatus, as well as trials on a model concrete core were carried out prior to construction. This proved that the geocomposite worked properly and that the geotextile met the high demands required. No penetration of the sharp-edged filter

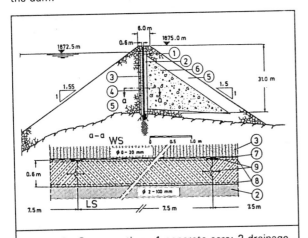

Figure 1. Cross section: 1 concrete core; 2 drainage zone; 3 fine grained zone; 4 transition zone; 5 stone rubble (max. diameter = 1.0 m); 6 moraine (max. dia. = 1.0 m); 7 geocomposite; 8 skin reinforcement; 9 waterstop.

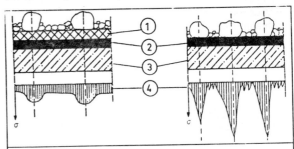

Figure 2. Stress relieving effect of the geotextile: 1 geotextile; 2 reinforced bitumen layer; 3 concrete core; 4 distribution of compressive stress in bitumen layer.

Photo 1. General view of the dam construction.

Photo 2. Application of the geocomposite to the concrete wall.

material into the bitumen layer nor any abrasion or other damage of the geotextile itself was observed. This was after a test period of 80 days at 1 MPa normal stress in the large scale penetration and shear test. The penetration of bitumen into the geotextile was no greater than 0.8 mm at a temperature of 18°C. At 5°C, the temperature inside the dam, the penetration should be much less. Note the viscosity of bitumen decreases by a factor of 100 from 18°C to 5°C. A rough estimation of the bitumen penetration, assuming a worst case situation, gives a value of 2.8 mm in 10 years.

APPLICATION OF THE GEOCOMPOSITE

The geocomposite sliding layer was only applied on the upstream face of the concrete core. The installation work was carried out by two workers. They heatfused the bitumen side of the geocomposite to the previously bitumen coated concrete wall by using the fill level as the working platform (Photo 2). The fine grained gneiss filter material (maximum particle size 20 mm) was placed directly onto the geocomposite and compacted by a vibrating roller.

PERFORMANCE

Although the geocomposite sliding layer was only applied to the upstream side of the dam, the measurements in the base of the concrete core showed a significant reduction of compressive stresses in the concrete. These amounted to approximately 25%.

CONCLUSIONS

The use of a needlepunched nonwoven geotextile as protection for a reinforced bitumen layer allowed the construction of the sliding layer for the concrete core diaphragm element in Bockhartsee dam.

Geotextiles used for this purpose should have:

* low inherent stiffness
* high abrasion resistance
* sufficient mechanical strength
* stress relieving capacity

REFERENCES

Henzinger, J., "Application of a Geotextile to Protect a Bitumen Slip Layer", Proc. 3rd. Int. Conf. on Geotextiles, Vienna, April 1986, Vol. 2, pp. 545-549.

Schober, W. and Henzinger, J., "Membranartige Betonkerndichtungen für hohe Staudämme", Mitteilungen des Institutes für Bodenmechanik, Felsmechanik und Grundbau der Universität Innsbruck, Austria, 1984.

Schober, W. and Lercher, H., "The Concrete Core Diaphragm Wall of the Embankment Dam Bockhartsee, Monitoring and Interpretation", Proc. of the 15th. Int. Conf. on Large Dams, Lausanne, July 1985, Vol. 1, Q.56, R.66, pp. 1257-1272.

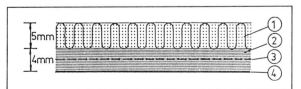

Figure 3. Structure of the geocomposite:
1 geotextile; 2 bitumen layer; 3 glass reinforcement;
4 separation foil.

GEOMEMBRANE WATERPROOFING FOR REHABILITATION OF CONCRETE AND MASONRY DAMS LAGO NERO DAM, ITALY

D. Cazzuffi
ENEL CRIS
Milano, Italy

F. Monari
C.A.R.P.I.
Oleggio, Italy

A. Scuero
Sibelon
Novara, Italy

Italian experience of using geomembranes for the rehabilitation works on concrete or masonry dams and spillways is very significant. In 1979 a complete waterproofing of the upstream face of the Lago Nero dam was engineered using a geocomposite formed by a PVC geomembrane thermocoupled to a polyester geotextile. The geotextile was prestressed and fastened to the main structure of the dam with specially designed steel ribs.

THE DAM

The dam, built in 1929/1934 and owned by ENEL (the Italian Electricity Company), is located in the high valley of Serio River, Italian Alps, at an El. 2,000 m asl. It is a massive concrete gravity structure with a maximum height of about 40 m. Its length at crest level is 146 m. The upstream face surface is 3,500 m². The capacity of the reservoir approximates 3,350,000 m³.

REHABILITATION DESIGN

As a consequence of the lack of preliminary testing of the concrete and poor construction procedures, the dam had seepage problems through its foundation and its body. Degradation of the structure increased despite various repairs (Photo 1). In 1979 major remedial works, including reinforcement of the foundation, restoration of the downstream face, loading the central portion of the wall etc., were completed. The most interesting part of this work was the installation of a waterproofing geomembrane on the upstream face (Photo 2).

ENEL discarded other alternatives such as reinforced gunite or steel plate membrane and chose the installation of a synthetic geomembrane. This was selected because of simplicity of installation, especially in regards to the covering of structural joints, rapidity of construction, low costs, and ease of future maintenance and repairs.

The problems to be dealt with were:

- choice of the geomembrane's synthetic material,
- installation procedures for a sub-vertical face, and
- drainage of condensation water behind the geomembrane.

GEOMEMBRANE SELECTION

ENEL's CRIS laboratories tested the different geomembranes provided by manufacturers in order to verify their main characteristics and suitability.

Sibelon CNT 2800, a particular brand of extruded PVC flexibilized and stabilized (now manufactured by

Table 1. General properties of the geomembrane from tests at ENEL-CRIS laboratory.		
General Properties	Test Method	Sibelon
Thickness (mm)	ASTM D374-79	1.93
Tensile strength (MPa)	ASTM D638M-81	18.0
Strain at failure (%)	ASTM D638M-81	285
Moisture vapour perm. (g/m² in 24h)	ASTM D1653-72	3.2
Abrasion test (mm³/1000 turns)	ASTM D1044-78	60

Sibelon, Novara, Italy) was finally chosen. Test results are given in Table 1. The choice of this geomembrane was made not only because of its good properties in resistance, deformability and welding potential, but also because of previous successful experiences on the part of ENEL and others in the installation of the same type of geomembrane in similar environment (like Lago Miller dam).

The geomembrane was manufactured in a width of 2.05 m and a length, depending on the structure to be covered, so as to avoid horizontal seams. The colour was a light grey shade. A polyester needle punched nonwoven polyester geotextile was heat coupled during manufacturing. The geotextile is 1.95 m in width and has a mass per unit area of 200 g/m².

GEOSYNTHETIC INSTALLATION

The PVC geocomposite was installed with an original system, now patented by the installer C.A.R.P.I., Oleggio, Italy. This system is based on the use of metallic ribs. It allows continuous fastening along vertical lines, horizontal prestressing which eliminates sagging due to self weight, and acts as the main drainage system by means of small holes along the side of the ribs themselves.

The geotextile provides protection against puncturing resulting from the existing coarse surface on the upstream facing. It is also designed to provide local drainage so as to eliminate the water between the concrete body of the dam and the geomembrane.

Particular attention was devoted to the waterproofing of the base of the upstream face. An additional concrete wall was poured along the interior borders of the dam.

Mechanical fastening of the geocomposite to the wall was made by means of metal plates and anchors which were then tested at 2 MPa pressure. The testing

Photo 1. Lago Nero Dam before rehabilitation.

Photo 2. Lago Nero Dam after installation of geomembrane.

confirmed the water tightness of the system. The installation of the geomembrane was performed employing self-hoisting platforms secured to the dam's crest. The installation took 90 days for completion.

PERFORMANCE

Daily measurements of water losses showed a maximum total loss of 2.7 l/s. Only 14% of the total losses were attributable to the PVC geomembrane.

Because of the importance of this application, regular inspections are carried out on site, whenever the reservoir is drained. These inspections have ensured that no yielding or loosening of the geocomposite nor any other detectable alteration has taken place. The general behaviour has been satisfactory.

DURABILITY

In 1976 a previous application of a PVC geomembrane made by Sibelon was carried out on the upstream face of a masonry dam, the 11 m high Lago Miller dam, built between 1925 and 1926 and owned by ENEL. Table 2 summarizes mechanical characteristics of samples taken in 1985. The geomembrane is exposed to the action of ice and of UV as Lago Miller dam is at El. 2,170 m asl.

The results show that permanence of the dead load causes an increase in the longitudinal tensile strength, while longitudinal strain at failure tends to decrease. The strain decrease makes the material more rigid. The results are encouraging, due to the long period of exposure.

CONCLUSIONS

The main benefits involved in the geocomposite solution are:

- total waterproofing of construction joints,
- new and efficient upstream face drainage system, created by the geotextile and the metallic vertical ribs,
- prefabrication off the site,
- low cost of civil works for preparation of the face,
- reduced time of installation,
- easy and practically cost-free maintenance,
- long durability,
- competitive price of first installation.

The described patented method is suitable for most types of dams, as proved by the following list, including name, country of the dam and year of geomembrane installation:

- masonry gravity dams (Italy: Lago Miller/1976, Camposecco/1992)
- concrete gravity dams (Italy: Lago Nero/1980, Lago Barbellino/1987, Lago Cignana/1989; France: Migoelou/1989, Chambon/1991; Portugal: Pracana/1992)
- multiple arches concrete dams (Italy: Lago Molato/1985, Pian Sapejo/1990, Ceresole/1992)
- concrete arch dam (Italy: Publino/1989)
- roller compacted concrete dams (France: Riou/1990; Honduras: Concepcion/1991)
- embankment dams (Italy: Gorghiglio/1979, Valle Cornuta/1990, Saforada/1992; France: Crueize/1988)
- cofferdam (Italy: Alento/1988)

On the basis of the results obtained so far, this system has proved to be highly suitable both for maintenance and new construction purposes, provided that adequate attention is given to all installation details.

REFERENCES

Cazzuffi, D., "The use of Geomembranes in Italian Dams", Water Power and Dam Construction, March 1987, pp. 17-21.

Monari, F. and Scuero, A.M., "Ageing of Concrete Dams: the Use of Geocomposites for Repair and Future Protection", ICOLD, 17th International Congress, Vienna 1991, Vol II, Question 65, pp. 769-783, R. 42.

Table 2. Results of tensile tests conducted at ENEL-CRIS on Sibelon PVC geomembrane after 9 years in operation at Lago Miller Dam (El. 2,170 m).		
Tensile test (UNI 8202/8)	Longitudinal (Vertical)	Transversal (Horizontal)
Tensile strength (MPa)	21	15.4
Strain at failure (%)	258	284

GEOTEXTILE ANTI-PIPING BARRIER FOR METABASIC FOUNDATION SOIL TUCURUI DAM, BRAZIL

P.R. Aguiar
Geosint Eng. Associados
Sao Paulo, Brazil

A geotextile was used as an anti-piping barrier on the downstream face of the cut-off trench of Tucurui Dam, Brazil. The geotextile was used in areas where the foundation rock had a high coefficient of permeability. This high permeability was due to a great concentration of tubular cavities in the region known as "metabasic".

DESCRIPTION

Tucurui Dam is a zoned earthfill dam situated in the north of Brazil (Amazonian region), in the valley of the Tocantins River. Its construction began in 1976 and the dam was inaugurated in 1984. The dam is part of a very big power generating plant (capacity 8,000 MW) and has the following characteristics:

- total length of the dam: 8,530 m;
- compacted earthfill: 80,000,000 m³;
- soil excavation: 23,000,000 m³;
- rock excavation: 22,000,000 m³;
- reservoir area: 2,160 km²;
- maximum height of the embankment dam: 103 m.

The area of the foundation soil, known as "metabasic", extends a length of 250 m. It is situated on the right bank of the Tocantins River. The depth profile of the metabasic stretch is given in Table 1.

The lower horizon varies from highly fractured rock interbedded with soil, to hard altered rock and/or very slightly fractured solid rock. The altered rock exhibited high loss of water, with a coefficient of permeability in the range of 1 µm/s. The solid rock, although less permeable, revealed some areas with high loss of water.

Although the metabasic residual and saprolitic soils had coefficients of permeability less than 1 µm/s, they exhibited areas of high permeability that were considered abnormal for the type of soil tested.

Further investigations showed that these high permeabilities were due to a great concentration of tubular cavities. The cavity diameters varied from a few millimetres to more than 200 mm. The cavities form sub-vertical developments that can reach great depths (over 20 m). Some cavities are interconnected with the open fractures of the underlying altered rock. The cavities proved to be more subject to erosion when submitted to concentrated flows of water.

DESIGN

The foundation treatments which were implemented are presented in Figure 1.

The geotextile was applied on the downstream face of the cut-off. Its function was to stop possible piping of soils from the compacted earthfill through a possible undetected or unplugged cavity.

The self-sealing soil (slightly clayey alluvial gravelly sand) placed on top of the geotextile was used as a complement to the anti-piping barrier.

Table 1. Cross-section of the metabasic stretch (from the ground surface to the deepest layer)	
Soil Characteristics	Thickness
Colluvial deposits, 2<N<4	about 2 m
Alluvial terrace	0 to 3 m
Metabasic residual soil, 6<N<9 $k = 1 \times 10^{-6}$ m/s	3 to 15 m
Saprolitic soil, N>11	3 to 15 m
Soft altered rock (highly fractured) $k = 1 \times 10^{-6}$ m/s	4 to 6 m

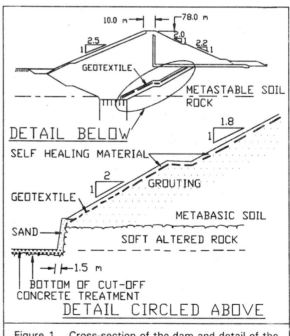

Figure 1. Cross-section of the dam and detail of the geotextile application.

ISSMFE., Committee TC9 - Geosynthetics Case Histories.

Photo 1. Placement of geotextile over the metabasic soil.

GEOTEXTILE REQUIREMENTS

In this application, the geotextile must fulfil the requirements discussed below.

Mechanical Requirements

In the metabasic stretch, even after filling the tubular cavities, it is reasonable to assume that any undetected cavities with a maximum diameter of 50 mm may remain unfilled. The portions of the geotextile in contact with an unfilled cavity may become deformed under the applied stresses. The maximum value of these stresses was calculated to be 800 kPa. In other words, the bursting strength of the geotextile should be 800 kPa on a 50 mm opening or 800 x 50/35 = 1,143 kPa, if measured with testing equipment having a 35 mm opening.

Due to the low shearing resistance of the foundation material, puncturing of the geotextile on the edges of the cavity was considered an unlikely event and no puncture requirement was specified.

Retention of Fines Requirements

Retention of fine soil particles is the main function of the geotextile in the metabasic stretch. The geotextile must act as an anti-piping barrier, retaining the clayey gravelly sand of the cut-off. Using Giroud's retention criterion [1982], the geotextile opening size (O_{95}) should be less than 380 μm.

Permeability Requirements

The gradients in the clayey gravelly sand, in the proximity of the geotextile, are on the order of 1. This was judged insufficient to cause clogging of the geotextile. The minimum permeability required for the geotextile is on the order of 500 nm/s using Giroud's permeability criterion [1982].

GEOTEXTILE SELECTION AND INSTALLATION

The geotextile used was a polyester continuous filament nonwoven (Bidim OP-60). Its main characteristics, measured according to the recommendations made by CFGG (French Committee on Geotextiles and Geomembranes), are the following:

- Tensile strength   38 kN/m
- Strain at failure   41%
- Permeability (no load)   2,200 mm/s
- Permeability (under 800 kPa)   40 mm/s
- Opening size (O_{95})   59 μm
- Bursting strength (AFNOR-G-07112)   6,000 kPa

The factors of safety are 6,000/1,143 = 5.25 for bursting strength and $40 \times 10^{-3}/500 \times 10^{-9}$ = 800 for permeability. These factors of safety are high, which is justified by the fact that the geotextile application was done in a zone that is inaccessible after construction of the dam.

The quantity of geotextile used was 11,000 m². The geotextile was placed over the previously regularized cut-off face with overlapping of 500 mm. Special care was taken during compacting to avoid damage to the geotextile. During work interruptions the geotextile was protected from sunlight and rain using opaque plastic covering sheets.

PERFORMANCE

Three years after the reservoir filling, it was observed that the water flow through the compacted fills of the cut-off was slow as expected, due to the low permeability of the earthfills. No piping was observed, which indicates that the anti-piping system composed of the geotextile barrier and the self-healing clayey gravelly sand performed satisfactorily.

REFERENCES

Borges, C.M., Dib, P.S., Ono, S. and Sa, M.B.L., "Consideracoes sobre o Projeto da Barragem de Terra e Enrocamento de Tucurui", XI Sem. Nac. de Grandes barragens, Rio de Janeiro, Brazil, 1983, Vol. 2.

Dib, P.S. "Compressibility Characteristics of Tropical Soils Making up the Foundation of the Tucurui Dam in Amazonas (Brazil)", Proc. of the 1st. Int. Conf. on Geomechanics in Tropical Lateritic and Saprolitic Soils, Brasilia, Brazil, 1985, Vol. 2.

Dib, P.S., and Aguiar, P.R., "Tucurui Dam: Non-Woven Geotextile as one of the Anti-Piping Barriers", Proc. of the 3rd. Int. Conf. on Geotextiles, Vienna, Austria, 1986, Vol. 1, pp. 279-284.

Giroud, J.P., "Filter Criteria for Geotextiles", Proc. of the 2nd. Int. Conf. on Geotextiles, Las Vegas, USA, 1982, Vol. 1, pp. 103-108.

GEOGRID REINFORCEMENT TO PREVENT CRACKING IN DAM CORE
CANALES DAM, SPAIN

S. Uriel
Politechnical University
Madrid, Spain

J.R.P. Rodríguez
Laboratorio de Geotecnia
Madrid, Spain

Canales Dam, which is currently the highest embankment dam in Spain, with a height of 158 m, was completed in October, 1986 (Photo 1). A polymeric geogrid (Photo 2) was used to reinforce a portion of the top 6 m of the core, as shown in Figure 1. The purpose of the reinforcement is to diminish the possible effects of transverse cracking in the dam crest.

DESCRIPTION

In order to study core cracking, tests were carried out in the laboratory (Brazilian tests) and in experimental embankments where the tensile behaviour of the core could be studied on a large scale. These tests and their results have been reported by Bravo et al. [1982]. As a summary, the strain required for cracking to appear is shown in the Table 1.

Table 1. Strain required for cracking to appear.			
Test No.	Moisture Content (%)	Bulk Unit Weight (kN/m³)	Cracking Strain (%)
1	19.0	15.6	0.24
2	17.5	16.0	0.26
3	18.3	15.4	0.24
4	28.6	14.9	0.53
5	18.3	15.8	0.20

For normal compaction conditions, with a moisture content of 18%, it was deduced that the tensile strain required for cracks to appear would be of the order of 0.25%. After calculations with the finite element method, it was concluded that in the zone situated in the vicinity of the broken back on the right-hand abutment extending for some 65 m in length and up to about 5 m in depth, the strain would be greater than 0.25%. In these circumstances it was decided to adopt an additional measure to alleviate the eventual cracking.

DESIGN

The additional anti-cracking measure consisted of reinforcing the core with polymeric geogrids (Tensar 2). The aim of this is not to eliminate the cracks, but to spread them so that a lot of narrow cracks may occur rather than a few wide ones, like the effect of the reinforcement in reinforced concrete. To check the effectiveness of this reinforcement, experimental embankments were constructed with geogrids laid every 300 mm. Zones with and without geogrids were tested in the same embankment to compare cracking deformation. The deformations experienced are summarized in Figure 2. As may be seen

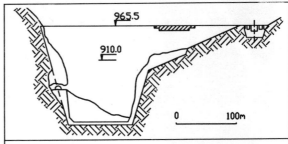

Figure 1. Longitudinal profile of Canales Dam showing the reinforced zone.

in this figure, the effect of the geogrid is clear. The area of extension is widened and the tension peaks are reduced by about 35%. It was therefore decided to use geogrids in the dam.

An original theory was developed to establish a relationship between the required amount of geogrid, and the distance between cracks and their opening, depending on the following parameters:

E_p : Deformation modulus of geogrid (N/m)
E_s : Deformation modulus of soil (Pa)
d : Distance between geogrids (m)
k : Modulus of stress transfer between geogrid and soil (N/m³) (ratio between tangential stress and displacement between both elements)
m : ϵ_t/ϵ_o = ratio between the tensile strain imposed on the soil and that required for cracking.

Figure 3 summarizes data regarding expected cracking in Canales Dam. In the light of these results it was decided to lay geogrids every 150 mm in the area shown in Figure 4. The geogrid-reinforced zone extends to a depth of 6 m

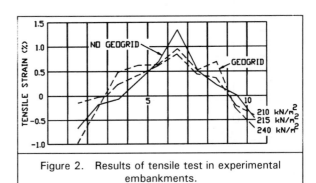

Figure 2. Results of tensile test in experimental embankments.

| Photo 1. Aerial view of Canales Dam. | Photo 2. Installation of the geogrid. |

below the crest (i.e., 1 m above the normal reservoir level) and to a width of 8 m inside the core. As a result of this, it is expected that crack openings will not exceed 10 mm and the distance between cracks will be about 6.5 m.

REFERENCES

Bravo, G., Uriel, S., and Pérez Rodríguez, J.R., "In Situ Tests for Control of Cracking of the Clay Core of Canales Dam (Spain)", Proc. 14th. Congress on Large Dams, Q.55, R.55, Rio de Janeiro, 1982.

Bravo, G., Uriel, S., and Pérez Rodríguez, J.R., "Anti-cracking Measures in the Canales Dam", Proc. 16th. Int. Congress on Large Dams, C7, San Francisco, 1988.

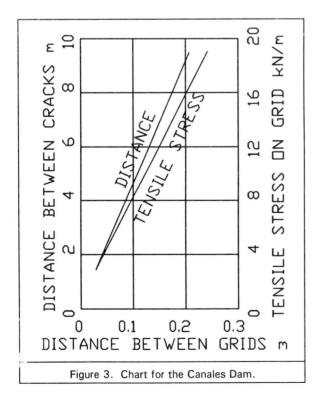

Figure 3. Chart for the Canales Dam.

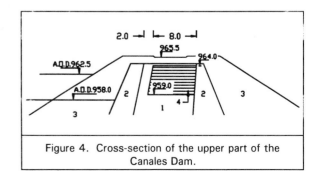

Figure 4. Cross-section of the upper part of the Canales Dam.

GEOCOMPOSITE FOR DAM SHAFT DRAIN
LA PARADE DAM, FRANCE

G. Navassartian
Sogreah
Pau, France

J.P. Gourc
Irigm-UJF
Grenoble, France

P. Brochier
Sommer BTP
Neuilly, France

The Garonne valley, in southwest France, is a major agricultural region. Irrigation of cereal crops requires the creation of water reserves that can be used during dry periods. It was with this aim in mind that a far-reaching programme for the construction of 10 m high earth dams was implemented. The dams are made of homogenous material with shaft drains. This is an interesting application for geotextiles. Since 1987, a geocomposite shaft drain (geosynthetic filter/drain) has been used instead of the granular drain in all the dams built within the context of this development programme.

The overall programme is being carried out under the authority of the Direction Départementale de l'Agriculture.

DESCRIPTION

La Parade hill dam described in this case history is just one example of a whole series of structures built in recent years.

All these dams are homogenous and the geocomposite shaft drain, named Somdrain and manufactured by Sommer, includes a polypropylene nonwoven draining core between two polypropylene nonwoven filters. The 175-17 includes two 170 g/m² filters surrounding a 500 g/m² drain, whereas the 106-10 has two 100 g/m² filters for a 600 g/m² drain.

Worthy of note is the special case of Peyrelongue dam, made completely of sandy material. Since the dam body is highly permeable, the geotextile acts as a filter drain (100 g/m² + 600 g/m²) associated with a PVC geomembrane for sealing purposes. This geomembrane is bonded to the textile in the factory and the name of this product is 106 ET5.

DESIGN

The Soils

Survey trenches were excavated along the dam centreline, before construction. These indicated an impermeable substratum at a depth of 6 m with an overlying alluvial layer having the following mechanical properties:

$$\phi' = 27° \qquad c' = 20 \text{ kPa}$$
$$\phi_u = 0° \qquad c_u = 35 \text{ kPa}$$

The borrow material to be used for dam construction was obtained from the future reservoir basin. The material was a marly clay with a natural water content between 19 and 22% and with a fine particle size:

$$D_{99} < 50 \text{ mm} \qquad\qquad D_{35} < 80 \ \mu m$$

The Atterberg limits were as follows:

$$41.0\% < W_L < 54\%$$
$$22.5\% < W_p < 28\%$$
$$18.5\% < I_p < 28\%$$

The optimum Proctor 16.4 kN/m³ $< \gamma_{opt} <$ 17.2 kN/m³ was obtained for a water content of 17% $< W_{opt} <$ 20%. This soil was difficult to compact beyond a value of (W_{opt} + 4%). It was therefore decided to compact it at its natural water content. Under these conditions, the average permeability of the dam body was equal to 10 nm/s. Its mechanical properties were as follows:

$$\phi' = 22° \qquad c' = 20 \text{ kPa}$$
$$\phi_u = 0° \qquad c_u = 50 \text{ kPa}$$

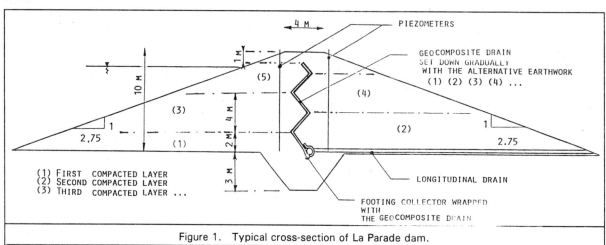

Figure 1.   Typical cross-section of La Parade dam.

| Photo 1. Laying of collector at the foot of the shaft drain. | Photo 2. Dam under construction. |

The stability analysis by the Fellenius method gave the following results:

- upstream stability under fast reservoir emptying F = 1.6
- downstream stability on completion of works F = 1.35
- downstream stability, reservoir full F = 2.1.

The Shaft Drain

The geocomposite shaft drain used has the following properties in the roll direction:

- Tensile strength: 6 kN/m. Strain at failure: 65%.
- Tear strength: 500 N
- Opening size: 115 μm
- Thickness T_g and transmissivity θ measurements under compression σ gave the following results:

σ (kPa)	2	10	25	50	100	200
T_g (mm)	7.8	7.1	5.8	5.0	4.0	3.1
θ (x 10^{-6} m²/s)	130	110	60	35	15	7

The shaft drain was designed in accordance with the recommendations of the French Committee on Geotextiles and Geomembranes (CFGG):

- Checking of filter criteria for the filter.
- Checking of draining capacity of the drain:
  - estimation of the maximum confinement pressure:
    σ = 86 kPa (weight of earth) + 100 kPa (compaction) = 186 kPa
  - transmissivity under compression:
    θ = 7 x 10^{-6} m²/s = 25 l/h/m
    or 20 l/h/m with surrounding soil (20% reduction)
  - drainage capacity for an 8.5 m high shaft drain:
    Q = 20 l/h/m / 8.5 m = 2.35 l/h/m²
  - inflowing water from the dam body (k = 10 μm/s):
    Q = 0.036 l/h/m²

Thus the ratio of theoretical safety to drainage capacity gives the following coefficient:

F = 2.35 / 0.036 = 65.

PERFORMANCE

Construction of La Parade dam was completed within one month, in July 1987. A granular shaft drain is installed by digging a trench in the compacted fill as the successive layers of the fill were laid.

A geocomposite shaft drain is installed in a different manner: 2 m thick layers of fill are placed alternately on the upstream and downstream parts of the dam body. The geocomposite is laid alternately on the upstream and downstream slopes on the last compacted fill layer. When covering the geocomposite, care must be taken to ensure that the material is not damaged during compaction.

All the dams, built with a geocomposite shaft drain, have given complete satisfaction, with no technical problem since their construction. Like the La Parade dam, all the dams, have only been subjected to qualitative inspection procedures since construction (dry downstream facing, drain discharging water). In June 1988, however, La Parade dam was equipped with a piezometer.

The association of a clay dam with a geocomposite shaft drain can therefore be considered to be an advantageous solution for several reasons:

- This type of dam is often located some distance from main roads. The transport of granular materials for a conventional drain would damage local roads designed only for light traffic. Making good such damage is a costly business for contractors.

- The cost of a geocomposite shaft drain works out to be half that of a granular drain.

- The only reserves that can be made is concerning the long-term behaviour of the drains. These remain unknown. Ten years would no doubt be necessary before any final judgment can be made. This justifies the decision to install measuring instruments in La Parade dam.

Other structures of the same type are planned using more permeable fill materials. At the present time, except for Peyrelongue dam, the permeability limit was restricted to less than 100 nm/s.

REFERENCES

Non supplied.

GEOTEXTILE FILTERS FOR SELF HEALING OF DIAPHRAGM CUT-OFF FÖRMITZ AND SCHÖNSTÄDT DAMS, GERMANY

F. List

Bayer. Landesamt für Wasserwirtschaft
München, Germany

The 33 m high Förmitz Dam, near the city of Hof, was constructed in the years 1974 to 1978 for the low flow improvement of the Saale River. The Schönstädt Dam with a height of 22 m was completed 1986 for the flood protection of the city of Coburg in Northern Bavaria. Geotextiles were widely used in both dams. The locations of both dams are indicated in the map in the contribution on Frauenau Dam (see p.20).

DESCRIPTION

The Dams

The data on both dams and their reservoirs are presented in Table 1.

In both cases only thin alluvial or weathering product layers cover the bedrock. These consisted of metamorphic phyllites in the case of Förmitz Dam and of rather jointed sandstone in the case of Schönstädt Dam.

On the Förmitz Dam site no suitable impervious material for a dam core was available. Only a semi-impermeable material was used for the core of the dam. As a cut-off wall (or diaphragm wall) a "dry trench" soil cement diaphragm was used. Details of the design and construction of the project and of the dam behaviour during the first years of operation are reported by List (1980). The cross-section of the dam is illustrated in Figure 1.

Table 1. Characteristics of Förmitz and Schönstädt dams.

Characteristics	Förmitz Dam	Schöstädt Dam
Drainage area (km²)	38.7	127.5
Total reservoir capacity (m³ x 10⁶)	10.8	6.7
Crest length (m)	800	350
Max. dam height (m)	33.0	22.0
Dam volume (m³)	550,000	420,000
Crest width (m)	8.0	9.0
On river	Fömitz	Itz
Construction period	1974/78	1982/86
Dam type	rockfill + earth	zoned earth

For the Schönstädt Dam core and the upstream blanket a loam was used. This was available as a restored product of weathering of the sandstone at the western hillside of the future reservoir. The cross-section of this dam is illustrated in Figure 2. The grain size distribution of this material varied within a very broad range. The percentage of fines (d < 0.06 mm) ranged between 18 and 60% and could be used directly for the core. For the fill an alluvial silty sand, with 5 to 25% of fines and different percentages of the gravel fraction, was used. The upstream slope was protected by the rockfill zone.

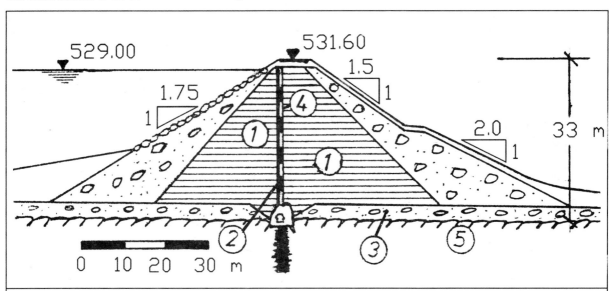

Figure 1. Cross-section of Förmitz Dam: 1) semi-impervious material, 2) dry trench diaphragm wall, 3) partially weathered rock & alluvions, 4) geotextile, 5) bedrock (phyllite).

| Photo 1. View of Förmitz Dam with a part of the reservoir. | Photo 2. View of Schönstädt Dam shortly after completion. |

The subsoil sealing for this dam was realized by a diaphragm wall with a medium depth of 10 to 12 m. To avoid uplift of the downstream fill by underseepage, relief wells, with a mean distance of 16 m, and a toe drain were installed.

Geotextiles in the Design of Both Dams

As erosion protection of the diaphragm wall geotextiles were used as given below.

For the Förmitz Dam a geotextile was used as a self-healing element in case of leakage.

In Schönstädt Dam geotextiles were used for the following purposes:

- as filter between the lower part of the upstream and the protective rockfill;
- as transition filter between the core and the downstream coarse filter; and
- as filter around the relief wells and the toe drain.

GEOTEXTILE SELECTION

For Förmitz Dam a three-layer nonwoven geotextile 1002 NS with a mass per unit area of 1100 g/m² and a thickness of 9 mm was chosen: this selection was

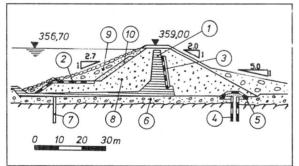

Figure 2. Cross-section of Schönstädt Dam:
1) core, 2) geotextile between rockfill and sand,
3) geotextile between core and filter, 4) geotextile filter of relief wells, 5) geotextile for drainage,
6) alluvions over sandstone, 7) diaphragm wall,
8) silty sand, 9) rockfill zone, 10) gravel filter.

considered to be most advantageous as a self-healing element for the "dry trench" diaphragm.

The same geotextile type was used for the filter downstream of the core in Schönstädt Dam, whereas for the relief well the type 1004 R of the Naue company with a mass per unit area of 900 g/m² was preferred. As a filter between rockfill and sand on the upstream shoulder and for the toe drain a Terrafix 600 geotextile was utilized.

To check the function of the geotextile as a self-healing element for the Förmitz Dam diaphragm, laboratory investigations of the process of self-healing were carried out. For this purpose soil-cement material of the diaphragm was placed in a permeameter and covered by a specimen of the 1002 NS geotextile. The soil-cement specimen had an initial coefficient of permeability of $k = 5$ nm/s. After a period of permeation an artificial crack was manufactured into the specimen. A great increase in permeability was recorded. Then a certain quantity of silt was added to the permeating water. This resulted in a complete reduction of the permeability down to the original value.

PERFORMANCE

During the first impoundment of Förmitz Dam a high increase in seepage through the diaphragm was noted. A total of 7.0 l/s was observed in the four seepage measurement sections of the dam. A detailed investigation of the reasons for this phenomenon was carried out by means of borings. These indicated many defective zones in the diaphragm wall. For this case it was extremely important that the geotextile prevented a further erosion in the diaphragm. After the defective areas were sealed by grouting, the seepage with the water at maximum reservoir level was reduced to the total of 0.4 l/s.

REFERENCE

List, F., "Experience during Construction and Reservoir Filling of Förmitz Dam with a Membrane Sealing and Grout Curtain" (in German), Wasserwirtschaft, 1980, No. 3, pp. 124-128.

GEOTEXTILES FOR EROSION AND FILTER CONTROL OF EARTH DAM FRAUENAU DAM, GERMANY

F. List
Bayer. Landesamt für Wasserwirtschaft
München, Germany

The Frauenau Dam was constructed for the water supply of the region of the Bavarian Forest and the adjacent Danube Valley (Figure 1) during the years 1976 to 1981. In this dam, geotextiles were widely used as filters.

DESCRIPTION

The Dams

The mean data of the Frauenau reservoir and dam are summarized in Table 1.

Weathered gneis was used for the dam core. This material has a variable percentage of fines (d < 60 μm) between 15 and 25% and almost no clay particles. To obtain a homogeneous impermeability for the dam, a diaphragm wall was added as a supplementary sealing element. Details of the dam's design and the construction and its behaviour after completion are given by List and Beier (1985). The composition and construction of the diaphragm wall are reported by Beier and List (1982).

Geotextiles in the Design of Frauenau Dam

Geotextiles were used in Frauenau Dam for three main different problems (see Figure 2):

(a) As a self-healing element for the protection of the diaphragm wall against erosion (see 3 on Figure 2). The inhomogeneous subsoil consists mainly of deposits of completely weathered rock in the right part of the valley and in the step right rock abutment. These may cause cracks in the core and the diaphragm wall. Should cracks occur a geotextile would prevent erosion.

(b) As erosion protection of the weathered rock deposits below the downstream fill (see 4 on Figure 2) -

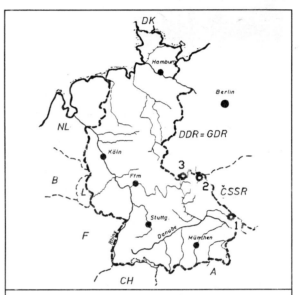

Figure 1. Dams in Bavaria (south-eastern part of Germany) with application of geotextiles: 1) Frauenau; 2) Förmitz; and 3) Schönstädt.

erosion could occur if underseepage results through the subsoil and the grout curtain. The geotextile filter will prevent this type of erosion.

(c) As protection against internal or surface erosion during construction of the slopes of the excavation trench for the dam core (see 5 on Figure 2).

GEOTEXTILE SELECTION

The selected geotextile in the dam core was a composite nonwoven geotextile with two coarse filter layers and a central drainage layer. This product (1002 NS of the Naue Company) has a total thickness of 9 mm.

The selected geotextile to act as a filter below the downstream fill was a composite geotextile. It was chosen to take into account the possibility of large total and differential settlements.

The selected geotextile as the protection of the core excavation slopes was a thermally bonded nonwoven geotextile. In all cases the design of the geotextiles was by assessing the allowable opening size for the protected material.

The mechanical and hydraulic properties of the used geotextiles were checked by extensive laboratory testing.

Table 1. Characteristics of Frauenau dam.	
Characteristics	Frauenau Dam
Drainage area	30.4 km^2
Total reservoir capacity	20.3 km^3
Crest length	640 m
Maximum dam height	84.0 m
Dam volume	2,500,000 m^3
Crest width	9.0 m
On river	Kleiner Regen
Construction period	1976/81
Dam type	zoned rockfill + earth dam
Subsoil	partially weathered gneiss
Sealing element of dam	core + diaphragm

ISSMFE., Committee TC9 - Geosynthetics Case Histories.

| Photo 1. Aerial view of the dam and reservoir. | Photo 2. Placing of the soil-cement into the dry trench; left the geotextile mats. |

MONITORING

Because of variable depth of rock surface across the valley, different flow nets were expected to develop in the cross-sections of the dam. These would cause percolation in the geotextile for the core. Therefore, this geotextile was separated by geomembrane bulkheads (dark mats in Photo 2) into 9 sections. Reliable values of the pore water pressures in the lowest part of the interface between the diaphragm wall and the downstream part of the core were obtained by measuring the water pressures at the lower boundary of the geotextile in each section.

PERFORMANCE

During the 6 years of operation since the completion of Frauenau Dam in 1981 the observations and measurements indicate that the geotextile elements of the dam fulfilled their functions in an excellent way. The total amount of seepage water is about 0.35 l/s for the 30,000 m² of diaphragm wall.

REFERENCES

Beier, H. and List, F., "Trench diaphragms as sealing elements", Proc. 14th. ICOLD Congress, Rio de Janeiro 1982, Q. 55, R. 13.

List, F. and Beier, H., "The Frauenau Dam: Monitoring and Observations", Proc. 15th. ICOLD Congress, Lausanne 1985, Q. 56, R.17.

List, F., "Use of Geotextiles in Dam Construction", Proc. 2nd. Int. Conf. on Geotextiles, Vol. 1, Las Vegas, 1982, pp. 189 - 192.

List, F., "Technical criteria for the use of geotextiles in embankment dam construction", 1. Nationales Symposium Geotextilien im Erdund Grundbau, Mainz 1984, pp. 139 - 144.

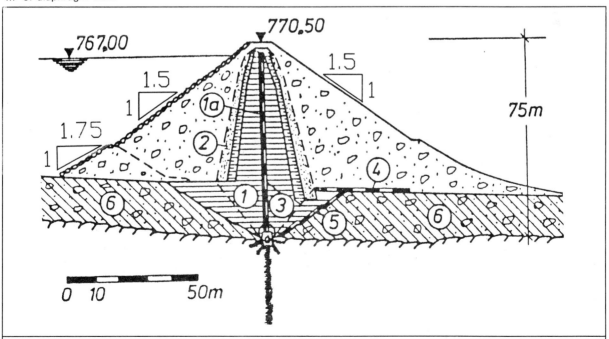

Figure 2. Cross-section of Frauenau Dam: 1) core, 1a) dry diaphragm wall, 2) transition zones, 3) geotextile for core, 4) geotextile for drainage, 5) geotextile for excavation slope, 6) weathered rock.

GEOTEXTILE FOR UNDERDRAINS OF TAILINGS DAM
ERGO TAILINGS DAM, SOUTH AFRICA

R.J. Scheurenberg
Watermeyer Legge Piesold and Uhlmann, Consulting Engineers
Rivonia, South Africa

The outer impounding walls of tailings or slimes dams for the disposal of mining residues in South Africa are generally constructed of the waste material itself. The fine wet slimes are retained behind stable confining walls of structurally competent material.

Underdrains are installed to have several functions. The seepage surface below the outer slope is drawn down and prevented from emerging on the face. The pore water pressures within the wall zone are reduced. The effective shear strength of the material is increased. And the wall stability is enhanced.

DESCRIPTION

The East Rand Gold & Uranium (ERGO) project recovers mineral rich material from old residue deposits. After the gold, uranium and pyrites have been extracted, the resultant barren residues are disposed in the ERGO tailings dam. The dam is sited across a shallow valley and on the side hill of the next valley. It is 10 to 15 km from the process plant.

The dam, one of the largest in the southern hemisphere, covers an area totalling over 1300 ha. Within a perimeter of 15 km, some 680 Mt of tailings can be deposited at the rate of 2.7 Mt per month.

The walls of the tailings dam are constructed of cycloned coarse tailings within low earthfill toe walls. The cyclone underflow produces a free-draining, free-standing, high strength outer wall within which the fine overflow material is deposited. The dam will eventually reach a maximum height of 76 m above the valley floor.

Construction of the predeposition works, including earthfill starter and toe walls and underdrains, began in 1976. Tailings were first deposited in the central valley during 1977. With the predeposition works extended to enclose 3 sides of the dam perimeter, deposition continued on this site until December 1984. The tailings dam extension on the side hill of the adjacent valley has been kept separate from the original dam. The predeposition works for this major extension were constructed during 1984 with further additions later. Tailings deposition is planned to continue until the end of the century.

The underdrainage system must function effectively both during the many years of the construction of the residue deposit and after its completion. Geotextiles are incorporated in the filter layers which separate the deposited material and the underlying soil from the drainage medium. The geotextile function is to prevent the ingress of fine soil and tailings while seepage water passes through.

TECHNICAL CONSIDERATIONS

Typical construction details of filter drains installed at the ERGO tailings dam are shown in Figure 1. The filter sand layer is designed to collect the seepage water, derived from the tailings slurry and from stormwater, into the drain without any appreciable head loss. The required water through flow rate thus determines the surface area of the sand layer. The coarse tailings layer acts as a protective cover until wet tailings have been deposited over the drain.

The stone and perforated pipe are sized according to the required longitudinal flow capacity along the drain. The stone serves the dual purposes of feeding the water into the pipe and of supplementing the longitudinal flow path.

By incorporating geotextiles into the filter drains, the grading requirements for the filter sand and stone can be relaxed and an intermediate natural gravel layer can be omitted. The material costs are thus reduced and construction is facilitated.

Laboratory flow tests were first carried out with the various brands of geotextile then available in South Africa and with samples of the tailings and sand. These tests were designed to model filter performance in terms of

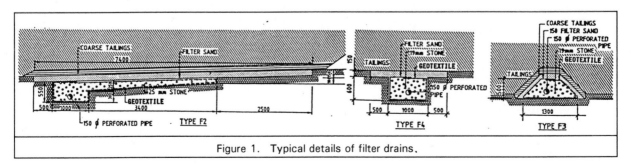

Figure 1. Typical details of filter drains.

| Photo 1. ERGO Tailings dam - Tailings deposition through hydrocyclones. | Photo 2. Filter drains under construction outside earthfill starter wall. |

through flow capacity and solids retention without clogging. A nonwoven needlepunched polypropylene or polyester geotextile (e.g. Bidim U14) was found satisfactory. Subsequent experience showed that a heavier grade of geotextile (e.g. Bidim U24) could better withstand the handling forces and damage during construction.

As further knowledge was gained, the geotextile properties could be specified for the required performance both during construction and in operation. Geotextile with a minimum unit mass was required to meet all the criteria tabulated. The established criteria are given in Table 1.

Acceptable grades which have been used successfully include:

- Bidim U24 (nonwoven needlepunched continuous filament polyester);
- Polyfelt TS600 (nonwoven needlepunched continuous filament polypropylene stabilised against UV radiation);
- Geoindustex S135T (woven fibrillated flat tapes, of polypropylene stabilised against UV radiation).

At all splices, the geotextile was lapped, folded and either stitched with a woven nylon thread or stapled at close centres.

Certain sections of drain have malfunctioned at various times in locations where water was forced to flow out of the sides of drains. The cause was either because of internal positive hydraulic heads at those locations or because of a downstream mechanical blockage. Where the drain became exposed to the air, a reddish brown deposit formed and the geotextile surrounding the drain became clogged. This was due to the formation of ferric oxide precipitates which, together with micro-organisms, coagulated the fine particles of quartz tailings and trapped them in the pores of the geotextile.

The damaged filter drains were reconstructed and covered. They have since functioned satisfactorily.

REFERENCES

Scheurenberg, R.J., "Experiences in the use of geofabrics in underdrainage of residue deposits", Proc. 2nd. Int. Conf. on Geotextiles, Vol.1, Las Vegas, U.S.A., July 1982, pp. 199-204.

Scheurenberg, R.J., "Clogging of filters due to iron oxide deposits", Proc., Filters Symposium, Johannesburg, South Africa, October 1986.

Table 1. Established criteria for geotextile filters.		
Property	Specified Value	Test Method
Water through flow capacity normal to plane of geotextile under 100 mm water head and confining pressure 200 kPa	minimum 5 l/s/m^2	---
Effective opening size O_{90}	> 110 μm < 800 μm	wet sieving
Strip Tensile strength (in any direction)	10 kN/m	DIN 53857
CBR puncture resistance (minimum piston force)	2.0 kN	DIN 54307

GEOTEXTILE FOR DOWNSTREAM DRAIN
YANGDACHENG DAM, CHINA

W. Wei

Exploration and Design Institute of Water Resources
Jilin Province, China

In Yangdacheng dam, over 4,600 m² of geotextile were used as a filter around the downstream drain pipe. The results were satisfactory.

DESCRIPTION

Yangdacheng reservoir has a 86,000,000 m³ storage capacity. It is located on the Meng Guangli river in Jilin province. The homogeneous earthfill dam has a maximum height of 17 m and a crest length of 2,250 m. It is constructed with silty loam and silty sand fill.

The reservoir was put into service in 1980. When the water level reached 176.69 m water leakage was observed on the downstream slope . Owing to the poor quality of the construction of the drainage ditch, the ditch had become badly clogged in some parts. Seepage flow could not drain out freely. As a result, the phreatic line inside the dam rose. This caused flooding of over 300 ha of farmland and caused more than 1,200 ha of fish pond to become non functional, and unable to produce any benefit. Slides occurred on the left bank of the spillway apron and downstream of the culvert apron section. These were at least 70 m and 600 m long respectively . The reservoir was unable to store water.

DESIGN OF FILTER

Design Proposals

Permeability tests were conducted under different boundary conditions, corresponding to three typical sections of the dam. Based on these tests a pipe underdrain was selected as superior to the drainage ditch alternative. The pipe was made up of reinforced concrete with a 600 mm diameter and a greater than 2% open area. In selecting the filter material around the perforated pipe, a comparison was made between a sandy gravel filter and a geotextile. In accordance with the filter design criteria, the natural sandy gravel would have to be manufactured and made into an artificial graded material. Also, if it was chosen as the filter material, it would have to be delivered through a long distance (more than 100 km). A time and work consuming process. Since a tight construction schedule was demanded the quality assurance would be hard to control.

Geotextile is one of the new materials of construction. Its advantages are: high strength, good filtration, low cost, ease of installation and quality assurance. Moreover, the problems mentioned above may be resolved by its use. Thus, the geotextile was finally selected as the filter material in this project.

Geotextile Selection

Under unidirectional flow condition in this project, the following criteria were used:

$$O_g \leq d_{90}, \qquad k_g \geq 100 \, k_s$$

Where O_g is pore size of geotextile; d_{90} is the 90% finer than d size by mass of soil to be protected; k_g and k_s are the coefficients of permeability of geotextile and soil respectively.

Tests on the soil in the vicinity of the covered drainage pipe gave, d_{90} from 82 to 120 μm, k_s from 15.0 to 8.3 nm/s. The properties of geotextile adopted are shown in Table 1. It can be seen from Table 1 that the geotextile could meet the design requirement of this project.

CONSTRUCTION METHOD

According to the gradient requirement of the design excavation section and covered pipe layout, the excavation was carried out building small portions at different times. Due to high ground water table plus the disturbance by the workers, thin mud layers of various depths formed along the bottom of the trench. This made it difficult to fix each section of perforated concrete pipe to the specified elevation. To solve this problem, a number of concrete supporting pads (Figure 1) were put into the trench in advance and the space between two pads was filled with sand. Then the geotextile was placed over the sand. After that a 2 m long pipe section was set on to the geotextile and a survey level was used to adjust the pipe to design elevation.

To improve the drainage efficiency, a layer of crushed stone was placed over the pipe and a 20 mm wide

Table 1. Properties of selected geotextile	
Test	Data
Type	Nonwoven
Mass per unit area	400 g/m²
Thickness	4.3 mm
Tensile strength	463 N/50mm
Puncture strength	1044 N
ε_f	88 %
Permeability (hor.)	2,200 μm/s
Permeability (vert.)	49 μm/s
O_{90} (minimum)	62 μm
O_{90} (maximum)	54 μm

Photo 1. Pipes during geotextile placement.

Photo 2. Pipes after geotextile placement.

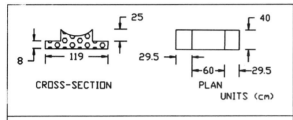

CROSS-SECTION

PLAN

UNITS (cm)

Figure 1. Supporting pad (unit:cm) (a) cross section. (b) plan.

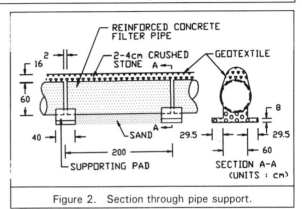

Figure 2. Section through pipe support.

space was left at each joint of the pipe sections. After that, the geotextile was laid over the crushed stone (see Figure 2) and the trench was finally backfilled with earth.

TECHNICAL AND ECONOMICAL STUDY

Cost Comparison

If sandy gravel were to be used as filter material, 5,840 m^3 of crushed stone and 4,789 workers would be needed. The total cost would be 335,000 Yuan. For a geotextile, only 400 workers and 4,600 m^2 of geotextile are needed. The cost would be 46,000 Yuan. It is seen from this comparison that the cost of the geotextile is only 13.7% of that for sandy gravel and the number of workers needed is 9% of that required for sandy gravel alternative.

Quality and Construction Period Comparison

Since the natural sandy gravel was poorly graded, using such material for the filter would not only result in difficulty controlling the layer thickness, but would often result in soil mixing at the interface. It would be a time and work consuming process. Controlling the filter grading would not be easy. Thus, the filter efficiency could hardly be guaranteed. However, the geotextile is convenient to place, easy to adjust and has an excellent filter effect. Thus, the quality is much easier to ensure and less time is needed for the construction work. The total length of pipe plus geotextile was 150 m and was placed in two months.

APPLICATION EFFECT

The project was completed on Nov. 10, 1986. Considering the water level at Section 1+800 as an example (Figure 3), in comparison to Sept. 1, 1986 before the pipe installation, the water level fell 0.394-0.429 m on

Nov. 1, 1986 and dropped 0.804-1.087 m by Feb. 9, 1987. The seepage water was clear. The water level in the fish pond fell 0.8-1.0 m. This permitted reuse of the land and the fish pond downstream of the dam.

CONCLUSION

This case history demonstrates that a geotextile can be successfully used for a dam downstream covered drain pipe. Also demonstrated are the ease of the construction work and quality control, and the economical benefits.

REFERENCES

Giroud, J.P., "Filter Criteria for Geotextiles", Proc. of the 2nd. Int. Conf. on Geotextiles, Vol. 1, 1982, pp. 103-108.

Hoare, D.S., "Geotextile as Filter", Ground Engineering, 1984, Vol. 17, No. 2.

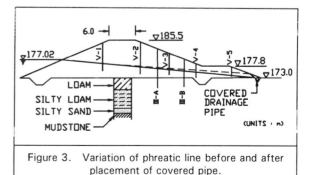

Figure 3. Variation of phreatic line before and after placement of covered pipe.

CHAPTER 2

CONTAINMENT PONDS, IRRIGATION AND RESERVOIRS

GEOSYNTHETICS IN HAZARDOUS WASTE LANDFILL
BATON ROUGE, LOUISIANA, USA

J.F. Beech, J.P. Giroud, and R.B. Wallace
GeoSyntec Consultants
Boca Raton, Florida, USA

A hazardous waste landfill, Cell 901, owned by Rollins Environmental Service (LA) Inc., was constructed in 1986 in Baton Rouge, Louisiana, USA. The landfill designer was Espey, Huston & Associates, Inc. The liner system design was done by GeoServices Inc. now known as GeoSyntec Consultants. In addition, GeoServices provided construction quality assurance (CQA) services for the construction of the geosynthetic components of the liner system.

This double-lined landfill was perhaps the first to include geomembrane liners, geotextile filters, geonet drainage media, and geogrid slope reinforcement.

DESCRIPTION

The landfill is 180 m long by 130 m wide with 3H:1V side slopes and a maximum height of 9 m. A more detailed description is provided by Lutz et al. [1987].

The liner system is composed of the following (top to bottom):

- a 600 mm thick protective soil layer;

- a leachate collection and removal system (LCRS), consisting of:
    - a geotextile filter (Bidim U-64),
    - a single (slopes) or double (bottom) geonet drainage layer (Tensar DN-3), and
    - sand-encapsulated, perforated HDPE pipes located within trenches;

- a primary liner, consisting of:
    - a 2 mm thick HDPE geomembrane (Schlegel Sheet), and
    - a 600 mm thick compacted low permeability soil layer (clay), located only at the bottom, where it forms with the geomembrane a composite liner;

- a leachate detection, collection, and removal system (LDCRS), consisting of:
    - a geotextile filter (Bidim U-64),
    - a geonet drainage layer (Tensar DN-3), and
    - sand-encapsulated, perforated HDPE pipes located within trenches; and

- a composite secondary liner, consisting of:
    - a 2 mm thick HDPE geomembrane (Schlegel Sheet), and
    - a 900 mm thick recompacted low permeability soil layer (clay).

DESIGN

The liner system used in this project is a double liner, as required by the U.S. Environmental Protection Agency (EPA) regulations for hazardous waste landfills. The double liner concept, as presented by Giroud [1973], is that the drainage layer (LDCRS) located between the two liners evacuates the liquid that may leak through the primary liner, which results in a very low head on, and therefore a very small leakage through, the secondary liner.

The liner system meets the design requirements of the EPA regulations for hazardous waste landfills: geomembrane for the primary liner; composite liner for the secondary liner; thickness of at least 0.9 m and hydraulic conductivity less than 1 nm/s for the soil component of the composite secondary liner. A composite primary liner was used at the bottom of the landfill to enhance the performance of the liner system on the basis of research work undertaken at the time when this project was designed. This work, which shows that the rate of leakage through a defect in a geomembrane placed on clay is several orders of magnitude less than if the geomembrane was placed on a permeable soil, was eventually published by Giroud and Bonaparte [1989], Giroud et al. [1989] and Bonaparte et al. [1989].

Geonets were used instead of the 0.3 m thick granular layer specified in EPA regulations for LCRSs and LDCRSs. This was possible because the authors demonstrated through theoretical analyses and transmissivity tests that a leachate head less than the geonet thickness could be maintained over the underlying liner, thereby meeting the EPA performance standard.

Stability of the liner system was a concern because the downslope driving force due to the weight of the protective soil layer could exceed the upslope resisting force resulting from shear strength at geosynthetic-geosynthetic or geosynthetic-soil interface. Furthermore, interface properties of the available materials were not well documented. It was therefore, deemed necessary to reinforce the protective soil layer using a geogrid (Photo 1) anchored at the crest of the slope (Photo 2). (Today, when geogrid reinforcement is used, the authors recommend a separate anchor trench for the geogrid to achieve a more effective geogrid-soil interface shear strength.) The method of design developed for this project was eventually published by Giroud and Beech [1989]. It is interesting to note that a geosynthetic problem (low interface shear strength) was solved by using an additional geosynthetic (geogrid reinforcement).

| Photo 1. LCRS geonet drain (right), geotextile filter (white), and geogrid reinforcement (left). | Photo 2. Anchor trench for geomembrane, geonet, geotextile, and geogrid. |

CONSTRUCTION

Cell 901 was constructed in 1986. Because of the critical role played by geosynthetics in this project, it was essential to provide thorough CQA services. In particular, comprehensive monitoring and documentation was provided for:

- geosynthetics handling and placement;

- trial seams and seaming operations for the geomembranes;

- seaming or joining operations for the geonets, geotextiles, and geogrids;

- nondestructive testing of the geomembrane seams;

- sampling and destructive testing of geomembrane seams;

- repair and nondestructive testing of geomembrane sampled locations; and

- placement of soils adjacent to geosynthetics.

The liner system was successfully installed and was documented in the CQA report and certification, which were submitted to the responsible regulatory agencies.

PERFORMANCE

The LDCRS makes it possible to monitor the performance of this landfill. In fact, in the USA, all modern, double-lined hazardous waste landfills are monitored on a permanent basis, but monitoring data are confidential. However, a generic analysis of monitoring data from a number of double-lined landfills performed on behalf of the EPA [Bonaparte and Gross, 1990; Gross et al., 1990] shows that measured rates of leakage are consistent with rates predicted using the method by Giroud et al., [1989]. This establishes the validity of the double composite liner concept.

The waste was to be placed in Cell 901 in such a controlled way that stability of the liner system would be progressively improved. Therefore, the most critical time for liner system stability was the period between the end of construction and the beginning of waste placement. This period was longer than foreseen, and the liner system was stable during the entire period.

CONCLUSIONS

This case history illustrates an application where regulatory and design requirements could only be met by using geosynthetics and where the performance of the many geosynthetics greatly depended on the thoroughness of the CQA program.

REFERENCES

Bonaparte, R., Giroud, J.P., and Gross, B.A., "Rates of Leakage through Landfill Liners", Proc. of Geosynthetics '89, Vol. 1, IFAI, San Diego, CA, Feb 1989, pp. 18-29.

Bonaparte, R. and Gross, B.A., "Field Behavior of Double-Liner Systems", Waste Containment Systems: Construction, Regulation and Performance, Bonaparte, R., Ed., ASCE Geotechnical Special Publication No. 26, San Francisco, CA, USA, Nov 1990, pp. 52-83.

Giroud, J.P., "L'étanchéité des retenues d'eau par feuilles déroulées", Annales de l'ITBTP, 312, TP 161, Dec 1973, pp. 92-112. (in French)

Giroud, J.P. and Beech, J.F., "Stability of Soil Layers on Geosynthetic Lining Systems", Proc. Geosynthetics '89, Vol. 1, IFAI, San Diego, CA, USA, Feb 1989, pp. 35-46.

Giroud, J.P. and Bonaparte, R., "Leakage through Liners Constructed with Geomembranes, Part II: Composite Liners", Geotextiles and Geomembranes, Vol. 8, No. 2, 1989, pp. 71-111.

Giroud, J.P., Khatami, A., and Badu-Tweneboah, K., "Evaluation of the Rate of Leakage through Composite Liners", Geotextiles and Geomembranes, Vol. 8, No. 4, 1989, pp. 337-340.

Gross, B.A., Bonaparte, R., and Giroud, J.P., "Evaluation of Flow from Landfill Leakage Detection Layers", Proc. 4th Int. Conference on Geotextiles, Geomembranes and Related Products, Vol. 2, The Hague, The Netherlands, May 1990, pp. 481-486.

Lutz, E.J. and Buchanan, R.J., "Design and Construction of a Resource Conservation and Recovery Act Minimum Technology Requirement Landfill Cell", Proc. 19th. Mid-Atlantic Industrial Waste Conf., Lewisburg, PA, USA, 1987, pp. 537-553.

GEOCOMPOSITE FIN DRAINS IN WASTE DISPOSAL SITES
FLÖRSHEIM, HOHENZELL AND SCHÖPPENSTEDT, GERMANY

H.R. Murray and J.A. Hunt
Geotextile Group, ICI Fibres
Frankfurt, Germany and Pontypool, United Kingdom

Until 1984, the use of composite geotextile drainage systems ("fin drains") in Germany was largely limited to the drainage of structures (bridge abutments, basements and the like). In the early 80's their potential for waste containment sites was recognised and by the mid-80's they had been designed into several such projects.

FLÖRSHEIM WASTE TIP

The site is located some 25 km west of Frankfurt and serves the local Main-Taunus communities for the disposal of domestic refuse. The waste mass is largely above the surrounding ground level and is contained by earth bunds approximately 8 to 12 m high. The base layer and the bunds are of silty clay to provide the required level of impermeability.

The role of the fin drain is two fold: (1) to ensure that aggressive waste water accumulating during the tipping and compaction of refuse is transported to the base drainage system, and (2) to ensure that gas (methane etc) generated during the decaying of the refuse is not allowed to escape freely over the top of the retaining embankments, with damaging results to the surrounding plant life.

Geotextile Selection and Placement

A fin drain, with adequate flow capacity when compressed under the design load of up to 15 m of waste, was required. 'Filtram' 1BZ was selected as meeting this requirement. Its backing LDPE geomembrane provided additional protection against water ingress into the embankments. No attempt was made to seal the joints between geomembrane strips.

The fin drain was laid in a strip along the length of the interior face of the embankments with its lower edge butting up to the drainage material. It was then covered with sand and the tipping operation commenced. When tipped refuse had reached the level of the upper edge of the first Filtram strip, the next strip was installed. This procedure was repeated to the top of the embankments. The final depth of waste above the fin drain will be about 15 m.

HOHENZELL WASTE TIP

In mid-1984, the Hohenzell domestic refuse tip near Fulda was to be extended. With the increased awareness of the dangers of aggressive leachate escaping through any weak spots in the impermeable layer, the authority responsible, the Main-Kinzig-Kreis, specified a "tell-tale" drainage layer to detect any leak in the sealing layer.

Construction

The whole tipping area - base and embankments - was sealed with an impermeable soil layer consisting of a graded aggregate 0/42 mm sealed with bentonite. Starting from the original soil level, the layers are:

- partial cover of 'Filtram' 1B1
- 100 mm filter layer
- 600 mm clay impermeable layer
- 'Filtram' 1B1

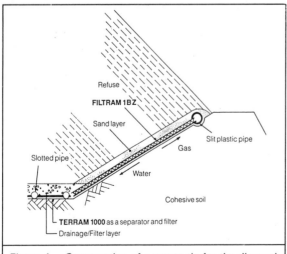

Figure 1. Construction of a waste tip for the disposal of domestic refuse. Flörsheim, Hesse, Germany.

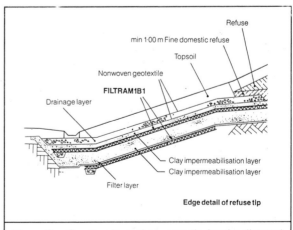

Figure 2. Construction of a waste tip for the disposal of domestic refuse. Hohenzell, Hesse, Germany.

Photo 1.   Flörsheim waste tip.

Photo 2.   Settlement lagoon, sugar factory,
Schöppenstedt.

Photo 3.   Hohenzell waste tip.

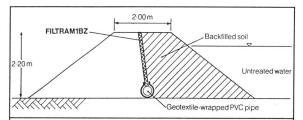

Figure 3.   Protection of agricultural land from polluted
water leaking from a factory-waste lagoon. Sugar
factory, Schöppenstedt, Germany.

- 400 mm sealed aggregate
- geotextile 150 g/m²
- 1.00 m fine domestic refuse
- normal refuse

The upper layer of fin drain will detect any leaks in the top sealing layer by transporting the leachate to polyethylene collector pipes installed at intervals. It thus also protects the lower sealing layer against such leakage water.

SETTLEMENT LAGOON, SCHÖPPENSTEDT

Untreated waste water from the sugar production plant at Schöppenstedt is pumped into a lagoon, where harmful solid waste settles out and can be removed. The sides of the lagoon were formed by constructing impermeable soil embankments around the perimeter. In the course of time these embankments had become permeable due to the ravages of rats, mice, etc. Problems had been caused by the leakage of waste water into the surrounding agricultural land.

Fin Drain Solution

The inside face of the embankment was excavated back to the centre line and a drainpipe laid below reservoir base level. This pipe was wrapped in a geotextile to prevent clogging by fines. 'Filtram' 1BZ was laid against the excavated face with its lower edge resting on the pipe,

and the geotextile protecting the pipe was fastened to the fin drain. The embankment was rebuilt. Should any water penetrate the inner face of the embankment it will be collected in the fin drain and transported down to the pipe. This would ensure that the surrounding land does not become contaminated.

CONCLUSIONS

Using composite geotextile drainage systems, solutions to the problem of gas and leachate drainage are possible. These problems would either have been impossible, or at least significantly more expensive, before the advent of these geosynthetic materials. With ever greater attention being paid to the environmental aspects of waste management, such novel construction materials look like playing an even greater role in the future.

REFERENCES

ICI Fibres Geotextile Group, "Filtram in waste-management schemes", March 1986.

Murray, H.R., "Composite Geotextiles for Soil and Structure Drainage", Proc. 23rd. Int. Man-Made Fibres Congress, Dornbirn, Austria, 1984.

GEOSYNTHETICS IN GAS BARRIER AND VENTING SYSTEM LANDFILL SITE CORBETT ROAD, ONTARIO, CANADA

G.A. Marshall
Terrafix Geosynthetics Inc.
Toronto, Ontario, Canada

M.J. Pullen and M.E. Samis
Marshall Macklin Monaghan Limited
Toronto, Ontario, Canada

The Corbett's Road Landfill site, located in Oshawa, Ontario, Canada, contains mostly industrial wastes. These wastes are reported to include paint sludges, waste metal, wood, and plastics from General Motors.

The landfill site has been closed since 1979. At that time, gas vents were installed through the final cover. A leachate collection system was retrofitted into the landfill. Gas probes on the adjacent lands have been continuously monitored since 1980. The monitoring indicated that some gas migration away from the landfill continues through a shallow sand layer. This migration is generally observed after the ground freezes and the gas is restricted from venting to the surface.

As a new subdivision was to be constructed on the adjacent lands, Marshall Macklin Monaghan Limited of Toronto, Ontario, the consulting engineers for the project, designed a gas venting system to provide a safeguard to the residential area adjacent to the site. Installation of the venting/barrier system was made part of the subdivision agreement between the developer and the City of Oshawa.

ALTERNATIVE SYSTEMS

The systems reviewed for application to the site included active systems, with mechanically induced negative pressures in the soil, and passive systems, using free venting to the atmosphere even through the winter.

Extraction Wells

The extraction well type of system incorporates a series of wells arranged in a line which are connected to a header pipe and blower system on the surface. A negative pressure is created in the wells, resulting in gas migration toward the wells. The gas is then vented or flared off. This active system is best suited when the transmissive layer is deeper than approximately 10 m and not in an area of shallow fluctuating ground water.

Interceptor Trench

The intercepter trench system involves the excavation of a trench which is then filled with coarse imported granular material. The granular material is encased in geotextile to provide separation between the native soils and the coarse granular material. Collection pipes are sometimes added at the top for gas collection and at the bottom for drainage. Polyethylene or other impervious material is sometimes installed in the granular material as a barrier to horizontal gas movement across the trench.

Gas Collection and Venting Barrier System

The gas collection and venting barrier system incorporates the use of a prefabricated drainage material or geocomposite (geowaffle) which was initially designed for foundation wall drainage. The materials consist mainly of a synthetic waffle which has a geotextile bonded to one or both sides, thus providing an open pathway for water and gases to flow. Perforated pipes are provided at the top of the barrier for gas collection and at the bottom for water drainage. In principle, this system is similar to the granular filled trench; however, the geowaffle replaces the coarse granular fill and adds a barrier to horizontal gas movement at the same time. The gas collection and venting system is shown in Figure 1.

DESIGN

In preparing the design for the system, a number of criteria need to be satisfied.

1. The long term integrity of the system has to be ensured.
2. The materials selected need to be chemically resistant to any volatile solvents that are reported in the landfill.
3. The system should be able to control a fluctuating ground-water regime.
4. The design should provide a barrier for horizontal movement and a mechanism for venting.
5. The design should be flexible enough to allow active venting if required in the future, but would be installed as a passive system initially.
6. Any innovative approach to the problem must be competitive in terms of materials and labour costs.
7. Last, and perhaps the most important, the system should be easily constructed and able to be maintained by inexperienced contractors.

To satisfy the above conditions, a geocomposite of Hitek 20 geowaffle bonded to needlepunched, nonwoven geotextile (200 g/m^2) on one side was used in conjunction with 150 mm perforated drainage pipe wrapped in a flap of geotextile bonded to the geowaffle. A similar 150 mm perforated pipe was installed at the top of the geowaffle as a gas collector. The perforated pipes and the geowaffle are manufactured from high density polyethylene and the geotextile from polyester. The design and subsequent installation called for the geocomposite barrier to be placed vertically from the top collection pipe to the bottom collection pipe.

The drainage pipe was placed on granular fill, set 1 m into the clay till that underlies the conductive sand

Photo 1.　Laying drainage pipe.

Photo 2.　Setting Hitek geocomposite.

layer and on the landfill side of the geowaffle barrier. The drainage pipe was laid with a 1% grade toward the drainage outlet.

At the top of the geocomposite barrier, a perforated gas collection pipe of the same specifications as the water drainage pipe was set. This gas collection pipe was placed at a depth of approximately 1.2 m. Along the length of the gas collection pipe, seven mushroom vents were installed to allow gas to escape.

To monitor the performance of the system, 12 probes were installed, in pairs, on either side of the geocomposite. This allowed for monitoring of combustible gas on both the landfill side and the subdivision side.

The whole system was backfilled to within 1 m of the surface with free draining material. The topmost meter was backfilled with clay till excavated from the toe of the system.

CONSTRUCTION

Construction started December 1986 and the system took two weeks to install. As some ground-water problems were expected, excavation of the trench started at the lowest end of the system, at the drainage outlet. Starting at the low end allowed the drainage pipe to drain the excavation as installation progressed.

The entire length of trench was approximately 750 m. The volume of fill removed and later backfilled was approximately 3,050 m³. Hitek panels were pre-manufactured for the various sections of the system to minimize the quantity of material lost to wastage. The total quantity of material used was 1,790 m².

The material was placed manually with a crew of three labourers. Two excavators were employed, one to

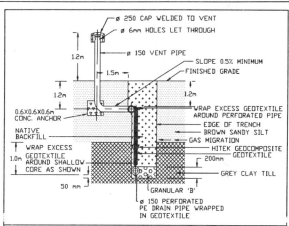

Figure 1.　Gas collection and venting system detail.

advance the excavation and one to backfill behind the installation. The progress averaged 85 linear m per day.

PERFORMANCE

The system has been operating as designed for a year and a half. Monitoring of combustible gas migration is ongoing on a monthly basis. To date, only low levels of combustible gas have been detected on the landfill side of the system. Minimal combustible gas has been detected on the subdivision side, and this gas is inferred to be natural in origin.

COST

The entire system was installed at a cost of 125,000 Canadian 1987 dollars. This included all materials, excavation placement, backfilling, vent installation, drainage pipe installation, monitoring probe installation, and hydroseeding of the work area.

GEOMEMBRANE SEALING OF A WASTE DISPOSAL AREA
MECHERNICH/EUSKIRCHEN, GERMANY

H. Steffen and D.B. Asmus
Consulting Engineers
Essen - Kettwig, Germany

The central waste disposal area in Mechernich/Euskirchen, Germany was designed in 1979. Due to the difficult topography of the slope surfaces a geomembrane was used on the slope surfaces as a sealing element.

DESCRIPTION

The Landscape

The planned region contained two V-shape valleys lying one behind the other and connected by a small steep-walled valley. The first valley was 150 m long and 70 m wide measured at its base; the second valley covers an area of 350 m long and 80 m wide. The height of the slopes was about 40 m with a maximum gradient of 1.2H:1V.

PRINCIPLE OF THE PLANNING

Choice of the Materials

The geomembrane had to fulfil the requirements of "Richtlinien über Depioniebasisabdichtungen aus Dichtungsbahnen". This standard requires a two-dimensional strain of 10%. Because of the steepness of the incline and certain roughness of slope this was increased to a minimum strain of 12%. The best solution offered at the time of tendering was a modified Lucobit geomembrane with a high percentage of polyethylene. The strain of this material at bursting was about 30% in the two-dimensional test.

Structural Boundary Conditions

Because of the very steep slopes some special structural measures were required to ensure that the geomembrane could not slide down the slope after it had been installed.

The resistance to sliding must be achieved by the frictional force between the surface of the geomembrane and ground. It should be independent of the resistance achieved by anchorage of the geomembrane in the small trench at the top of the slope.

These conditions imposed the requirement of a high roughness coefficient on the bottom side of the geomembrane. In addition it was necessary to lay sandsacks on the geomembrane as ballast to activate the frictional force. The trench at the top of the slope used for anchoring the geomembrane, was dimensioned such that it alone was large enough to prevent the geomembrane from sliding down the slope.

Both requirements for holding the geomembrane in place were considered sufficient security against the geomembrane sliding down the slope.

PROBLEMS DURING LAYING OF THE GEOMEMBRANE

During heavy wind conditions the laid geomembrane flapped and turned over due to delays in the positioning of the sandsacks. This problem was solved by the immediate placement of a sufficient number of sandsacks.

In the second stage of construction ultrasonic control measurements established that the thickness of the geomembrane had been reduced from 2.5 mm to 2.1 mm during installation. The reason for this was found to be in the incorrect placing of the geomembrane in the anchor trench. The geomembrane had been stretched in tension and then pressed into the trench during filling. Further negative influences occurred from quick changes of the climate and temperature. During periods of hot weather the geomembrane expanded and moved down the slope. This movement was induced by the force of gravity. The frictional resistance was insufficient.

During the following cooling period the geomembrane tried to contract against the force of gravity, but this was not possible. As a consequence waves in the geomembrane appeared, increasing to extreme folds. These had to be repaired by cutting along the full length of the folds and welding the cut edges together.

To avoid the reappearance of folds, the ballasting sandsacks were laid on the geomembrane (a) immediately after placement and (b) closer together. This gave a better weight distribution on the surface of the geomembrane and avoided reoccurrence of the folds. Now the geomembrane could only expand within a small distance resulting in only very small waves in hot weather that could contract in cold weather.

CONTROL TESTS

Nondestructive as well as destructive control tests were carried out after laying the geomembranes. The nondestructive tests of the welding seams were done with an air channel and were aided by means of an air pressure test and vacuum test. Random supplementary tests were carried out with ultrasonics. The destructive tests were carried out as two-dimensional burst pressure tests. Before the start of the second stage of construction it was possible to compare laboratory tests done on new geomembranes with those installed five years ago. The major part of the geomembranes were exposed, over five years, to the weather. Other areas were exposed to the

Photo 1. Wrinkled geomembrane.

Photo 2. Patching of geomembrane.

Photo 3. Transition area from old to new geomembrane liner.

stored waste. The latter had to be uncovered, since the new geomembrane, laid in the second stage of construction, had to be connected by welded seams to the existing geoomembrane. The laboratory tests showed no evidence of any property differences between the old and new geomembranes.

CONCLUSIONS

The perceptions gained from this described case are:
(1)   It is possible to use geomembranes, even on very steep slopes, if sufficient resistance to sliding is provided.
(2)   Testing before construction was necessary in order to select the correct material for the special problem described.
(3)   The design should account for the most disadvantageous loading case. Especially the time required to laying out the geomembrane. These requirements, specified in the design, must be fulfilled quickly to avoid any damage during geomembrane installation.
(4)   Accompanying care with continuous quality controls (destructive and nondestructive tests) during installation is necessary to identify early any possible damage of the geomembranes and to have immediate repair.

REFERENCE

Minister für Umwelt, Raumordnung und Landwirtschaft, "Deponiebasisabdichtungen aus Dichtungsbahnen", Ministerialblatt für das Land Nordrhein-Westfalen, 06 September 1985.

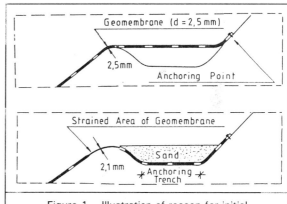

Figure 1. Illustration of reason for initial geomembrane damage.

GEOTEXTILE FOR WASTE PIT COVER
GEORGSWERDER-HAMBURG, GERMANY

G. Heerten
Naue-Fasertechnik GmbH & Co. KG
D-4990 Lübbecke, Germany

In 1986, for the first time, a nonwoven needlepunched geotextile made of high density polyethylene fibres was used in waste pit engineering. The HDPE geotextile's function was to act as a filter and separation layer in the covering system of an old existing waste pit near the city of Hamburg, Germany.

THE PIT HISTORY

The problems at the waste pit Georgswerder is a result of the rapid increase in refuse quantities in Hamburg since World War 2. These problems serve as a warning example for the method of refuse disposal used in the past with its damaging effects to the environment. These damaging effects are obvious today. At first the pit was used as a tipping place for refuse and rubble. Later the area became the main disposal site of Hamburg. From 1967 to 1974 more than 200,000 m³ of special waste, coming from industry and trade, were deposited at the pit. Altogether, approximately 14,000,000 m³ of waste have been delivered to the pit since 1979.

Today's job is to redevelop the dump in such a way that it is no longer feared as permanent source of harmful substances. Plenty of examinations and overlapping steps are necessary. Within the scope of the project a lot of new technological research and development is required.

FIRST STEP OF THE REDEVELOPMENT PLAN

The first step in the redevelopment plan was the covering of the upper area to the dump. This was to mainly avoid the penetration of rain and thus a further washing out of dump substances.

The main components of the covering system are:

- gas drainage layer
- mineral sealing (clay layer)
- HDPE geomembrane
- mineral drainage layer
- nonwoven filter layer
- cover substratum

GEOTEXTILE REQUIREMENTS

As a component of the cover system, the geotextile has to meet the following requirements:

- Resistance, in both dry and wet conditions, against the gas and its components which are released in the waste pit.
- The nonwoven geotextile is required to deform to the different settlements of the waste pit surface without tears.
- Even in a stretched condition the nonwoven geotextile must keep its filter stability with regard to the cover substratum.

For these requirements, test reports by independent institutes were obtained. During production of the geotextile a complete self-supervision and supervision by external authorities was required. All supervision was documented to ensure adherence to the requirements.

Problems arose in proving the resistance of the geotextile against the components of the refuse tip gas. Although well-known fibre research institutes' opinions were obtained, the resistance of known fibre raw materials against irregular mixtures of the numerous components in changing temperatures and different humidities could not be proven. For this reason, only HDPE (high density polyethylene) was allowed as the geotextile's raw material. The reason for this decision was (1) it is used for drainage tubes and synthetic liners, (2) HDPE is known for its superior resistance against chemicals and (3) it had already been applied frequently as geomembrane liners in waste pit sealing systems.

HDPE GEOTEXTILE DEVELOPMENT

Specifically for this application, Naue-Fasertechnik has developed, together with a fibre manufacturer, a nonwoven geotextile, Depotex 455 R, of HDPE staple fibres with a fibre linear density of 17 dtex. This geotextile was determined as having the requirements that could satisfy the required functions.

The filter design specification of the geotextile filter layer considered the following:

a) opening size
   (O_g = effective opening size in a wet sieving method)
b) filtration length (thickness requirements)
c) permeability

The geotextile has a mass per unit area of 450 g/m², a thickness of 4.3 mm, strain in the strip tensile strength test of approximately 200% and an opening size of O_g = 130 μm. It was also necessary to prove that, in contact with the soil layers (mineral drainage layer/cover substratum), the geotextile interface would develop sufficient friction to prevent interface failure. This proof was obtained using the big shear test at the Franzius-Institute for Coastal Engineering and Hydraulic Research, University of Hanover [Kohlhase et al., 1986]. During construction in 1987 the geotextile came up to all expectations.

Photo 2. Installation of the HDPE nonwoven geotextile on top of the drain layer.

Photo 1. Construction details of the covering system from below: HDPE geomembrane, drain layer, HDPE geotextile, cover soil.

REFERENCES

Die Deponie Georgswerder, Antworten auf ein Erbe. Freie und Hansestadt Hamburg, Baubehörden 1986.

Kohlhase, S., Saathoff, F. and Bassen, R., Anwendungsorientierte Versuche für die Deponie Georgswerder am Vliesstoff Depotex 455 R. Untersuchungsbericht des Franzius-Institutes für Wasserbau und Küsteningenieurwesen der Universität Hanover, 1986.

CONCLUSIONS

With the HDPE geotextiles made of HDPE staple fibres now developed, a complete HDPE product range is available for waste pit technology - drainage tubes, geomembranes, drainage geonets and nonwoven needlepunched geotextiles.

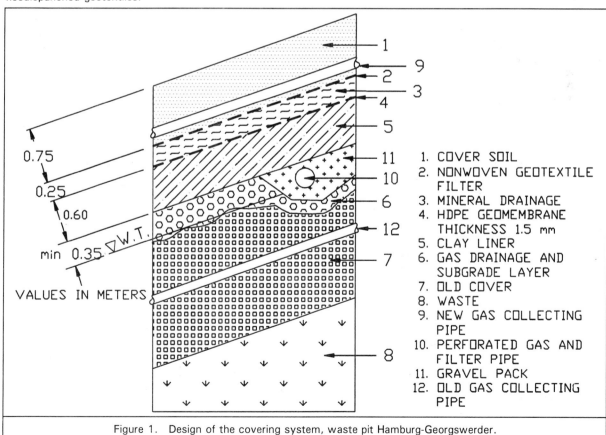

1. COVER SOIL
2. NONWOVEN GEOTEXTILE FILTER
3. MINERAL DRAINAGE
4. HDPE GEOMEMBRANE THICKNESS 1.5 mm
5. CLAY LINER
6. GAS DRAINAGE AND SUBGRADE LAYER
7. OLD COVER
8. WASTE
9. NEW GAS COLLECTING PIPE
10. PERFORATED GAS AND FILTER PIPE
11. GRAVEL PACK
12. OLD GAS COLLECTING PIPE

Figure 1. Design of the covering system, waste pit Hamburg-Georgswerder.

GEOSYNTHETIC SEALING OF WASTE DISPOSAL AREA
BASTWALD/VOGELSBERGKREIS, GERMANY

H. Steffen and C. Schmidt
Consulting Engineers
Essen - Kettwig, Germany

In 1985 the government of Hessen, Germany demanded a combined sealing system for a waste disposal area. A geotextile was required as protection for the selected geomembrane against the covering coarse drainage material. This was to be positioned between the two layers.

DESCRIPTION

Characteristics of the Waste Disposal Site

This kind of combined sealing system for cover of a waste disposal area was planned the first time in Bastwald (Vogelsbergkreis/Germany). The ground storage covered an area of about 180 000 m².

The estimated working life is 17.5 years, neglecting any possible reduction of the waste volume. The maximum height of the storage is 25 m. The sealing system must be designed for a maximum surcharge of about 400 kPa inclusive of the top cover on the storage.

Design of the Combined Sealing System

Before planning and construction of the sealing system, a report was made regarding the design of the combined sealing system. Laboratory tests were required to give a statement concerning the effectiveness and permeability of the sealing system. Based on these reports the design was made as follows: two layers of mineral sealing, each of thickness 300 mm after compaction; over that a geomembrane of 2.5 mm thickness (Niederberg Chemie, CHD - foil); this to be covered by a 300 mm thick coarse-grained drainage layer of broken basalt chips. The use of basalt chips was necessary, because in this area no other material with a low content of lime was available.

Between drainage layer and the geomembrane a geotextile was used as a protection layer. This was designed to avoid any damages of the geomembrane from the coarse granular skeleton of the drainage material. The design of the combined sealing system is shown in Figure 1.

Choice of Protection Geotextiles

The selected geotextile was required to take a maximum load of 400 kPa resulting from the granular drainage material and to prevent damage of the geomembrane. Laboratory tests were carried out to find the best combination of geotextile and the local available basalt drainage material. The drainage material was made of a mixture of field and twice field size freshly crushed grains.

In the laboratory program the use of different geotextiles and their effectiveness was investigated. From these tests, a geotextile was selected having the appropriate properties for this special loading case.

Laboratory Tests

The test program was carried out in a pressure pot of 255 mm diameter. The drainage material was a basalt chip layer graded 2 to 5 mm onto which a layer of 5 to 8 mm chips are embedded.

The opened pressure pot is shown in Photo 1. On this photo the embedded layer of chips is seen. The embedded basalt chips layer formed a trough. The trough forced a strain of 10% on the geomembrane.

The test used field size crushed basalt material of grading 2 to 5 mm and twice field size crushed basalt material of grading 5 to 8 mm. Photo 2 gives a visual impression of the two materials.

On the layer of chips the geotextile was positioned. Over that a specimen of the geomembrane was restrained, the pressure pot was closed, and the pressure was applied to the geomembrane. The pressure was increased in time-steps of 0.5 hours to a maximum pressure of 10 bars and then kept constantly for 4 hours. At the end of the test the pressure was decreased to zero in one step.

Photos 3 and 4 show typical results from the tests. Several materials were tested with different mass/m². Chosen from the results of the tests was a geotextile "Naue - Fasertechnik 816 R" with a mass of about 800 g/m².

Laying During Construction

After laying out the geomembrane the chosen geotextile was positioned over it with an overlapping of 500 mm in each lane. Subsequently the drainage material was placed above the geotextile as seen in photo 5.

CONCLUSION

Laboratory tests and field inspections showed, that a geomembrane can be securely protected by a geotextile against coarse drainage material. The arrangement of a geotextile must be designed for the special loading case. It must distribute the load so as to avoid any damage of the geomembrane.

REFERENCES

Non supplied

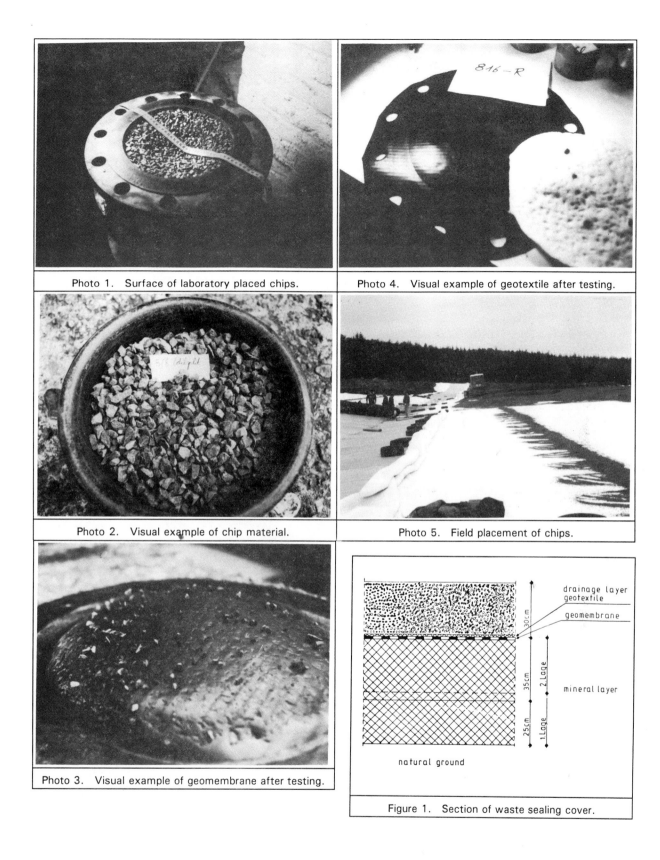

Photo 1.   Surface of laboratory placed chips.

Photo 4.   Visual example of geotextile after testing.

Photo 2.   Visual example of chip material.

Photo 5.   Field placement of chips.

Photo 3.   Visual example of geomembrane after testing.

Figure 1.   Section of waste sealing cover.

GEOTEXTILE FILTERS FOR INTAKE POOL OF A PUMPING STATION
LIANG ZHAI PUMPING STATION, CHINA

J.M. Zhu and N.H. Li
Nanjing Hydraulic Research Institute
Nanjing, Jiangsu, China

The Liang Zhai Pumping Station, located in the southeast of Feng county Jiangsu province, is constructed to divert water from Zheng River to Feng county which was poor in water resources.

In 1987, a geotextile filter was used in the intake pool and the drain pipes of the retaining wall in place of the conventional granular filter.

DESCRIPTION

The Station

The section of the station is given in Figure 1.

There are five pumps in the station. The upstream water level is 37.5 m and the downstream water level is 42.0 m.

The Subsoil Properties

From the ground level to 30 m below, there is a loose silty sand layer. The properties of the subsoil were obtained from tests as follows:

- Natural density $\rho = 1950$ kg/m^3

- Natural moisture content $W = 29.1\%$

- Specific gravity $G_s = 2.68$

- Grain size distribution $d_{85,s} = 0.072$ mm
  $d_{15,s} = 0.158$ mm

- Uniformity coefficient $C_u = 3.53$

- Coefficient of permeability $k_s = 31.0\ \mu$m/s

GEOTEXTILE SELECTION

Because it is difficult to obtain specified granular material, a nonwoven geotextile filter with a mass per unit area of 550g/m^2 was used to protect the above-mentioned silty sand from piping.

According to the engineering requirements, the following geotextile filter criteria were considered:

$$O_g < d_{85,s}$$

$$k_g > 10\ k_s$$

where: O_g = opening size of geotextile

k_g = coefficient of normal permeability of the geotextile

A test for compressibility of the nonwoven geotextile (in either dry case or saturated case) was conducted under different pressures. The response curves e vs. σ and T_g vs. σ are shown in Figure 2.

At the same time, the change of coefficient of permeability of geotextile with the compressibility of geotextile and the pressure was taken into account, according to the equation proposed by Giroud (1980) for needlepunched nonwoven geotextiles:

$$\frac{O_g + d_f}{O'_g + d_f} = \sqrt{\frac{T_g}{T'_g}}$$

where:

O_g = average opening size between geotextile filaments (μm), corresponding to thickness T_g (mm) for the considered geotextile;

O'_g = average opening size between geotextile filaments (μm), corresponding to thickness T'_g (mm) for the same geotextile;

d_f = diameter of filaments (μm).

In Table 1 the requested values of geotextile opening size are given.

Thus, the properties of the selected geotextile were as follows:

- Mass per unit area $\rho_g = 547$ g/m^2

- Thickness $T_g = 3.51$ mm

- Opening size $O_g = 72\ \mu$m

- Coefficient of permeability $k_g = 1.6\ \mu$m/s

- Tensile strength $\sigma_f = 20$ kN/m

A long-time permeability test was conducted in order to check the performance of the geotextile. The result of the above test shows that the permeability of the geotextile tended to be almost constant and no clogging phenomenon was observed (see Figure 3).

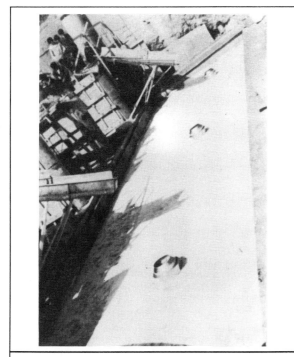

Photo 1. Application of the nonwoven geotextile filter on the intake pool.

Table 1. Geotextile properties			
Geotextile Location	Overburden Pressure (kPa)	Compressive Deformation (mm)	Opening Size (μm)
Intake pool	9.8	0.85	72
Drain Pipes in the retaining wall	98.0	1.51	61

Until now (more than one year after construction), the outflowing water has always been clear. This indicates that the drainability and the protection ability against piping of the geotextile filter are good.

CONCLUSIONS

The nonwoven geotextile with a mass per unit area of 550g/m² has satisfied the engineering requirements in this application.

Moreover, the observation shows that it works very well when it is required to function as a filter.

Compared with the conventional sand gravel filter the nonwoven geotextile filter has many advantages.

The cost of the geotextile filter including placing fee ranges between 20% to 30% of the cost of the conventional granular filter.

REFERENCES

Giroud, J.P., "Introduction to Geotextiles and their Applications", Proc. of the 1st. Canadian Symposium on Geotextiles, Calgary, Sep. 1980, pp. 3-31.

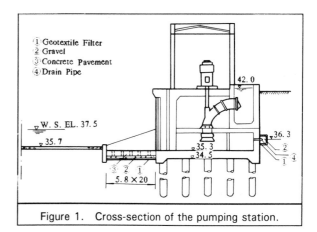

Figure 1. Cross-section of the pumping station.

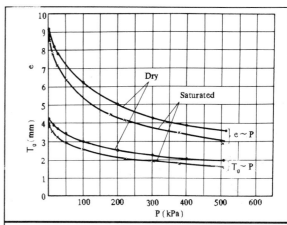

Figure 2. Results of compressibility test on the selected nonwoven geotextile.

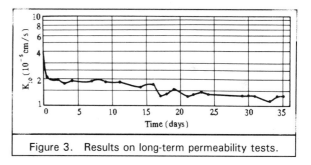

Figure 3. Results on long-term permeability tests.

Hoare, D.J., "Synthetic Fabrics As Soil Filters: A Review", Proc. ASCE., Journal of the Geotechnical Engineering Division, Oct. 1982, pp. 1230-1245.

GEOTEXTILE FILTER UNDER BITUMINOUS CONCRETE RESERVOIR LINING
GEESTE RESERVOIR, GERMANY

H. Schmidt
Bezirksregierung Weser-Ems
Oldenburg, Germany

More than 2,000,000 m² of geotextile filter were installed under a bituminous concrete lining of Geeste Reservoir. The geotextile essentially acts as a separator between the sandy supporting soil and the crushed stone on which the bituminous concrete lining is constructed.

THE PROJECT

The Energy Supply Company Vereinigte Elektrizitätswerke Westfalen AG, Dortmund, Federal Republic of Germany, built together with Elektromark AG through Vewelektromark Speicherbecken Geeste o HG in the Federal Country of Lower Saxony, Rural District Emsland the "Reservoir Geeste" (Photo 1). This reservoir was built between 1983 and 1986. It has a capacity of about 23,000,000 m³ and a water surface when full of about 1.8 km². The base and interior embankment of the artificial basin are sealed with asphaltic concrete. During periods when the river Ems has a flow of less than about 5 m³/s the reservoir is required to supply additional water for the operation of the cooling tower of the 1,300 MW Nuclear Power Station in Lingen.

The essential components of the reservoir are the ring dam which was erected with sand obtained from the interior of the basin, the sealing layer composed of asphaltic concrete, and the appurtenant structures for the filling and discharge of the basin.

CONSTRUCTION OF THE SEAL

The seal has the following design above the sand foundation:

- a polyester nonwoven needlepunched geotextile with a thickness of at least 4.5 mm,
- chips layer from crushed limestone with a grain size of 11/32 mm and a medium thickness of 200 mm,
- binding layer of 70 mm (at least 50 mm) from asphaltic concrete with a grain size of 0/16 mm,
- asphaltic fine concrete seal of at least 70 mm with a grain size of 0/11 mm,
- mastic cover out of bitumen and filler in the zone of the embankments (protection of the seal against UV-radiation).

FUNCTION AND STRAIN OF THE GEOTEXTILE FILTER

The geotextile forms the separating layer between the sands outcrops in the base and the layer of chips to be built above. The geotextile is intended to provide a filter-stable transition. The filter efficacy of the geotextile is generally evaluated according to two criteria - the hydraulic and the mechanical filter specification. Concerning the application of the geotextile in this reservoir, the hydraulic filter efficacy is not a safety requirement.

The mechanical filter efficacy of the geotextile guarantees erosion protection at the chips/sand interface under hydrodynamic loading should the geotextile be required to filter away the sand grains under the effect of the flow forces. Depending on the flow direction, the following cases could result concerning the Geeste reservoir:

- flow of fine-grained sand into the chips layer (hydraulic descent from the bottom to the top at an increasing ground water level)
- flow from the chips layer into the fine-grained sand (hydraulic descent from the top to the bottom at leakages in the seal) and
- flow in the chips layer parallel to the chips/sand layer interface.

CONSTRUCTION INSTALLATION AND CONTROL TESTS

Before the installation, samples were taken from each geotextile filter delivery (as a rule about 12,500 m²) in the presence of the building owner and the federal local building supervision (Water Conservation Bureau Meppen). The following control tests were executed on the site:

- thickness
- mass per unit area
- tensile strength longitudinally and widthwise

Furthermore, test institutes named in an agreement with the Water Conservation Bureau Meppen executed the following control tests on the geotextile filter samples which were taken on average from each 75,000 m² of geotextile filter delivered:

- material (fibre raw material)
- thickness
- mass per unit area
- mechanical filter efficacy
- hydraulic filter efficacy
- water permeability
- digging-wet maximum tensile strength (DIN 53 858)
- seam test
- temperature resistance
- disruptive strength

A total of 103,230 m² of geotextile filter was rejected and could not be used for installation. Therefore, a waste of 4.9% resulted with respect to an installed geotextile filter area of 2,093,000 m².

Photo 1. Aerial photo.

Photo 2. Basin seal on the soil.

A total of 229 control tests were carried through on the site and 28 control tests in test institutes.

The results of the control tests have shown that the delivered geotextile filter material differed considerably from the pre-construction material. This difference occurred mainly in relation to the mass per unit area and the tensile strength.

The required average tensile strength of 800 N was only reached with mass per unit area of about 600 g/m² and greater.

In addition it was found that the geotextile material was not uniform.

The manufacturer delivered the geotextile filter ready made and rolled up in a width of 6.20 m and a length of 50 m. After the execution of the described control tests and the installation release by the federal local building supervision, an "Unimog" transported the geotextile rolls to the place of installation. Here the geotextile was unrolled on the prepared sand foundation using an overlapping width of of at least 500 mm. Possible foreign matters such as, for example, stones and chips were required to be previously removed.

Especially in the embankment area, the geotextile was not allowed to be permanently fixed to the ground. This was so that any tensile stresses occurring at the surface of the chips layer and the seal would be immediately reduced. Direct passing over of the installed geotextiles with building implements or heavy vehicles was forbidden. The installation of the chips layer above the filter geotextile took place with angle dozers in such a manner that the dozer did not pass directly over the geotextile until it had been covered with a 200 mm thick chips layer. In order to protect the filter geotextile, one had to drop the chips from a low height (below 2 m) onto the filter geotextile. The drivers of heavy vehicles were advised to avoid turning sharply or on one spot.

During the installation of the geotextile filter, inspections to examine the condition of the geotextile and of the seams, as well as of the overlapping width proved to be essential. It was possible to identify large areas of unevenness (e.g. thinning which resulted from production). Also, due to carelessness, chips were allowed to get under the geotextile into direct contact with the sand foundation.

In these areas, holes appeared in the geotextile. The damaged geotextile then had to be underlain with undamaged geotextile filter. During the winter pause, the parts of the geotextile which were not covered with crushed stones were lain on the seal layer and covered with crushed stones. Here it was also necessary to examine visually whether the geotextile was damaged and whether or not crushed stones lay between the geotextile overlaps. Such stones could easily destroy the geotextile.

FINAL REMARK

The laying of the asphalt seal with the largest paved area in the world (Photo 2) was completed in November 1986. The continuous delivery of about 2,000,000 m² of filter geotextile - distributed over 3 years (except winter) - raised problems concerning the production technique. Once this was finally mastered the installation took place speedily and rationally. The type of the building installation has stood the test.

REFERENCES

Schmidt, H and Täubert, U., "Einbau und Kontrolle des Filtervlieses beim Bau des Speicherbeckens Geeste", Wasserwirtschaft 77/1987, Booklet 6.

Täubert, U., "Das Speicherbecken Geeste - Zwei Millionen Quadratmeter Filtervlies und Asphaltbeton-Dichtung", Mitteilungen des Franzius-Instituts für Wasserbau und Küsteningenieurwesen der Universität Hannover, Booklet 62 (1986), pp. 146-159.

GEOMEMBRANE FOR RESERVOIR WATERPROOFING
MT. ELBERT FOREBAY RESERVOIR, COLORADO, USA

R.K. Frobel
Geosynthetics Consulting Engineering
Evergreen, Colorado, USA

In 1980, the Mt. Elbert Forebay Reservoir was lined with 1.15 mm thick reinforced chlorinated polyethylene (CPER) geomembrane. The 117-ha installation was the largest single cell lining installation in the world. The owner, the U.S. Bureau of Reclamation (USBR), lined the reservoir with a continuous polymeric geomembrane due to excessive seepage through a previously constructed compacted earth lining which was threatening the stability of an ancient landslide in the hillside directly south of the reservoir [Morrison et al., 1981].

DESCRIPTION

The 117-ha Mt. Elbert Forebay Reservoir is located immediately north of Twin Lakes, a pair of glacial-age lakes located 24 km southwest of Leadville, Colorado, USA. Located at an elevation of 2,940 m, the reservoir serves as the forebay for the Mt. Elbert Pumped Storage Powerplant, which is 133 m below the reservoir. The forebay reservoir and power plant are used to provide peaking power for the East Slope Power System of the Bureau's Fryingpan-Arkansas project.

The reservoir has a capacity of 14,250,000 m^3 of water of which 8,800,000 m^3 are available for electric power generation. Two 103-MW hydroelectric turbine-generators, which generate the power, are designed also to operate as 127-MW reversible pump turbines to pump water back from Twin Lakes to the forebay during off-peak hours.

The original reservoir was completed in 1977 by construction of a 27 m high zoned earth dam across the open north side of a topographic depression and a small dike in the open southwest corner of the depression. Because the original compacted earth lining failed to restrict water flow out of the reservoir, a decision was made to dewater the reservoir and place a continuous polymeric geomembrane over the entire forebay bottom and side slopes [Frobel and Gray, 1984].

Once the decision was made to cover the reservoir with a continuous geomembrane, an exhaustive state-of-the-art survey was completed on existing geomembrane products, seaming methods, and material availability. Specifications for the Mt. Elbert lining were issued by the USBR in January, 1980 [USBR, 1980], the contract for installation was awarded April 16, 1980, and final installation of the 1.15 mm thick CPER geomembrane and earth cover was completed on September 20, 1980.

Geomembrane

The CPER geomembrane is of three-layer construction consisting of two equal thicknesses of CPE (chlorinated polyethylene) laminated to one layer of 10 by 10, 1,000-denier polyester scrim. The specified physical properties requirements for this lining are given by Frobel and Gray [1984].

The lining was fabricated into "blankets", each 1,300 m^2 in size and weighing approximately 2,300 kg. Two shapes of blankets were furnished: 61 m by 21 m containing 14 factory seams made with a Leister™ hot-air gun, and 30 m by 43 m, containing 29 factory seams made dielectrically.

To install the geomembrane lining, labour crews unfolded and positioned the blankets. Adjacent blankets were overlapped a minimum of 150 mm. A three-man crew thoroughly cleaned the contact surfaces with trichloroethylene solvent, and the manufacturer's bodied solvent CPE adhesive was applied to a minimum width of 100 mm. After the field seams were tested and approved, a cap strip was applied over the field seam. The cap strip consisted of a 0.76 mm thick non-reinforced CPE, 75 mm in width. An extensive QA (quality assurance) program [Frobel, 1983] was conducted in conjunction with the Mt. Elbert flexible membrane lining installation.

PERFORMANCE

Reservoir

The forebay reservoir was filled beginning January 1981 and has maintained the operating level of 2,940 m since that time with the exception of short periods of pool drawdown.

Piezometers and observation wells installed in the hillside south of the reservoir continue to be monitored. In general, there has been no appreciable rise in ground-water levels since the relining of the forebay. Inclinometers installed along the south side have not indicated any movement of the old landslide mass.

Geomembrane

In an effort to monitor long-term performance of the CPER geomembrane system, a special test section was installed in the reservoir. The 6 m by 30 m test section was installed at a location within the reservoir that would allow periodic access for retrieval of test coupons.

Eleven test panels (or coupons) comprised the total test section. Each test panel was made up of all three types of seams used in the project, which included hot air, dielectric, and bodied solvent adhesive (field seams). The

Photo 1. Overview of reservoir under construction

test panels were placed on a 50 mm layer of fine sand directly above the Mt. Elbert forebay lining and then covered with the same 450 mm earth cover. Thus, the panels can be extracted and tested without disturbing the original CPER geomembrane lining system.

The first coupon panel test program for the test section was begun in the spring of 1981, and test panels were taken on a yearly basis for 5 years. Since no significant changes occurred after 5 years, coupon extracting and testing will be accomplished at greater time intervals until all coupons are tested. The last sampling was accomplished in the fall of 1987.

The following physical and mechanical property tests were conducted on the coupons to determine changes in the CPER sheet material and seams:

- Mass and Thickness
- Mullen Burst Hydrostatic Resistance (ASTM D751-79, Method A)
- Large-Scale Hydrostatic Resistance (USBR Procedure)
- Ply Adhesion (ASTM D 413-76, Machine Method A)
- Tongue Tear Resistance (ASTM D 751, Method B)
- Seam Peel Strength (ASTM D 1876-78)
- Seam Shear Strength (ASTM D 751)

Original test specimens were taken from the same blanket samples as those used to fabricate the test section. Thus, results from extracted coupons are a direct comparison of statistical properties within the same original blanket panel.

Generally, any significant changes in the CPER and seams occurred within the first 3 years of service. There has been very little additional change even after 7 years of exposure [Morrison, 1988]. The following summary observations on test results after 7 years of exposure can be made:

- Mass Gain - The CPER moisture absorption has levelled off at 18%, which is slightly above the expected absorption rate indicated by laboratory testing.
- Mullen Burst Hydrostatic Resistance - This mechanical property has dropped approximately 15% and primarily reflects some change in scrim strength or total composite.
- Large-Scale Hydrostatic Resistance - No significant change.
- Ply Adhesion Resistance - This mechanical property dropped an average of 30%, reflecting a reduction

in scrim/CPE bond and/or CPE polymer strength at the "strike-through".
- Tongue Tear Resistance - Inconclusive due to the wide range of results.
- Seam Peel Strength - The thermal dielectric and hot air seams showed a loss in peel strength of approximately 25%, whereas the adhesive field seams showed a lower percent loss in strength of approximately 11%.
- Seam Shear Strength - The thermally bonded seams (hot air and dielectric) showed a strength loss of approximately 55% after 3 years, and this has not changed significantly after 7 years. The adhesive seams showed a loss in strength of approximately 30%.

The loss in shear strength does not reflect actual seam interface failure (i.e., CPE to CPE bond using adhesive or thermal welding) but rather the polyester scrim pullout at the seam overlap. It is apparent that the scrim/CPE bond within the CPER laminate has deteriorated, and this weakening of bond is being reflected in loss in mechanical properties such as the Mullen hydrostatic, ply adhesion, and most notably the overlap seam shear strength. Because the specified overlaps resulted in only 25 mm of scrim-to-scrim bond (for the thermally welded bonds), the 25 mm overlap is the only contributing area for the seam shear values. The adhesive field seam requires a 100 mm wide bonded area and thus had more scrim-to-scrim contact area, which resulted in a less dramatic loss in tensile shear. In all cases of seam shear testing, the scrim pulled out of the overlaps relatively easily as compared to original unsaturated testing [Frobel and Gray, 1984].

The water absorption of the CPE sheet material is primarily responsible for the observed mechanical property changes in the CPER and CPER seams. These changes are not considered detrimental to the overall integrity of the Mt. Elbert Forebay geomembrane [Frobel and Gray, 1984]. In fact, the test results obtained at 3 years of exposure did not change significantly after 5 and 7 year testing. The Mt. Elbert geomembrane is serving its intended design function and is expected to continue to do so for many years to come.

REFERENCES

Frobel, R.K., "Quality Assurance Program for the Mt. Elbert Forebay Flexible Membrane Lining Installation", Proc., Symposium on Waterproofing Membranes for Dams, Paris, France, Feb 1983.

Frobel, R.K. and Gray, E.W., "Performance of the Fabric-Reinforced Geomembrane at Mt. Elbert Forebay Reservoir", Proc., Int. Conf. on Geomembranes, IFAI, Denver, CO, 1984, pp. 421-426.

Morrison, W.R., Gray, E.W., Paul, D.B. and Frobel, R.K., Installation of Flexible Membrane Lining in Mt. Elbert Forebay Reservoir, USBR REC-ERC-82-2, 1981.

Morrison, W.R., Personal communication, Feb 1988.

U.S. Bureau of Reclamation, Mt. Elbert Forebay Reservoir Membrane Lining, Fryingpan-Arkansas Project, Colorado, USBR Specifications No. DC-7418, 1981.

GEOMEMBRANE RESERVOIR WATERPROOFING
THE MUNA RESERVOIR PROJECT, SAUDI ARABIA

B. Rawlings
Niederberg-Chemie GmbH
Lübbecke, Germany

The Muna Reservoir Project involved the construction of a large bulk water storage reservoir. The reservoir is located in the Sarayai hills near the holy area of Muna, in the Kingdom of Saudi Arabia. The reservoir was planned to provide an adequate supply of drinking water for the pilgrims visiting Mecca during the Haj Season.

DESCRIPTION

The contract required the construction of a large water-storage reservoir in the basin of a valley. The ground consisted of natural rock formation, in the base and on three sides. The fourth side was created from imported infill materials, forming an artificial dam. It included the trimming and compaction of the reservoir embankment slopes, the spreading and compaction of a 400 mm thick shell layer, the laying of an asphalt concrete sub-base layer and the final waterproof lining using an impermeable geomembrane lining system. The function of the asphalt layer was to reduce the possible scouring effects on the underside of the geomembrane and importantly to provide a more flexible sub-base capable of withstanding any settlement that might occur in the embankments. It was also considered that an asphalt layer would reduce water loss in the event that the geomembrane lining was damaged during the operating of the reservoir. The actual waterproofing of the reservoir was to be achieved solely by use of the impermeable geomembrane.

CONSTRUCTION

The asphalt sub-base lining consisted of a 120 mm thickness of bituminous wearing course, laid in two layers each 60 mm thick. A layer of prime coat was applied to the compacted shell layer, prior to laying the first 60 mm asphalt base course. Then a tack coat was applied to this first asphalt layer and another 60 mm asphalt surface (wearing course) was laid. The asphalt paving was carried out in four metre wide widths, with staggered vertical joints using a paving unit. The paving unit was supported on the steep embankment slopes by means of a winch portal placed at the embankment crest and pulled up the slopes by cable. Each layer was compacted, first by a 1.5 tonne tandem vibro roller and then by a 4.5 tonne tandem vibro roller, working from the embankment base to the embankment crest. A final compaction ratio of more than 90% was essential. A 2.5 mm thick Carbofol geomembrane was selected.

GEOMEMBRANE

For the impermeable layer the specification dictated that the geomembrane will be supplied from the manufacturing facility of Niederberg-Chemie GmbH, in large panels 6.00 m wide with a minimum length not less than 55.00 m. Geomembrane sheets of this length were required to cover the complete embankment, without the need for horizontal joints along the embankment slope. The large geomembrane sheets had to be tough and at the same time flexible. They had to be manufactured from material that was completely watertight. They must also provide adequate resistance to puncture, tear and abrasion. An elongation of at least 300% before breaking was specified. The geomembrane had to be able to accommodate any stress likely to develop either during construction or in the operating conditions of the reservoir, in both short and long term duration. Fully developed geomembrane connection details were required at the top of the embankment, around the massive concrete columns, and against the inlet and outlet structure. The concrete

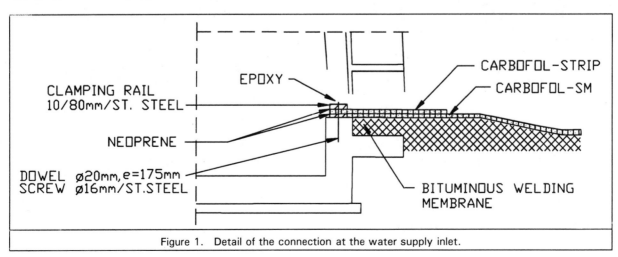

Figure 1. Detail of the connection at the water supply inlet.

Photo 1. Photograph showing asphalt wearing course on embankment slope.

Photo 2. Photograph showing the Carbofol geomembrane lining system and support columns for the roof structure.

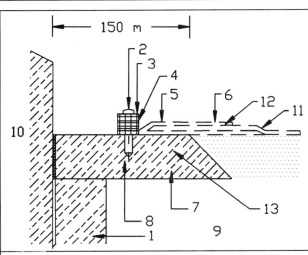

1 CONCRETE BASE
2 STAINLESS STEEL BOLT
3 STAINLESS STEEL RAIL
4 NEOPRENE 5 mm
5 FLEECE 800 g/m^2
6 ASPHALT
7 CONCRETE COLLAR
8 DOWEL
9 COMPACTED SOIL
10 COLUMN
11 CARBOFOL - SEALING MEMBRANE
12 CARBOFOL STRIP
13 MECHANICAL FASTENING

Figure 2. Detail against the massive concrete roof support columns.

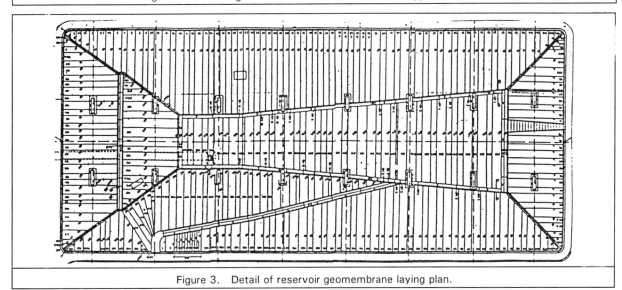

Figure 3. Detail of reservoir geomembrane laying plan.

columns were also lined to a height of 30 m with an impermeable geomembrane. This provided waterproofing to the exposed concrete surface, below the operating level of the reservoir.

FINAL COMMENT

Carbofol geomembranes and systems include air pressure methods of inspection and testing of the site welded seams. The double welded seam has a monitoring channel, running through the centre of the seam for pneumatic testing of the seam tightness. This method has been recognised by the leading authorities as being the most practical and effective method.

REFERENCES

Non supplied.

GEOMEMBRANE SEALING FOR AN IRRIGATION CANAL
KIRKUK, IRAQ

B. Kopp
Niederberg-Chemie, GMBH
Lübbecke, Germany

Frequently water occurrences in desert regions are accumulated for use by large irrigation projects. This is true of the main canal near Kirkuk, Iraq.

DESCRIPTION

An irrigation project starting near Kirkuk, Iraq, consists of a 120 km long main canal. The construction has progressed over many years. The canal transports the water of the river Tigris through desert areas. Near the city of Kirkuk some of the Tigris water flow is conducted through a retaining dam into the canal. On the way to the city of Dakuk the canal water supplies newly constructed agricultural areas, by means of numerous smaller secondary canals. The main canal passes through regions where the soil, in large areas, consists of gypsum formations. In similar projects involving these formations erosion of such gypsum formations (called dolines) has led to the destruction of the whole canal. Such destruction caused an interruption of the water supply.

Decision for Use of a Geomembrane

The decision for the use of an artificial waterproofing on this project was made because of following aspects:

- very high water tightness requirement
- short construction time
- cost
- testability of the geomembrane
- possibility of connection to various constructions
- root resistance
- no danger of erosion caused by waves
- geomembrane layer and therefore less earth excavation

Geometry of the Canal

The total length of the canal is approximately 120 km. Two sections of the canal were constructed with a thermoplastic waterproofing geomembrane. The waterproofed sections involved a length of about 32 km near Kirkuk with a total surface area of 2,500,000 m^2, and a further 25 km near Dakuk, with a total area of 1,800,000 m^2. The cross section of the canal was adapted to the geometrical conditions of the landscape. The designed strata sequence of the canal is:

- 100 mm protective concrete
- 300 g/m^2 protective nonwoven geotextile
- Carbofol geomembrane, type CHD
- fine gravel formation
- large gravel

The protective concrete was laid with bay joints (about 3 x 5 m field size).

GEOMEMBRANE

Material Values

In all Geomembrane systems the most important factor is the jointing behaviour of the geomembrane. Carbofol can be welded nearly independent of the weather at outside temperatures between -5° to +50°C. The large range of material welding temperature makes welding much easier than some other geomembranes and reduces the danger of a welding failure. The mechanical properties of Carbofol geomembranes are specified in Table 1. It has an elongation at break amounting to about 500% at low deformation modulus - sliding modulus is about 2.5 N/m^3 - they are very deformable.

Table 1. Mechanical and physical characteristics (median values) for Carbofol lining geomembranes 2 mm, standard sheets		
	Test Spec.	Result
Ultimate tensile strength, long. (MPa)	DIN 53 455	10
Ultimate tensile strength, trans. (MPa)	DIN 53 455	8
Elongation at failure long./trans. (%)	DIN 53 455	550
Hardness (Shore A)	DIN 53 505	80 ± 2
Tear resistance, long./trans. (MPa)	DIN 53 363	150
Mod. of elasticity (MPa) (1-2% Moduli) long.	DIN 53 457	55
(1-2% Moduli) trans.	DIN 16 726 E	55
Slotted disc water (h) pressure test at 15 bar	DIN 16 726 E	100
Water vapour permeability (g/m^2)	DIN 53 122	0.75
Water vapour diffusion resistance coefficient	-	≥ 20,000
Cold bend test (°C)	DIN 53 361	-25
Fire classification	DIN 4 102	B2
Dimensional change after storage at 6 hours/80°C (%)	DIN 16 726 E	< 0.5
Test certificate and expert opinions of government. Testing laboratories and recognized independent institutes are available for inspection.		

Photo 1. After completion of the slope base the prefabricated geomembranes were installed.

Photo 2. Overflowed canal.

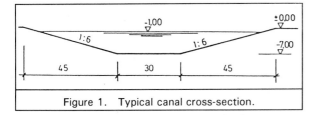

Figure 1. Typical canal cross-section.

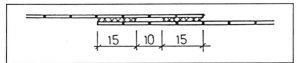

Figure 2. Welding seam as double seam with testing canal.

Biochemical Behaviour

The canal was constructed with the intention that it must operate for a long time. Long-time performance of the material, more than 50 years, was considered essential. Therefore, the climatical, chemical and biological resistance of the water-proofing material are of utmost importance. Carbofol complies with the following requirements:

- indifference to influences of natural acid, alkaline or saline ground, dammed-up or seepage water as well as the normal chemical influences of the adjacent structural parts
- high long-time behaviour
- resistance to rooting
- no tendency to soften
- resistance to micro and macro organism
- high resistance to heat and cold
- high UV-resistance

Furthermore, in particular cases, the material is resistant to penetrations and rodents.

Connection and Laying Method

Carbofol geomembranes are welded homogeneously by means of hot gas welding using hot air or contact welding along with a hot plate. The prefabrication is a very important factor for correct installation.

The welding of Carbofol geomembranes can be performed under many conditions as follows:

- nearly independent of the weather
- adapted to the rough site conditions
- a welding factor of more than 0.9
- easy to handle
- control is possible
- independent of the geometrical conditions

Welding Seam Testing

Welding seams were executed as overlapping seams with a double seam. All welded seams were tested for tightness and strength by means of air pressure. Connection works and repair works were tested for tightness with vacuum testing equipment. Prior to the installation of the protective geotextile a visual check, with regard to mechanical damages was also carried out.

CONSTRUCTION DETAILS

Suspension Ditch

The edge termination was executed with a so-called suspension ditch. It must be observed that there is no underflow of water below the geomembrane and that all forces acting on the slope will be absorbed by the friction resistance between the ground and the geomembrane.

Connections and Terminations to Structures

All connections and terminations were constructed in accordance with DIN 4031, now renamed DIN 18 195.

CONCLUSIONS

The project commenced in 1980. All geomembrane lining works have been carried out on time and according to quality standards. In spite of extreme climatic conditions (summer temperatures up to 50°C in the shade, winter -5°C) the geomembrane lining installation continued throughout the full year. The first part was put in service in 1982, the second part in 1983. Permanent checking of the control drainage has proved satisfactory function and performance of the installed geomembrane.

REFERENCES

Non supplied.

GEOTEXTILE FILTER TO ACCELERATE SLUDGE CONSOLIDATION CALLENMANSPUTTE BASIN, BELGIUM

F. De Meerleer
UCO Technical Fabrics N.V.
Lokeren, Belgium

For the dumping of toxic dredging sludge from the Gent-Terneuzen canal, the Belgian Ministry of Public Works built at Callenmansputte, near Gent, a basin with a depth of 20 m, a length of 700 m and a width of 220 m. In order to accelerate consolidation a geotextile filter, a very permeable sand layer, and a vacuum system, were used.

DESCRIPTION

The Dumping Area

A cement bentonite diaphragm wall, shown in Figure 1, in combination with an existing thick clay layer was used to prevent migration of contaminants into the surrounding soils of the basin and the ground water. The sludge has a very high water content, a very low permeability and consists of fine soil particles. The basin filled rapidly so that the dumping of new dredged material was no longer possible. As the entrance for sea going ships into the canal had to be guaranteed, extra storage area was required to be created quickly.

Design

A cost effective solution is illustrated in Figure 1. The area is covered with a polypropylene woven geotextile. Drainage pipes are placed on the geotextiles. These are covered by a very permeable sand layer approximately 1 m thick and a geomembrane.

According to the initial design, accelerated consolidation is to be creating by a vertical pressure on the sludge, using an applied partial vacuum of 60 kPa. This will increase the storage capacity by about 4 m in a short time period. The new sludge dumping will further accelerate consolidation.

Construction of the Drain

The bearing capacity of the dredged sludge is almost nil, making access impossible. Therefore extra water is pumped over the whole area. This allows the flotation of the woven polypropylene geotextile (specific gravity 0.9). After spreading the geotextile, a pontoon is used to disperse a 1 m thick sand layer. The sand is a ballast to the geotextile.

TECHNICAL CONSIDERATIONS

Geotextile Selection

During towing on the water of the 150,000 m² geotextile blanket, important forces will occur on the fabric and on the seams. The tensile strength necessary for this

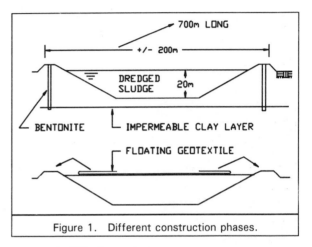

Figure 1. Different construction phases.

purpose is difficult to calculate. A rough calculation of the probable stresses indicated that the woven geotextile UCO SG 52/60 would do the job.

The opening size (O_{90}) of 350 microns was deemed large enough to prevent the phenomena of clogging and blocking. Water circulation during the whole consolidation period is in fact essential.

The basic chemical material, polypropylene, is resistant to the chemicals in the sludge. Due to exposure of several months to sunlight, UV stabilization is of paramount importance.

The characteristics of the selected geotextile are:

Mass per unit area	:	270 g/m²
Tensile strength (roll direction)	:	52 kN/m
Tensile strength (cross-roll direction)	:	60 kN/m
Strain at failure (roll direction)	:	20%
Strain at failure (cross-roll direction)	:	8%
Coefficient of normal permeability	:	35 mm/s
Opening size	:	350 μm

Construction

The geotextile was installed in July 1987. At one side of the pond, a ramp was prepared. The geotextile was unrolled parallel to the embankment and the 10 m wide strips were sewn together as the work progressed (approximately 2,000 m of seams per working day). The lengths of the strips were already adapted to follow the irregular geometry of the pond. The geotextile, fixed to floating tubes, was towed over the water by winches installed on the opposite embankment. To avoid friction of the lateral embankments, the lanes were folded lengthwise.

| Photo 1. Unrolling of the 10 m wide geotextile parallel to the embankment prior to seaming. | Photo 2. Towing the geotextile (700 m x 220 m), fixed to floating reclamation tubes over the water. |

| Photo 3. Towing the geotextile (700 m x 220 m), fixed to floating reclamation tubes over the water. | Photo 4. Geotextile, drainage tubes and sand supplying pontoon. |

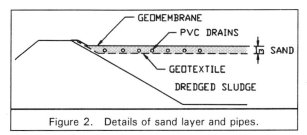

Figure 2. Details of sand layer and pipes.

Drainage pipes to accelerate evacuation of water from the sand, were sewn into seams on the geotextile as shown in the Figure 2. When the whole pond was covered, the geotextile floating on the water was ballasted locally to allow navigation of a sand supplying pontoon. Speed of the pontoon was monitored carefully to obtain a sand layer of uniform thickness, even with changing rates of discharge of the sand supplying unit.

PERFORMANCE

Due to a very important increase in the quantities of dredging sludge to be stored, it was decided to abandon the initial proposal of vacuum consolidation. The existing embankment was raised slightly more than 6 m height. This created new storage capacity very rapidly. Under these conditions it was not possible to monitor the consolidation process.

CONCLUSIONS

Although it seems impossible to handle a geotextile blanket 700 m x 220 m, this case study proves the opposite. This technique of covering water surfaces with a geotextile and ballasting it with sand will certainly find other applications, such as reclamation of mining ponds.

REFERENCE

De Meerleer, F., "Application and recent new ideas for cost-effective design with geotextiles", Proc. Post-Vienna Conference on Geotextiles, Singapore, 1987, pp. 277 - 285.

GEOTEXTILES FOR CONSOLIDATION OF SLUDGE LAGOONS
TRURO, UNITED KINGDOM, AND CARLING, FRANCE

P. Risseeuw and W. Voskamp
Akzo Industrial Systems bv.
Arnhem, The Netherlands

Local authorities and/or companies often have a major problem in finding effective means of disposing of industrial waste materials in the form of liquids of chemical material. Often such materials are mixed with soft clay and give a consistency of soft sludge.

DESCRIPTION

Consolidation of Sludge Lagoons

Typical examples of this nature are a water treatment work in the United Kingdom and a waste disposal lagoon for a large chemical factory in the north east of France. For many years, the owners have pumped their leftover sludges into lagoons with depths between 5 and 6 m. The sludge material dries out only after a very long period of time. The idea in each example was to cover the lagoon with sand/gravel to speed up consolidation once the lagoons had reached their highest levels.

Design and Construction

The very weakness of this "heavy water" does not permit anyone to even walk on its surface. Its weakness also meant that a sand/gravel "capping" material would sink almost immediately.

In 1983, the Dutch company Akzo, proposed a method of construction which enabled each client to dump sand-fill evenly in thin layers, on top of a double layer of heavy-duty polyester reinforcing geotextile by small bulldozers. After an initial layer of 0.50 - 1.00 m of fill had been placed on top of the geotextile, over the total area of

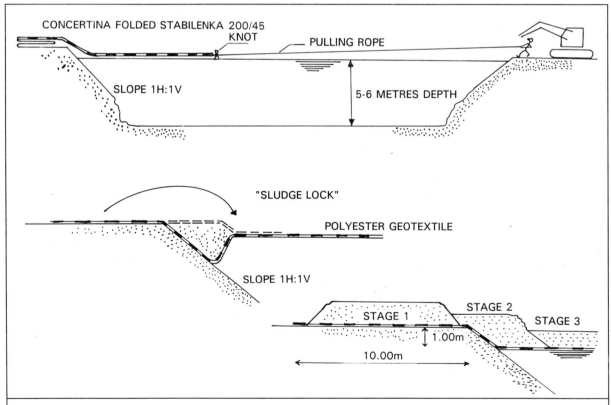

Figure 1. Method of installation of geotextile.
Top: Pulling geotextile across sludge.
Centre: After the geotextile had been installed, a "sludge lock" was created to prevent sludge from squeezing out during initial fill placement.
Bottom: Completion of installation.

Photo 1. The installing of the Stabilenka 200/45 geotextile over the lagoons and anchoring into position.

Photo 2. Once installed, the geotextile was strong enough to give support to 4 t bulldozers, while spreading fingers of fill material during the initial filling process.

the lagoons, it was clearly seen that no mud waves had developed. This meant that, after a short period, the top fill could be raised to a 3.00 m layer of fill.

PERFORMANCE

Consolidation of the Sludge

Three years after the project was completed, it was established that the fill settled uniformly down into the sludge material and speeded up the consolidation process. The initial void ratio had dropped from 2.5 to 1.5.

Installation Method

In such projects, the lagoon sides are first prepared for installing the geotextile by grading the slopes to a gradient of 1H:1V (see installation scheme). As far as possible, the sludge surface was cleared of roots, bushes, glass and metal. Stabilenka geotextile type 200/45 on 5.00 m wide rolls were sewn together to panels of 140 x 120 m; this gives a dead-weight of 8 tonne. The geotextile sheets were folded in a concertina fashion at the edges of the lagoon and then pulled across the surface by ropes. The two geotextile layers were laid in opposing directions to guarantee enough and uniform strength in all directions. An overlap of 5 m to 10 m at the borders was necessary to enable the geotextile to be folded back after the filling of "a sludge lock" or as an anchoring length.

Once the geotextile had been installed, small 4 tonne bulldozers started to spread forward small fingers of fill material to a maximum height of 1 m. These extended out towards the middle of the lagoon.

From these access strips, a uniform filling was performed afterwards.

REFERENCE

Sludge lagoons, Truro-U.K. and Carling-France

Client: 1.   South West Water Authority, Truro.
            2.   CDF, Société Chimique des Charbonnages, Carling.
Consultant: City of Truro/CDF Chimie S.A.
Contractors: City of Truro/Müller Fréres
Construction period: 1983, 1984.

GEOTEXTILE FOR BENTONITE SLUDGE POND CLOSURE
SOUTHEAST WYOMING, USA

J.N. Paulson
Exxon Chemical Company
Atlanta, Georgia, USA

The Wyoming Department of Environmental Quality required closure and capping of a bentonite-mine sludge pond that presented a hazard to livestock from adjacent ranches. Typical bentonite sludge pond closures in this area utilize the mixing method of stabilization, where local soils are mixed with the sludge to increase soil shear strength. The extremely soft sludge dictated another solution which utilized a geotextile as reinforcement. A high-strength reinforcing geotextile followed by 500 mm of lightweight sawdust fill and 3-4 m of soil cover was selected as the final closure cross section.

DESCRIPTION

The pond is located in southeast Wyoming. Pond dimensions were approximately 135 m long by 7 m wide, surrounded by perimeter dikes. Sludge depths varied from 4 to 8 m. Closure was begun in late 1986 and was completed in early 1987.

TECHNICAL CONSIDERATIONS

Site Conditions

The bentonite tailings were so soft, with shear strengths of consistently less than 5 kPa, that conventional displacement and mixing methods were thought to be ineffective. The alternative selected was a geotextile-reinforced soil cap. The geotextile provided separation between the underlying soft clays and the upper closure fill, and tensile reinforcement to prevent lateral spreading.

The reinforcement minimize mud waves, and prevent rotational-type failures during cover fill placement. A 500 mm layer of sawdust and wood chips was spread over the geotextile prior to the cover soil placement. This resulted in a reduction in bearing pressure induced by the fill weight and placement equipment.

Geotextile Considerations

A stitchbonded composite woven polypropylene geotextile, GTF-800 manufactured by Exxon Chemical Company, was used as the geotextile reinforcement. This is composed of four layers of flat tape fabric stitched together using closely spaced (10 mm) stitchlines and 200 to 300 stitches/m. This material has a wide-width strip tensile strength (ASTM D4595) of 100 kN/m in the roll direction and 90 kN/m in the cross-roll direction.

The stitchbonding process produces a stiff fabric with flexural rigidity (ASTM D1388) at a very high 290,000 mg-cm. This contributed to the workability and ease of installation, both of which are critical for softsite closures [Paulson, 1987].

Seams

Seam strengths of 50 kN/m were specified. These strengths were achieved by using field sewing with a union special 80,200Z sewing machine sewing two stitch lines with Kevlar 420 thread and a "J" seam (FED SSn-2).

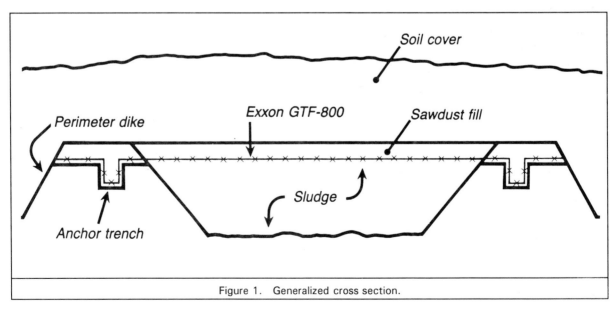

Figure 1. Generalized cross section.

Photo 1. Installation was completed in 30 minutes.

Photo 2. Compaction within anchor trench.

Photo 3. Lightweight wood chip placement.

GEOTEXTILE FABRICATION AND INSTALLATION

Field Fabrication

Because the sludge in the pond was too soft to walk on, the geotextile cover had to be sewn together and then installed as a single piece. To do this, 32 special-size panels, 61 m long by 3.8 m wide were unrolled in a stack at one end of the project site. As the panels were stacked, alternating edges (lengthwise) were sewn together. In this way, the entire panel, which folded accordion-style into a stack, was ready to be pulled over the pond surface.

The leading edge of the panel was looped back onto itself over a 25 mm diameter steel cable that ran the entire width of the leading edge of the panel. Tracked construction equipment was then placed at each end of the cable. These machines raised the leading edge of the panel off the ground and carried it to the other end of the pond, unfolding the fabric as they progressed. Seam strength was critical in assuring that the geotextile integrity was maintained during installation and subsequent covering operations.

Site Closure Procedure

Pond closure was achieved using the following sequence:

(1) An anchor trench was excavated around the pond perimeter, in the stable dike soil.

(2) The geotextile was installed over the entire pond area, the edges were embedded in the anchor trench, and the trench backfilled.

(3) A clay soil cap was placed on the top of the anchor trench to enhance anchoring prior to cover filling.

(4) A 500 mm thick layer of lightweight sawdust fill was blown over the entire pond area to help distribute earth work equipment track loads during the cover process.

(5) Cover soil was placed, filling from the perimeter towards the centre of the pond. Lifts of 600 mm or less were used. Once the initial lift thickness was placed, the whole process was repeated until the 3 to 4 m total height of cover soil was in place.

CONCLUSIONS

The use of a high strength woven geotextile provided a separation and reinforcing layer, and facilitated construction of this muck pond closure. High wide-width tensile seam strengths are necessary to maintain the integrity of the geotextile. Flexural rigidity can be an asset during the installation process. Close attention to seam construction, and installation details are important to the success of these types of geotextile applications.

REFERENCES

Paulson, J.N. and Langston, M.C., "Stitchbonded Composites", Proc., Geosynthetics '87, New Orleans, LA, 1987, pp. 193-204.

CHAPTER 3

SCOUR EROSION CONTROL

GEOTEXTILES FOR SCOUR PROTECTION OF A STORM SURGE BARRIER EASTERN SCHELDT, THE NETHERLANDS

K.A.G. Mouw
Rijkswaterstaat/President of The
Netherlands Geotextile Organization (N.G.O.)

A. Engelaan
Rijkswaterstaat/Board member of The
Netherlands Geotextile Organization (N.G.O.)

As part of the Delta Project a storm surge barrier has been built across the Eastern Scheldt estuary in the remaining channels Hammen, Schaar van Roggenplaat and Roompot.

The barrier consists of 66 piers and 63 sliding steel gates which can be lowered between the piers in case of emergency.

The 66 prefabricated piers were built in three separate construction docks. After transportation to the project site by the lifting vessel Ostrea they were installed on the sea bed without the need of pile foundations. To ensure the stability of the sandy soil beneath the piers a filter construction was placed on the sea bed. This construction, consisting of prefabricated mats, forms the foundation bed directly supporting the piers.

These filter mats were assembled in a specially designed plant. The plant was scheduled to supply the required number of mats within a period of 1.5 years.

FILTERMATS

Function of Filtermats

The mats consist of a filter construction of three graded layers of sand and gravel. They prevent migration of the sand of the sea bed and form a carefully composed transition to the layers of quarry stone that were placed around the base of the piers. They hold the underlying sand of the sea bed in position despite the pressures to which the barrier may be exposed. At the same time they provide sufficient drainage for the water. This latter function is of prime importance, since it ensures that the upper layer of sand is not washed away if the barrier is exposed to severe current action or heavy waves.

The lower mats, approximately 42 m wide and 200 m long, have a mass of about 5,500 t each. In order to prevent the mats from being damaged before and during the installation of the piers, a second smaller mat (upper mat) 30 m x 60 m was used immediately below the base of the pier.

In view of the very high standards required, both regarding quality and exact position, it was decided, after various ways of production had been considered, to prefabricate the mats and to transport them to their location. The filtermats were assembled on shore and simultaneously wound on to a 16 m diameter cylinder floating in front of the manufacturing plant.

Composition of Filter Mats

The lower mat that was laid directly on the prepared sea bed, is composed of three layers of material, in the following thicknesses:

- 110 mm sand   (0.3 to 2 mm grainsize)
- 110 mm gravel-sand   (2.0 to 8 mm grainsize)
- 140 mm gravel   (8.0 to 40 mm grainsize)

After laying the mats on the sea bed they were compacted by a beam. The thickness after compaction was 320 mm.

The underside of the mat consists of a supporting geotextile reinforced lengthways with steel wires. The wires increased the strength up to 725 kN/m width while limiting the elongation to no more than 0.2 %. The filtration of the bottom sand was realized by a nonwoven geotextile, used as an interlay.

All sand and gravel layers were separated by interlays. Each layer was related to the permeability of its underlying grains.

U-shaped steel wire baskets, of which the top edges are turned inwards 180° to enclose the geotextile filter, are inserted in all filter layers. This divides the mat breadthways into partitions. With the help of approximately eight 6 mm diameter steel pins/m^2, vertically injected through the mat and secured on both sides, the filter layers were consolidated into a compact mat. The filter material was thus protected from migration and shifting during the winding and unwinding operations.

The upper mats have a length of 65 m, a width of 30 m, and the same thickness as the lower mat. They were assembled in exactly the same way as the lower mats. In these mats the filter material consists only of gravel (8-40 mm). The supporting geotextile, as well as the top covering geotextile, both consisting of nine approximately 5 m widths that were stitched together to an overall width of 42 m. The side ends of these geotextiles, which during the assembling process had been turned up vertically, were also stitched together.

Both ends of the mats were stapled to wooden end units thus closing the mats.

Special Demands

Many tests were performed on the mats during the fabrication, winding, positioning and laying operations so as

Photo 1.   Filter mat assembly plant.

to obtain a thorough understanding of the mechanics and behaviour of the mats. One of the results of these tests made certain that no stretch was permitted in the supporting layer. This ensured that the thickness of the filter layers could not be destroyed through an increase of the mats length. A strength of more than 540 kN/m was needed to carry the weight of the hanging part of the mat during unwinding, in combination with current effects, and ship and anchoring forces. The maximum water depth involved was about 35 m. The top covering geotextile, being on the outside during the winding of the mat on to the cylinder had to stretch as much as 25%. As a result of the fixing points of the steel pins, this geotextile also had to stretch as much as 15% crosswise.

The primary function of the geotextiles of the filter mat is to act as packing for the filter materials during transport, laying operations, and during construction of the sill around the piers. They also have a long term function of acting as a second filter. By choosing this mat concept, double safety was obtained.

BOTTOM PROTECTION

On both sides of the barrier the bottom was to be protected from erosion over a length of about 650 m (partly 850 m). A strip of asphalt layers (three layers having a total thickness of 300 mm) connects the filter

mats to the earlier laid block mats. These mats are each 200 m long and 30 m wide. They consist of a supporting geotextile on which concrete blocks weighing 400 kg/m² are cast over 50% of the geotextile surface. After laying the mat, it was additionally ballasted with rubble to a weight of 200 kg/m². More than 4,500,000 m² of concrete block mats were used to protect the sea bed.

The method of prefabricating the mats and simultaneously winding and unwinding them on to floating drums, along with the positioning and laying of the mats was used as the guidelines for the design and operating systems of later filter mats.

A large number of applications for geotextiles are to be found in various parts of the barrier, and in the supporting supplies on the building sites.   It   would take too many words to describe them all. For those interested further the best advice is to visit the barrier.

REFERENCES

de Waal Malefijt, B.W. and Delfsma K.A., "The stormsurgbarrier in the Eastern Scheldt - A giant based on geotextiles", Proc. 4th. Int. Conf. Geotextiles, Geomembranes and Related Products, Vol. 3, The Hague, The Netherlands, 1990, pp. 1215-1218.

GEOTEXTILES FOR SCOUR PROTECTION OF RIVER BANK
RIVER IJSSEL, THE NETHERLANDS

H.A.M. Wichern
Nicolon B.V.
Almelo, The Netherlands

Since the introduction of geotextiles in Holland in 1957, the geotextile industry has worked on all aspects of their improvement. Using a modern geotextile for its hydraulic properties and durability is one thing. Using its mechanical properties to improve the economics of a river is more difficult. The latter was done for the first time at River IJssel.

DESCRIPTION

The River IJssel

The flow of the River IJssel is highly variable. It depends highly on the flow of the Upper Rhine. After the canalization of the Rhine, the targeted summerflow is between 250 to 350 m^3/s. This compares with the highest known flow of approximately 2,300 m^3/s. The canalization work caused a growth of shipping in the River IJssel that resulted in considerable riverbank erosion. The embankments consist prominently of sand that decreased in the downstream direction from coarse to fine grained. As a navigable waterway the River IJssel is suitable for ships up to 1,300 tonne.

The Slope protection

Originally the slope protection used was osierwood mattresses up to the mean summer water level. Above this stretcher bond stone revetment reposed on a row of creosoted wooden stakes was used. Geotextiles were already considered to be ideal filter material.

The question was how to use it below mean summer level? After thinking about the required criteria the solution was found to be very simple; as it should be. The geotextile was attached to a single layer (Photo 3) of osierwood grid. This grid gives sufficient floating capacity and rigidity to the total construction to allow a tug to tow it from the building site to place of application. The fastening of the geotextile to the grillage was simply done with ropes through the loops.

Once at the site sinking the mattress required only a small quantity of stones. The sinking was done with a sinking beam and the pressure of the current (if any). See Photo 1. Later the bulk of the rock layer was mechanically placed.

TECHNICAL CONSIDERATIONS, 20 YEARS AGO

The hydraulic criteria at that time of construction were plain and simple.

1) The permeability of the mattress needs to be at least 20 times that of the underlying soil. Instead of testing the sandy soil to obtain its permeability it was assumed the permeability of the mattress would be satisfactory for coarse sand if it could pass over 150 l/s/m^2 under a water head of 100 mm.

2) Sand tightness was also an estimated risk at that time. The devised method of test was basically to fill a bag made out of the geotextile with the local soil (only noncohesive sand was used). Then the bag was dipped a number of times in water. The number of dips was related to the energy of the person conducting the test. The sand remaining in the bag was then weighed. It there was less than a 15% loss the geotextile was approved. The 15% lost was considered of no consequence for the volume of the soil. During production of the geotextile, sand tightness was indicated in microns. The size of mesh was measured by means of light projection. Thus it was strictly a two dimensional method. Translation to practice was simple:

- Static conditions - mesh size $< d_{50}/3$.

- Turbulent conditions - mesh size $< d_{50}$.

- Turbulent conditions with the geotextile under ballast - somewhere in between. This was a matter of feeling.

TECHNICAL CONSIDERATIONS NOW

Today it is clear that the result of this pioneering approach was satisfactory. This is best proven by the fact that over 2,000,000 m^2 of this system has been used in the River IJssel and the method is constantly tested by performance and economy.

Focusing on the geotextile it is seen that only minor aspects have changed. There has been a change in the pattern of the loops. The dimensions supplied now are larger. Description of the properties changed together with the progress in specification testing. Today design engineers use up to date standards that require testing for mechanical and hydraulic properties. These include the cone drop, tear strength, permittivity, coefficient of permeability, sieve analysis etc. What is required and what is provided is in essence the same product. Two of these products from the supplier's brochure dated 1968 have not been changed and a third one was changed only for economic reasons.

Photo 1. The River IJssel.

Photo 2. Towing the mattress.

Photo 4. The old method of mattress construction.

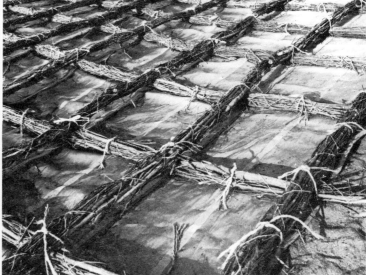

Photo 3. The new method of mattress construction.

CONCLUSION

The language changed but the message is still the same. Fabric became geotextile, feeling became designing. This case history is just made to prove that we are on the right track.

REFERENCES

Hoogendoorn, J., "A case history of the large scale application of woven synthetic fabrics on the banks of the River IJssel", Proc. 1st. Int. Conf. on Geotextiles, Vol. 2, Paris, France, 1977, pp. 243-247.

GEOTEXTILE MATS FOR SCOUR CONTROL AROUND PLATFORM OFF NORTHWEST COAST, AUSTRALIA

P.J. de Geeter
Marecon Pty Ltd
Perth, Australia

H.J. Dunnewind
Robusta Fabrics
Genemuiden, The Netherlands

In 1986 and 1987 a total of 500 scour control mats were installed around the main jacket structure and flare support structure of Rankin A gas production platform. The platform is located off the northwest coast of Western Australia.

This method of scour control was adopted by the operator of the platform, Woodside Offshore Petroleum Pty Ltd, after various alternative solutions were studied and discarded.

DESCRIPTION

The platform is located 130 km from shore in a water depth of 125 m.

The silty non-cohesive bed material had to be protected against an estimated 3 to 5 m scour over the 50 year design life of the structure.

The mats had to be stable under cyclonic wave and flow conditions with a design wave height of 12 m. Under design conditions the steady flow rate, at one metre above the sea bed, was anticipated to be in the order of 1 m/s.

Protection of the seabed against erosion had to extend to a distance of at least 10 m from the edge of the mudmats of the structural footings. This requirement was established by scale tests at the Civil Engineering Department of the University of Western Australia.

DESIGN

After studying various alternatives for preventing scour, such as dumping of rock or iron granules, it was decided to opt for installation of a geotextile matting, weighed by concrete blocks.

The main reason for using the geotextile was the softness of the seabed. The seabed had insufficient bearing capacity to support dumped particles of sufficient size to withstand the anticipated design currents.

Rock particles with the minimum required size of about 300 mm would insink more than 500 mm into the seabed. They could not be placed in a continuous layer with sufficient homogeneity at that water depth.

The required submerged weight of the concrete blocks (in relation to the optimum spacing between blocks) and the hydrodynamically required shape of edge blocks (in order to minimize drag and lift forces) was determined by using a special verified computer program.

This program took into account all relevant parameters influencing the potential overpressure that could be generated below the matting. This included the passage overhead of the height (*throw height*) of the design wave, as well, inertial forces, drag and lift forces generated a combination of the steady current and the design wave.

Parameters taken into account are:

- compressibility of bed material in relation to compressibility of water;
- elasticity modulus and tensile strength of geotextile layer (in the area between blocks);
- hydrodynamic drag-lift and inertia coefficients of edge blocks and inner blocks (as a function of block size and shape);
- long-term permeability of geotextile in relation to permeability of supporting bed material (a 50% reduction in geotextile permeability over time was assumed); and
- submerged weight and height of concrete blocks.

Cyclic flow velocity and particle acceleration at bed level was calculated by means of the generally accepted Airy/Stokes wave theory.

Steady flow velocity at bed level was derived from the flow velocity at 1 m above bed level by 1/10 exponent velocity profile above the boundary layer and 1/7 exponent profile within the boundary layer, in line with common practice.

GEOTEXTILE SELECTION

It was found that an open weave geotextile with maximum long-term permeability and, at the same time, the capability to prevent the passage of fine sand was required.

Furthermore the material had to be strong enough to allow installation of the mats by lowering from the water surface by means of a spreader beam/clamp type launching frame as shown in Photo 1. Although a heave compensator was used on the installation vessel, the vertical forces induced in the geotextile whilst in suspension under water were calculated to be about 100 kN/m, necessitating the use of strong, heavy-duty geotextile.

Also, the geotextile had to be sufficiently durable to last at least 50 years (the operational design life of the structure) in a tropical marine environment with relatively high seawater temperature.

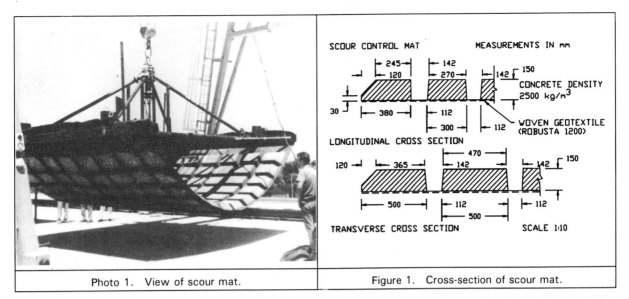

| Photo 1.   View of scour mat. | Figure 1.   Cross-section of scour mat. |

In order to meet these requirements it was decided to adopt one of the Robusta range of woven polypropylene geotextiles (the strongest and heaviest version, with a mass per unit area of 1,200 g/m²).

Properties of this geotextile, as tested to ISO 5081 by the Fibre Research Institute of T.N.O. Delft and Delft Hydraulics Laboratory, are as follows:

- tensile strength
  (roll direction): 300 kN/m
- strain at failure: 22%

From repeated computer calculations it was found that, for a concrete density of not less than 2,500 kg/m³, the lowest submerged mat weight required would necessitate an average spacing between blocks of 112 mm in relation to a block height of 150 mm and block width and length as shown in the cross-sections of Figure 1.

Other particulars of the mats are:

- total length of concrete area: 5.0 m
- total width of concrete area: 4.8 m
- mat mass in air: 4,980 kg
- submerged mat mass/unit area: 119 kg/m²

Each block was connected to the geotextile by means of two poly-oxymethylene pins of high durability and two steel pins which had the temporary function of absorbing excess shock loadings (if any) during handling of the mats on board of the installation vessel prior to launching.

Concrete was cast on the geotextile by a precast concrete company in Perth and hauled by road to Woodside's supply base near Karratha, 1400 km north of Perth.

REFERENCES

Koerner, R.M., "Designing with Geosynthetics", Prentice-Hall, Englewood Cliffs, NJ 07632, 1986, 424 p.

Veldhuijzen van Zanten, R., "Geotextiles and Geomembranes in Civil Engineering", Balkema, Rotterdam, Boston, 1986, 685 p.

Kroezen, M., Vellinga, P., Lindenberg, J. and Burger, A.M., "Geotechnical and Hydraulic Aspects with regard to Seabed and Slope Stability", 1982, 13 p. (publication no. 272 of Delft Geotechnics, The Netherlands).

Ogink, H.J.M., "Investigations on the Hydraulic Characteristics of Synthetic Fabrics", 1975, 42 p. (publication no. 146 of Delft Hydraulics Laboratory, The Netherlands).

Bezuijen, A., Klein Breteler, M. and Pilarczyk, K.W., "Large Scale Tests on a Block Revetment placed on Sand with a Geotextile as Separation Layer", Proc. 3rd. Int. Conf. on Geotextiles, Vienna, Austria, 1986, pp 501-505.

GEOTEXTILES WITH CONCRETE BLOCK REVETMENT FOR SCOUR PROTECTION
MITTELLANDKANAL, GERMANY

G. Heerten
Naue-Fasertechnik GmbH & Co. KG
D-4990 Lübbecke, Germany

W. Mühring
Neubauämter Mittelland Canal Osnabrück and Minden
Waterway Authority, Bundesrepublik, Germany

Since 1973, much experience has been gained with a flexible interlocking revetment system installed in many sections of the Mittellandkanal, Germany. This report is based on the long-term behaviour of a revetment system installation of 75,000 m² done in 1974/1975.

DESCRIPTION

Mittellandkanal

The Mittellandkanal is the connecting waterway between the river Ems region and the river Elbe region of Germany. The canal is one part of the connection between the Rhine/Ruhr area and the German seaports of Bremen and Hamburg. It is also the major part of the waterway connection to Berlin. Since the mid-sixties the Mittellandkanal has been improved for the use of larger barges. The development of the canal has been in accordance with the category IV criteria for European waterways:

Standard vessel:
1350 t motor vessel (Waterway Class IV)
Permissible speed:
10 to 12 km/h
Cross-sectional ratio (canal/ship):
n = 7

The reported section has a trapezoid cross-section with 2.5H:1V slopes.

Revetment System

At the time of construction only one concrete block/geotextile revetment system (Terrafix) was available in Germany. This revetment system consists of two components complementing each other functionally; (1) a heavy needlepunched nonwoven geotextile (multi-layer fabrics, thickness > 15 mm, mass per unit area > 1,500 g/m²) being the revetment filter layer, and (2) the interlocking concrete blocks being the revetment armour layer. The geotextile is composed of a fine and coarser filter layer. The fine layer has a minimum thickness of 6 mm and the very coarse rough layer (for stabilizing the boundary layer between geotextile and subsoil) a minimum thickness of 10 mm.

The interlocking concrete blocks are trapezoid-shaped with moulded-on conical pegs at the front and matching holes at the rear. Pegs and peg holes ensure an optimum interlock in horizontal and vertical direction, permitting tilt and rotation movements of the blocks. The flexibility provides for a good adaptation to the installation surface as well as compensation for any possible settlements. The distance between the blocks, as dictated by the interlocking elements and the special shape of the blocks, guarantee the necessary permeability to water, greenability and wave dampening effect. On account of the interlock, the weight per unit area of the revetment system can be reduced considerably in comparison with rip-rap revetments. Weights per unit area of approximately 1,300 to 2,500 N/m² have proved very successful even in the case of highly stressed waterways.

At high and steep slopes, with danger of toe scouring or with bad subsoil conditions, the hanging revetment constitutes a safe and proven solution. Wires connect the interlocking concrete blocks through special holes. This permits a transmission of longitudinal forces from the toe of the embankment to its upper edge, and thus a safe force distribution within the hanging revetment.

Site Conditions

At this site the revetment construction had to be done under wet conditions. Special consideration was given to preparing the slopes, placing geotextile and blocks underwater, and the influence of ongoing ship-traffic. The subsoil was silty fine sand with the following average characteristics:

permeability	k	= 10 μm/s
angle of friction	ϕ'	= 32.5°
cohesion	c'	= 0
unit weight	γ	= 2.0 kN/m³,
	γ'	= 1.0 kN/m³

The subsoil was a typical problem soil with a high amount of fine particles that had high movability. There was danger of downslope migration of soil particles underneath the geotextile. Under these conditions it is of very high importance to create stable boundary conditions between the geotextile and the subsoil.

INSTALLATION

The NV 12 interlocking blocks (block weight: 230 N, block dimensions: length/width/height: 660/140/120 mm) were assembled into revetment sections of 14.0 m in length and 5.60 m in width on a movable pallet of a special designed floating barge. Anchor wires were inserted at the lower edge. The anchor wires were attached to a wooden toe beam and the wooden anchor stakes (bongossi) at the top of the embankment without preloading. By retracting and tipping the pallet from the floating barge, the section hanging from the anchor wires was gradually lowered onto the slope upon which the heavy needlepunched nonwoven geotextile had just been laid. When the concrete block

| Photo 1. Floating barge for underwater installation laying the concrete block revetment system on the multilayer geotextile. | Photo 2. The concrete block revetment greened over after only a few years. |

sections had been placed, the upper part of the embankment was fixed. The joints between the revetment sections were filled with hydraulically bonded grouting material. As a result of recent development, the joints are not grouted today, but half blocks are used at the edges of the revetment sections forming a flexible, close section joint.

FIELD INVESTIGATIONS

To report some data of the long-term behaviour of this geotextile/concrete block revetment system, the Federal Institute for Waterway Engineering, Karlsruhe (BAW) carried out the following field investigations:

- tensile force measurements in the anchor wires during block panel installation
- tensile force measurements in the anchor wires after installation
- soundings to control the canal cross-section.

The maximum tensile forces, measured during laying of the block sections, gave a safety factor of 2.0 in relation to the wire breaking load. After installation the tensile forces were constantly reduced in all measuring zones. This ensures a sufficient shear strength between the subsoil and the geotextile and between the geotextile and the concrete blocks. These results are confirmed by soundings on the slope profiles. During the 6 years of measurement since completion of the revetment no significant changes have been noted. Maintenance and repair have been limited up to now to a few panels where the original installation was not sufficient. The inspection of some panels is showing that abrasion resistance of the geotextile is of high importance for long-term use of concrete block/geotextile revetments. A special abrasion test has been developed by BAW.

In the last years the requirements for a most favourable layout of revetment structures, considering environmental aspects, has become more and more important. Due to the large pore volume and the movability of the fibres in the labyrinth of the needlepunched nonwoven fabric, and the special joints between the concrete blocks aquatic growth generally develops above and below the water level. This encourages the development of small marine life.

CONCLUSIONS

Since 1973 interlocking revetment systems have been used, providing hydraulic engineering with a new economical method of bank production. The long-term experience over nearly 15 years has shown that a concrete block/geotextile revetment can be a satisfactory solution for canal embankments. Special attention has to be paid to the geotextile/subsoil boundary in order to avoid downslope migration of subsoil particles underneath the geotextile and to ensure a sufficient long-term abrasion resistance of the geotextile that is in contact with sharp edged concrete blocks.

REFERENCES

Heerten, G. and Mühring, W., "Proposals of flexible toe design of revetments". Flexible Armoured Revetments Incorporating Geotextiles, Proc., Int. Conf. Organized by the Institution of Civil Engineers, London, 1984, pp. 25-27.

Heerten, G., Meyer, H., and Mühring, W., "Experience with a flexible interlocking revetment system at the Mittellandkanal in Germany since 1973". Flexible Armoured Revetments Incorporating Geotextiles, Proc., Int. Conf. Organized by the Institution of Civil Engineering, London, 1984, pp. 179-192.

GEOSYNTHETICS FOR SCOUR PROTECTION OF RIVER GROYNES
WESER RIVER, NORTH SEA COAST, GERMANY

G. Heerten
Naue-Fasertechnik GmbH & Co. KG
D-4990 Lübbecke, Germany

In 1982 the first newly designed groynes were built at a large river training works in the tidal area of the river Weser on the North Sea coast of Germany.

DESCRIPTION

With the increase in the size of ships many estuaries and important ports have been deepened. As well as the increased use of large-scale dredging, river works to control flow and tidal range such as groynes and training walls have been erected. At present, the river Weser has been deepened to 12.0 m below chart datum up to Nordenham, and to 9.0 m below chart datum up to Bremen. For this, several groynes are under construction. In this large river training program, 100 groynes will be built. The groynes will serve to stabilize the shipping channel and to minimize the increase of the tidal range mainly by raising the tidal low water.

DESIGN

Groyne Design Requirements

The groyne design had to consider the performance of existing groynes that were built in the tidal area of river Weser since approximately 1920. Many of these groynes are affected by scouring at the groyne heads. Some scouring occurs at the groyne shanks. The scouring problems result in a lot of costly maintenance work. Therefore, the new design had to consider the scouring problems and must give a better scour protection and stability to the groynes. The following requirements for a scour protection solution have been specified by the River Weser Waterway Authority:

- It must be flexible enough to adapt to a developing scour.
- It should support soil sedimentation from outside and should be able to retain the underlying soil to a large extent.
- It has to be rot-proof.
- The mattress has to be oil- and UV-resistant.
- It must be heavy enough to resist current and wave action over a long term.
- Load must be applied in such a manner that it cannot be displaced by current and wave action.
- The load must not affect the flexibility of the mattress.
- The load has to be frost resistant.

Groyne Design

In the new design, geotextiles are used in the groyne section down to tidal low water. In the underwater section the conventional construction method of using a willow-fascine mattress for the groyne foundation is used. On a heavyweight needlepunched nonwoven geotextile (1,100 g/m²) the rip-rap core of the groyne is dumped. With an overlap of approximately 500 mm on both sides of the groyne a special scour protection mat is installed. By fixing the upper stones of the groyne core by grouting with concrete mortar, an increase in stability is achieved.

The filter mat in the foundation base of the groyne has to fulfil the tough requirements for geotextiles in hydraulic engineering, established by the Federal Institution of Waterway Engineering (BAW), Karlsruhe, Germany. This means, for the given local soils of silty sand, clay and mud, that the geotextile has to pass its filtering efficiency in the very tough turbulent tests and its penetration resistance in a special test with a dynamic load of 600 Nm, corresponding to a 300 N stone falling from a height of 2.0 m. Standard requirements, confirmed in more than 10 years of installing millions of square metres of geotextiles in revetments and other hydraulic structures, are a minimum thickness of 6.0 mm and a strength (DIN 53858, grab test) of 800 N for safe installation and adequate long-term behaviour.

The scour protection is composed of four parts:

- woven or nonwoven filter layer: soil-tightness, permeability and acting load have to be considered;
- sedimentation layer: approximately 50 mm thick, made of needlepunched and chemically bonded curled coarse fibres, it reduces the drag forces in the boundary layer of the seabed, so that sedimentation takes place, increasing the weight and stability of the structure;
- reinforcement geotextile: by means of wide meshes (approximately 20 mm) and very high tensile strength, the geotextile combines and reinforces the ballast elements securely, providing a high degree of flexibility and adaptability with plenty of strength in reserve;
- ballast elements: approximately 500 mm in diameter and 100 mm in height, with a minimum distance of approximately 200 mm between the rims of the elements, they stabilize the scour protection mattress during the sedimentation phase.

INVESTIGATIONS

Special investigations have been carried out to learn about the possibilities to stabilize a movable sandy seabed with a fibre structure. The main idea was to reduce the drag forces in the boundary layer to create sedimentation in the fibre structure and to form a stable fibre/soil seabed.

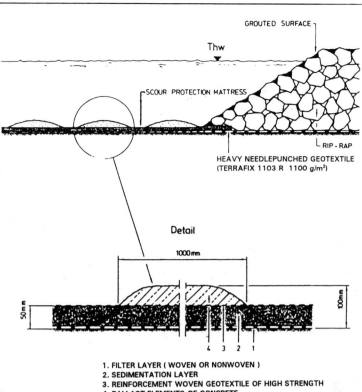

Photo 1. Demonstration of the effectiveness of the scour protection - the scour protection mat stabilizes the edge of the scour.

Figure 1. Construction details of the groynes and the scour protection mattress.

GROUTED SURFACE

Thw

SCOUR PROTECTION MATTRESS

RIP - RAP

HEAVY NEEDLEPUNCHED GEOTEXTILE
(TERRAFIX 1103 R 1100 g/m²)

Detail

1000 mm

50 mm

100 mm

4 3 2 1

1. FILTER LAYER (WOVEN OR NONWOVEN)
2. SEDIMENTATION LAYER
3. REINFORCEMENT WOVEN GEOTEXTILE OF HIGH STRENGTH
4. BALLAST ELEMENTS OF CONCRETE

Photo 2. Finished groyne opposite Nordenham, river Weser tidal area.

Hydraulic model tests carried out in the Federal Institute of Waterway Engineering, Karlsruhe, have shown the very high influence of the fibre structure to create a sufficient seabed stabilization. Sufficient seabed stabilization was obtained with the following characteristics of the sedimentation layer:

Fibres: Coarse curled polypropylene (PP) fibres, 300 μm diameter (650 dtex), mechanically and chemically bonded.

Structure mass per unit area:
1,000 g/m² (proportion of fibre 600 g/m²).

Thickness: 50 mm

Number of Fibres: 18 per cm²

CONCLUSIONS

Since 1982, at least 30 groynes involving more than 10,000 m² of toe protection mattresses have been installed. Up to now, the mattresses fulfil all expectations. Even heavy ice winters did not affect the scour protection mattress in its effectiveness.

REFERENCES

Heerten, G., Experiences of Different Scour Protection Techniques at Offshore-Structures in the North Sea. Proc. 5th. Australian Conf. on Coastal and Ocean Engineering, Perth 1981, pp. 22-28.

Heerten, G., Geotextiles in Coastal Engineering - 25 Years Experience, Geotextiles and Geomembranes, Vol. 1, No. 2, 1984, pp. 119-141.

GEOTEXTILE FILTER MATTRESS FOR RIVER BOTTOM EROSION CONTROL
EIDER BARRIER, GERMANY

H.U. Hollmer
Wasser-und Schiffahrtsamt Tönning
Bundesrepublik Deutschland, Germany

The dam across the mouth of the tidal river Eider at the North Sea coast of Schleswig-Holstein is an essential element of the "Master Plan for Strengthening Dykes, Shortening Dykes, and Shore Protection" of 1963. This dam, which was constructed in about 1967, protects the vast Eider lowlands against storm surge flooding and cuts by about 60 km the length of dykes to the dam built in the 1930's and located 35 km upstream in Nordfeld. In addition to flood protection, the purpose of this second dam is to improve drainage and to keep the river navigable.

DESCRIPTION

The Dam

The dam, which is 4.8 km long, consists of dykes high enough to cope with storm surge sea levels, a barrier with five gates of 40 m span each, and a shipping lock. As a rule, the barrier is kept open to let the tides pass freely. The gates may be used, however, to enhance drainage (low water sluicing mode) or to reduce siltation (flood throttling mode).

Bed Protection

Long-term natural data were gathered and investigations as well as model tests were made before the dam was built and, in particular, before the river bed immediately adjacent to the barrier was protected. Scouring of the Eider bed where the barrier controls the flow had to be kept at bay. To this end, the bed was covered with rigid protection, which extended, from both sides of the barrier foundation, 150 m upriver and 150 m seaward. Beyond the rigid protection, 30 m long areas provide a flexible transition to the natural river bed. The bed protection was designed and constructed for current velocities of $v = 4.65$ m/s normally, and $v = 5.00$ m/s as short-time maximum.

Construction

The rigid protection is adjacent to the concrete foundation slab of the barrier, and slopes at a 75H:1V gradient. It rests on a graded filter which consists of (from bottom to top) polyamide geotextile covering the silty sand, 100 mm gravel of 15/30 mm, and 200 mm cobbles of 60/90 mm. The top layer is formed by hewn granite blocks of 0.6 tonnes each near the barrier, and by 0.4 tonne blocks further away. They were laid tightly enough to prevent the cobbles and gravel from being washed out. The bed protection (1.65 t/m²) is permeable over the whole area so that hydrostatic uplift cannot occur. This construction complied fully with the requirements established by previous calculations and investigations

concerning the roughness required for scour control, as well as with the safety margins according to ISBASH (1969 version) regarding the granite block weights. A conventional filter constructed from graded natural material to prevent erosion would have been much more expensive due to its required thickness, and a mixed filter would not have provided sufficient safety. Therefore a synthetic geotextile was selected as the filter material.

GEOTEXTILE SELECTION

The polyamide (Nylon 6.6) woven geotextile used in the 1960's for the Eider Barrier is not produced any longer. Geotextile selection was based on the then available knowledge. The mesh size corresponded to the particle size distribution of the bed soil. The Bundesanstalt für Wasserbau (i.e. Federal German Waterways Engineering Laboratories) tested samples of this geotextile which had been stored under unknown conditions. The results were: mass per unit area, 200 g/m²; water permeability, 7.9 μm/s; maximum tensile force per unit width, 42.6 kN/m (roll direction) and 45.0 kN/m (cross-roll direction); strain at maximum tensile force, 22% (roll direction) and 20.4% (cross-roll direction).

PERFORMANCE

After four years of operation of the Eider Barrier, damage was discovered in the rigid bed protection in the immediate vicinity of the seaward side of the barrier. Inspections by divers and measurements showed that granite blocks had changed their positions to various degrees (and, thus, the roughness as well as the width of the joints were altered), depending on their distance from the gates. They had settled, tilted, moved horizontally, etc. The geotextile was found damaged in various places. The Technical Universities of Braunschweig and Hannover, the Bundesanstalt für Wasserbau in Karlsruhe, and the Bundesanstalt für Materialprüfung in Berlin (i.e. Federal German Institute for Testing Materials) were engaged to establish the cause of the damage. Also, geotextile samples were analyzed to evaluate the damage.

GEOTEXTILE CONDITION

The examination of geotextile samples gathered at distances of 20 and 100 m from the Eider Barrier did not suggest harmful chemical or microbiologic action. The result of the technical investigations was that geotextile damage could be interpreted as purely mechanical. Samples were found torn, cut, chafed, and compressed, but sometimes also completely intact. Tests on the geotextile yielded a permeability to soil clearly under 25 grams in 34 hours. Water permeability varied from 6.7

Photo 1. View of Eider Barrier.

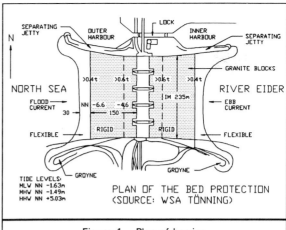

Figure 1. Plan of barrier.

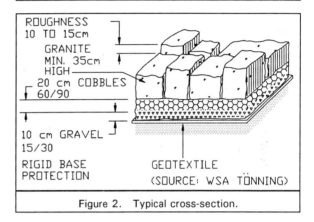

Figure 2. Typical cross-section.

μm/s for samples less stressed to 180 μm/s for samples from the barrier vicinity. The effectiveness as an hydraulic filter did not meet today's requirements, and the reduction of strength was abnormally high. The pressure by heavy construction vehicles' wheels while spreading the gravel and cobble layers and placing the granite blocks was suspected as one possible cause of geotextile mechanical damage, particularly since a considerable part of the gravel was found to be sharp-edged. In order to allow a safe assessment of such effects on the geotextile the Bundesanstalt für Wasserbau conducted full-scale tests. They found that, by driving on the gravel and cobble layers, sharp-edged gravel can crush and incise the geotextile to various degrees. Such test damage was, however, considerably less extensive than that encountered in reality. Consequently, all experts unanimously considered hydrodynamic forces acting on the bed protection as the primary cause for the observed damage. Model tests confirmed that surface roughness and structure of the bed protection lead to turbulence, with pressure cycles, increasing with current velocities. They caused rocking and jogging of the granite blocks, which movements were transferred to the underlying layers. Thus, the geotextile could be chafed, weakened and torn. Then, sand could be washed out from underneath through the geotextile filter. As a result, blocks settled. The rocking movements finally caused some blocks to be removed once the current exceeded a critical velocity.

CONCLUSIONS

In order to repair the damage once and forever and to prevent further damage, the possibility of movement of the granite blocks of rock - which was considered the primary cause of damage - had to be eliminated all over an area extending about 50 m from the barrier. To this end, the joints between the granite blocks were filled with colloidal grout so that relative movements of the blocks are no longer possible. Today, the rigid bed protection has been thus strengthened over its entire area in order to permit currents even faster than 5 m/s. Since completion of the grouting no further damage has been detected. It is believed that the rigid bed protection of the Eider Barrier met the requirements which were established at the time of construction, according to the then available state of the art. The damage which occurred is the result of circumstances not known at the time of design and construction. It should also be noted that problems occurred only in the area close to the barrier.

REFERENCES

Bundesanstalt für Wasserbau (BAW) Karlsruhe, Untersuchungen des Kunststoffgewebes der Sohlensicherung des Eider-Sperrwerkes, 5 Berichte, unveröffentlicht, 1979.

Bundesanstalt für Materialprüfung (BAM) Berlin-Dahlem - Prüfzeugnis über die Gewebeproben aus der Sohlensicherung, unveröffentlicht, im Auftrage der BAW, 1979.

Cordes, F., Eiderdamm Hundeknöll-Vollerwik. Die Bautechnik, Heft 11 und 12, 1970 Heft 10 and 11/1971 und Heft 7 und 8/1972.

Führböter, A., Gutachten über hydromechanische Belastungen an der Sohlensicherung des Eider-Sperrwerkes, TU Braunschweig, unveröffentlicht, im Auftrage des MELF S.-H., 1979.

Partenscky, H.W., Gutachtliche Stellungnahme zu den Tide- und Seegangs-verhältnissen am Eider-Sperrwerk, TU Hannover, unveröffentlicht, im Auftrage des MELF S.-H., 1979.

GEOSYNTHETIC CONCRETE MATTRESSES FOR SCOUR PROTECTING AT SEA DIKE CLOSURE NEAR HATTSTEDTER MARSCH, GERMANY

W. Saggau
Amt für Land- und Wasserwirtschaft
Husum, Schleswig-Holstein, Germany

Schleswig-Holstein, which is the most northerly federal state in Germany, is flanked by the North Sea and the Baltic Sea so coastal protection is of major importance. In 1982 the largest coastal protection project in the history of the country commenced in the Bay of Nordstrand.

PROJECT DESCRIPTION

The project involved the construction and refurbishment of a series of protection dikes comprising:

a)   An external dike of length 8.9 km for Hattstedter Marsch;

b)   A dike with a length of 6.9 km at Sönke-Nissen-Koog;

c)   A 3.3 km external dike for Ockholm; and

d)   The longest 14.9 km dam between the mainland and the island of Pellworm.

These measures were designed to improve safety and simultaneously prevent the perpetual erosion of the mudflats and the scouring of the tidal channels in the planning area. The external dikes aim to reduce directional tidal effect whilst the protective dikes are for restricting the tidal flow.

The 8.9 km external dike was divided into 3 stages of construction to take account of the prevailing tidal and flow conditions. During the construction period prior to closure of two of the dikes in 1987, two tidal basins had formed. Volumes at mean tide of approximately 3,000,000 m^3 are calculated for the northern part and this increases to 33,000,000 m^3 for the southern part. Details of these southern dike closures are described below as they involved the largest tidal volumes experienced in any previous dike closure along the German coast.

DESCRIPTION OF THE BED PROTECTION

The initially proposed construction method for the southern dike closure consisted of building a multi-layer rock mound from the sea bed. It was ascertained in the planning stage that as each step in rock placement progressed the effective cross-section of the closure area would be reduced. This in turn would increase turbulence and the tidal flow rate to a multiple of the original levels. The previously balanced system of flow conditions and bed contours would therefore be subjected to drastic change. The stability of the rock dike would be undermined by erosion brought about by scouring forces acting on the unprotected areas. The following criteria were established for the selection of an appropriate bed protection system: it should maintain adequate sand tightness; remain stable as forces of current and turbulence act on the rocks;

possess adequate strength for damage free placement; and provide a good service life at reasonable cost.

The selected bed protection system incorporated natural and man made components to form a flexible, reinforcing separator beneath the rock mound. This simple module comprised a polypropylene geotextile onto which layers of young willow branches were laid to a depth of 80 mm. To this layer, 100 mm diameter "Sausages" of firmer willow were added. Laid in parallel rows at 1 m centres and tied through to the fabric these formed the module's foundation. A grid pattern of two willow sausages subsequently laced to the substructure provided pockets having a depth about 200 mm for a plan area of 1 m^2. The bed protection layout involved 2 rows of mattresses each overlapping by 2 m.

The geotextile had a maximum opening size of 300 μm and a water permeability of 1.5 mm/s. Compared with the traditional brushwood mattress protection the adopted solution improves resistance to penetration by sand and costs less.

The multi-functional combination of geotextile and willow was seen as the solution to many of the practical problems of installation, its buoyancy (approximately 25 kg/m^2) provided floatation for the holding stage and positioning at the point of placement. Its rigidity increased positional stability and prevented the mattress from distorting or folding over at the corners or along the sides.

Resilience in the willow layers provided protection to the geotextile against subsequent dumping of rocks, the bulk of which weighed between 60 to 300 kg; in some cases individual rocks were heavier. This aspect of the system's integrity was rigorously tested using 450 kg rocks dropped from heights of 2.4 and 6 m and were carried out on land. The geotextile remained undamaged.

Severe water currents at the dike closure over a prolonged construction period dictated a specific range of rock sizes and two different loading times that had to be accommodated. For the "winter load case" - the period between completion of the bed protection (1985) and commencement of construction work on the rock dike (1987) - rocks within the range of weights 10 kg to 60 kg were found to be adequate for stability. During placement of the rock dike, a construction period of 8 weeks, the range increased to between 60 kg and 30 kg and up to between 1 and 3 t depending on the bed level and the locational distance from the rock dike.

The installed mattresses and the rock fill were surveyed from land for the border areas and from the sea

Photo 1. Mattress for bed protection.

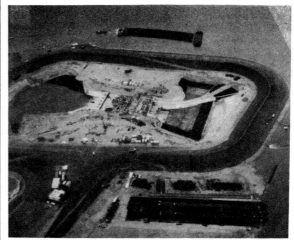

Photo 2. View of dike.

in the central area.

In the central area where depths reached 8 m, a survey vessel was used in conjunction with an echograph and polar location equipment.

CONCLUSIONS

The bed protection was successfully completed in 1985 and the dike closure was concluded with equal success in 1987. The geotextile willow system involved a total area of about 120,000 m². The sophisticated positioning equipment resulted in accurate construction and the total cost of the installed mattress was evaluated at DM 100/m².

The mattress bed protection constituted the main component in the method of rock dike enclosure for this prestigious project.

REFERENCES

Generalplan "Deichverstärkung, Deichverkürzung and Küstenschutz in Schleswig-Holstein", 1986, unpublished.

Saggau, W. and Schirmacher, R., "Küstenschutzmaßnahmen in der Nordstrander Bucht", Wasser und Boden, H. 2, 1987.

Saggau, W., "Deichschluß Süd im Rahmen der Küstenschutzmaßnahmen in der Nordstrander Bucht", Wasser und Boden, H. 3, 1988.

GEOTEXTILE COMPOSITE FOR CANAL BED SCOUR PROTECTION
MITTELLAND CANAL, GERMANY

W. Mühring
Neubauämter Mittelland Canal Osnabrück and Minden
Waterway Authority, Bundesrepublik, Germany

In the last twenty years there was a rapid development in design and construction of revetments in the widening of existing canals without disrupting the traffic. This work involved placement of a long-lasting filter layer covered by a cover layer of bonded rip-rap that protected the revetment against the erosive effect of shipping and water. A geotextile filter was used in the revetment on the slope, on the bottom of the canal and on the air-side of the canal dam.

DESCRIPTION

The Mittelland Canal belongs to the category IV as to the recommendations of the Conference of European Ministers of Transport with a cross-sectional area of at least 7 times the cross-sectional area of the fully loaded Rhine-Herne-Canal ship (1,350 t). Depending on local conditions and where possible, the construction is carried out with a water surface width of 53.0 m, a depth of 4 m and with slopes of 3H:1V.

Boundary Conditions

The hydraulic boundary conditions for the canal boundaries depend predominantly on ship induced loadings that give the front wave, the depression of water level and the transversal stern wave. Combined with the depression of water level, which acts for the period it takes the vessel to pass by, there is a high velocity current with changing directions. These produce high shear stresses. Screw race is only considered at moorings or in the area near lock gates.

The geotechnical boundary conditions depend on the different types of soil. Sometimes these are not sufficiently investigated, because the work has to be done under water into the existing, not replaced, soil. Geotechnical failure mechanisms, which have to be overcome, are mainly on the slope of the canal bed. The local stability involves the local bearing and the migration of soil particles downwards on the slope beneath the revetment, and, on the air-side of existing canal dams, local bearing and piping.

GEOTEXTILE SELECTION

When the work started in about 1964, there were no geotextile filters available. Design and filter criteria were developed after many years of experience, especially in the field investigations conducted since 1964. The course of development was from woven fabrics with pore distribution in the horizontal plane only, via nonwovens with a pore distribution in both the horizontal and vertical plane, to finally composite materials with varying pore openings between individual layers. On the basis of growing experience, composite materials have become increasingly popular over the last ten years [Mühring, 1984]. These composite materials are combinations of several layers of nonwovens of different thicknesses and with fibres of different linear densities. By careful selection of the pore-opening distribution and thickness of the different layers these kinds of geotextile filters can improve the filter effectiveness, especially for the fine-grained and layered soils as found in the construction of the Mittelland Canal [Mühring and Saathoff, 1986]. For the revetments on the canal slope inclined at 3H:1V geotextile composite materials with a stabilization layer are used as filters. This special stabilization layer was developed ten years ago due to a number of cases of revetment local stability failures resulting from migration of soil particles from beneath the geotextile filter. This development was the result of the consideration that, besides the solution of the filter problem itself (i.e. the determination of the pore-opening distribution in the overlying filter layer or filter layers), the necessary filtration length must develop within the layer thickness. Thus the solution of the transition failure could be overcome. This was possible by selecting the opening size of the stabilization layer, so that the soil particles which migrate from the unprotected soil surface of the slope into the stabilization layer are retained by coarse fibres of this layer. After loading with sufficient weight on the cover layer the soil retention ability must ensured a state of equilibrium beyond the maximum expected pressure gradient. The dimensioning of the geotextile fibres for the defined soil types is done in detail according to the Technical Terms of Delivery for Geotextile Filters of the Federal Office for Hydraulic Engineering in Karlsruhe. By reason of the specific working conditions under water, the difficult foundation conditions and the complicated instalment conditions, a geotextile filter with a thicknesses > 6 mm and effective opening sizes O_g = approx. 70 μm has been predominantly used. On slopes, filters with stabilization layers and opening sizes of 300 μm < O_g < 1,500 μm according to the recommendation of Working Group 14 GSSMFE have been installed.

PERFORMANCE

The used revetments consist of the above mentioned geotextile as filter and a 400 mm thick coverlayer of rip-rap with edge lengths of 150 to 250 mm. In permeable revetments located under water the rip-rap is grouted with about 80 litres of impermeable and 120 litres of permeable material (e.g. non-erosive concrete). In the surface area only a very little grouting is carried out for a better environmental integration of the revetment. According to the soil type, a toe protection is arranged. In impermeable revetments the pore volume of the rip-rap is completely

| Photo 1. Cross-section of a multi-layer geotextile with stabilization layer. | Photo 2. Construction sequence installing the geotextile filter. |

grouted with impermeable material. During installation of the geotextile filter problems did arise. This was especially true during installation in the bottom of the canal, where underwater currents are produced by passing vessels. The filter acted as a hanging wall during installation and continually changed its position. The problem was solved by keeping the filter during installation in as an exact position as possible. Another possibility is to unrolling the filter from a roll on the bottom of the canal.

CONCLUSIONS

Bank revetments as mentioned above were mainly installed in the widening of the Mittelland Canal. They are the most economic solution in regard to the costs of instalment and maintenance [Kniess, 1983]. In 1981, a break test has been made at one of those permeable embankment revetments. For a complete hour the revetment has been exposed to screw race currents, without finding any damages afterwards. Not even in the area of the filter. This suggests that the life of the revetments is considerably longer than supposed up to now.

REFERENCES

Bundesanstalt für Wasserbau, Karlsruhe, "Technische Lieferbedingungen für geotextile Filter" (TLG), Ausgabe 1987.

DVWK-Schriften 76, Anwendung and Prüfung von Kunstoffen im Erdbau and Wasserbau, Empfehlung des Arbeitskreises 14 der Deutschen Gesellschaft für Erdund Grundbau ue.V., Verlag Paul Parey, 1986.

Kniess, H.G., "Kriterien und Ansatze für die technische und wirtschaftliche Bemessung von Auskleidungen in Binnenschiffahrtskanälen". Mitteilungen aus dem Leichtweib-Institut der Technischen Universität Braunschweig, Heft 77, 1983.

Mühring, W., The development of geotextile filters in the construction of revetments in expansion work on canals, 1. Nationales Symposium Geotextilien im Erdund Grundbau, Mainz, 1984, pp. 23-29.

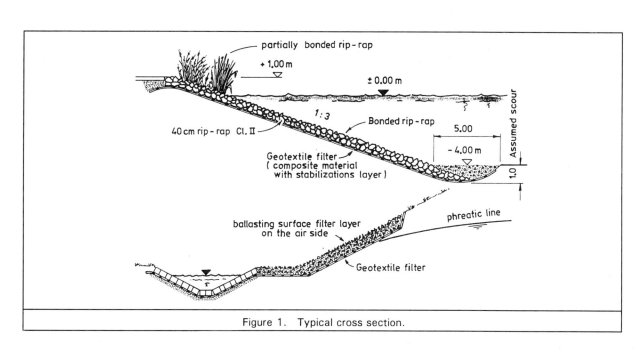

Figure 1. Typical cross section.

GEOSYNTHETIC CONCRETE MATTRESSES FOR RIVER SCOUR CONTROL
JIANG DU LOCK, CHINA

Z. Jian
Yangzhou Water Conservancy Bureau
Yangzhou, China

Jiang Du lock, a floodgate of Jiang Du pumping station, which is the most important part of the whole project for transferring water from southern China to northern China, is located on the north bank of the Yangtze River. It is also the throat for the Lixia River to draw water from the Yangzte. Because of the increasing flow rate, the riverbed, formed of powder sand, had been seriously eroded threatening the safety of the lock.

DESCRIPTION

The lock

The lock has nine water passages and their total net width is 90 m. The design-flood inflow is 505 m³/s, and the check-flood inflow is 940 m³/s. The actual flood inflow has ranged between 800-1,000 m³/s and its maximum is 1,340 m³/s. The depth of erosion has reached 6 to 7 m upstream and 2 to 3 m downstream. A cross section of the lock is shown in Figure 1.

Mattress Protecting the Upstream Riverbed

As protection for the upstream riverbed polypropylene woven geotextiles were sewn together to form mattresses. They were sunk to cover the riverbed upstream, loaded with precast concrete blocks and then stones were spread on the mattresses.

Mattresses Protecting the Downstream Riverbed

As protection for the downstream riverbed similar mattresses were sunk to cover riverbed. The head-on edges were fixed with steel piles (0.18 mm diameter, 1.5 m long) driven at 1 m spacing. These prevent the mattresses from moving and strengthen the antiskid resistance of the body of the mattresses. The concept is illustrated in Figure 2.

Mattress Protecting the Banks

To prevent aging caused by the sun's ultraviolet rays, the mattresses should be placed only with the top sides under the low water level while the bottom sides stretch far into the eroded riverbed.

Construction Time and the Mattresses

From March, 1979 to May, 1980, the project was finished by sinking six mattresses covering a total area of 24,150 m². Of this total, 18,550 m² are protecting the riverbed and 5,600 m² are protecting the banks. Each mattress was placed one at a time, with the largest being 10,350 m².

Geotextile Selection

The polypropylene woven geotextile used to protect the lock from water erosion was adopted for the first time in China. Every flat fibre was 0.08 mm thick and 1.5 mm wide. There were 64 warp and 60 weft fibres in every 100 cm². The allowable tensile strength is 29.4 N and limit tensile strength is 39.2 N. Also there are 3,700 sieve meshes in the above area. So the woven geotextile is lighter than water, but high in tensile strength, and the sieve meshes provide good permeability for the mattresses to sink easily.

DESIGN

Basis of Design

According to the mould experiment done by Nanjing Water Conservancy Science Institute, the mattress stability is closely related to the pressure load. When the flow rate is 3 m³/s, pressure load is 980 Pa and the mattresses can be kept stable.

Determination for the Edge Height

The edge height of the mattress protecting the riverbed upstream and downstream was designed to be 3.0 m below the water level and the top edge of the mattress protecting the banks was designed to be 0.8 m below the water level.

Determination for the Size of the Mattresses

The width of the upstream mattress was designed to be 115 m and that of the downstream mattress to be 120 m. The depth of erosion at the lock was 7 m.

The maximum erosion depth and the protected length should be in the ratio of 1:12; where the average depth of the erosion was 3 m this ratio should be 1:20. The length of the longitudinal curve line was carefully measured to establish the mattress length. The selected length of the mattress up to the lock was 90 m and down from the lock was 50 m. The size of each mattress was decided according to the construction conditions. The advantages of using large mattress are: less connecting joints, better in continuity, faster in carrying on the project.

Folding Rate of the Mattress

The factors that influence the folding rate of the mattress are closely related to the depth of the water, the waterflow speed, the wind speed, and the levels of the techniques. The completed project proved the fact that the

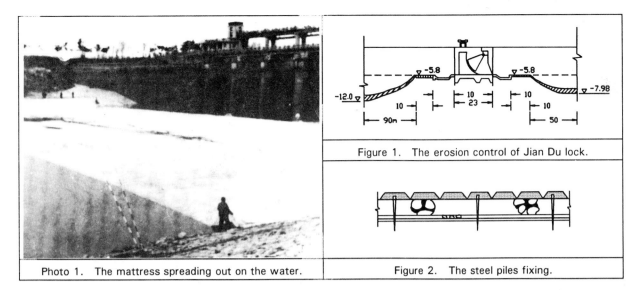

Photo 1.   The mattress spreading out on the water.

Figure 1.   The erosion control of Jian Du lock.

Figure 2.   The steel piles fixing.

folding rate in still water was 15%-16% and in moving water was 18%-20%.

Pressure Load

The pressure load is one of the key factors determining the success of sinking flexible mattresses. This project employed three methods: (a) Edge load - put the ladder-shaped precast concrete blocks around the four sides of the mattress; each block was 1 m long with a weight of 90 kg. (b) Net load - put the precast concrete blocks or cobbles packed in polypropylene bags in lines with a space of 10 m between each. (c) Spread load - spread stones on the mattresses at a rate of 90 kg/m.

Conditions of the Mattresses

The flexible mattresses have covered the riverbed and the banks around the lock for nine years; all the mattresses have remained steady and the state of covering has remained in good condition. What is more, the water has left a layer of silt about 44 mm thick. The erosion downstream of the lock has been stopped completely. According to testing results done in 1986, the limit tensile strength of a single filament remained 39.2 N and only its flexibility has decreased slightly.

Economic Benefit

24,150 m² of flexible mattresses have been put into use around the lock. The total cost of the whole project was 113,210 Yuan (or 5.3 Yuan /m²). This is only 11.1% of the cost of laying stones over the same area. In addition, Jiang Du pumping station has never stopped working and the Lixia River has never stopped flowing during the whole process. Instead, its flow quantity has increased by 146,000,000 m³. This has helped to combat any drought and the navigation has never been interrupted.

CONCLUSIONS

The main points learned from this case history is that flexible mattresses compared to natural rip-rap are:

- more effective against water erosion;
- stronger in entirety;
- longer in endurance;
- easier in transporting;
- faster in finishing the project;

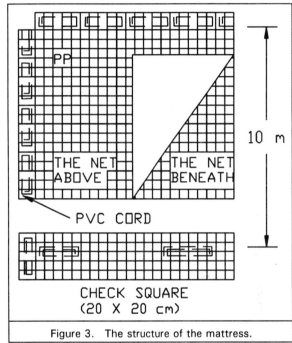

Figure 3.   The structure of the mattress.

- more adaptable to the changing conditions; and
- lower in cost.

Furthermore, should any side be eroded away, the constructed materials will still sink and again perform their function.

REFERENCES

Non supplied.

GEOTEXTILE MAT AND SANDBAGS AS TEMPORARY BREAKWATER DAM PLUIMPOT, THE NETHERLANDS

J.G. Vos
Akzo Industrial Systems bv.
Arnhem, The Netherlands

In 1957, sandbags made from synthetic manufactured fibre were used for the construction of a temporary breakwater dam. The construction took place in The Netherlands to cut off a small inlet from the sea. It is believed that this is the first time a synthetic fabric was used in a civil engineering project.

DESCRIPTION OF THE PROJECT

A temporary sandbag dam was used to cut off the Eastern Scheldt tidal inlet to one of the smaller islands in the South Western part of the Netherlands, called Pluimpot. Immediately after this small sea arm had been closed, the construction of the permanent dam could start. This would occur behind the sandbag dam, in shallow water, by means of hydraulic filling. After completion of the permanent dam, the nylon sandbags could then be removed and reused for other civil engineering projects.

The sandy bottom, at the place where the "nylon dam" had to be built, had a resistance to a maximum flow of 0.5 m/s. At the very moment of closure of the inlet much higher flow rates could be expected, lasting a very short duration. Thus, at the place of the definite gap closure, extra precautions were necessary to avoid serious scouring.

In July 1957, the usual method of bottom protection consisted of using willow sinkmats ballasted with stones. In this case, the sinkmat openings were too large. When this occurs it was normal practice to add a thick layer of reeds to the willow sinkmat. For this project, the idea was proposed to cover the ballasted sinkmat, at the place of the closure, with a woven nylon filter. The filter was to be as permeable as possible but to have sufficient sand tightness to retain the sandy bottom material. It was to be ballasted by a layer of mineheap stones (Figure 1).

The characteristics of the nylon sandbag dam were as following:

Length	:	approx. 150 m
Height	:	approx. 4 m
Width at the top	:	approx. 4 m
Slopes	:	1.2H:1.0V
Number of bags	:	40 per linear m
Mass of one bag	:	approx. 1500 kg
Size of empty flat bag	:	2.20 m x 1.30 m
Rate of handling	:	30 bags/hour
Length of final gap to be closed		
(at low tide)	:	10 m

Some details of the construction are given in Figures 2, 3, 4, 5, 6 and 7.

MATERIAL SPECIFICATIONS

The characteristics of the two selected geotextiles, respectively "sinkmat of nylon" and nylon sandbags, were as follows:

Specification For "Sinkmat of Nylon"

Polymer	:	polyamide 6
Yarn linear density	:	23.5 tex
Number of filaments per yarn	:	35
Yarn twist	:	200 t/m - z
Yarn tensile strength	:	16 N
Yarn strain of failure	:	26%
Fabric count	:	1600 ends/m
		1400 picks/m
Type of weave	:	plain
Fabric width	:	approx. 2 m
Ready made size of sinkmat	:	8 m x 5 m (*)

*)   This has been realized by sewing together 27 fabric lengths of 8 m.

Specification For Nylon Sandbags

Polymer	:	polyamide 6
Yarn linear density	:	94 tex
Number of filaments per yarn	:	140
Yarn twist	:	180 t/m - z
Yarn tensile strength	:	75 N
Yarn strain at failure	:	20%
Fabric count	:	1000 ends/m
		1000 picks/m
Type of weave	:	plain (*)
Fabric width	:	130 cm

(*)   A double fabric connected only to each other at the selvedges and at the places where the bottom and the filling opening of the sandbags were situated: this is called "tubular weaving" on a flat loom; the method was developed in Enka's Research Weaving Department. It was improved later by Nicolon weaving experts at the time of manufacture.

The sandbag fabric on the roll is shown in Figure 2. By melt cutting at the places marked 'A' the fabric could be divided in bags. These bags would have both a dense woven bottom and top along with an opening for filling the bags in the middle. These dense woven strips can be seen very well in the photographs. Figure 3 shows an "in macro" view underneath 2 cross sections over the warp ends of the fabric (a) in the middle of the bottom strip and, (b) at the selvedges of the fabric.

Photo 1. Overall view of the moment of strong current.	Photo 2. Measuring the flow rate in the final gap.	Photo 3. Delivery of bags to the dragline.

Photo 4. Start of the final shutting - sandbags were dropped from 1 to 2 m height.	Photo 5. Extra storage of sandbags at both sides of the closure to ensure continuity in the closing operation.	Photo 6. Shutting-off completed.

REFERENCES

Lingsma, J.S., "Gids voor de Deltawerken" (translation: Guide for the Delta Works), N.V. Uitgeverij Nijgh & van Ditmar, Rotterdam-'s Gravenhage, Netherlands, 1964, second edition, pp. 203-214.

Snip, J.G., "Man-made fibres in dyke building", Proc. World Congress of Man-made Fibres, Comité International de la Rayonne et des Fibres Synthétiques, London, 1962

Vos, J.G., "Enkalon-weefsel in dienst van de Deltawerken", (translation: Enkalon woven fabrics used by the Delta Works), Technical-Scientific Journal Het Ingenieurs Blad, Royal Flamish Society of Engineers, Antwerp, Belgium, Vol. 33, No. 11, November 1964, pp. 569-575.

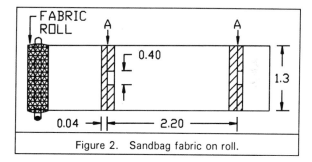

Figure 2. Sandbag fabric on roll.

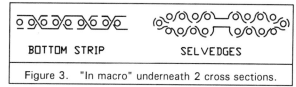

BOTTOM STRIP   SELVEDGES

Figure 3. "In macro" underneath 2 cross sections.

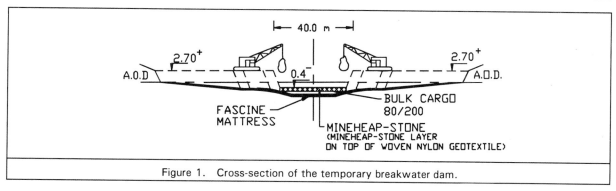

Figure 1. Cross-section of the temporary breakwater dam.

CHAPTER 4

SLOPE, BANK AND PIPELINE EROSION CONTROL

GEOTEXTILE FILTER FOR ARTIFICIAL ISLAND CONSTRUCTION
MACKENZIE RIVER, NORTHWEST TERRITORIES, CANADA

F. Claridge
Komex International Ltd.
Calgary, Alberta, Canada

S. Shinde
Imperial Oil Resources Ltd.
Calgary, Alberta, Canada

Six artificial islands were built in the MacKenzie River at Norman Wells, N.W.T., between the winter of 1983 and the fall of 1984 (over the two summer seasons). They are owned by Imperial Oil Resources Ltd of Calgary, Alberta, and built by Northern-Loram of Vancouver, B.C.

DESCRIPTION

The working surface of each island is 45 m by 80 m, and at the island-river bed interface is 170 m by 250 m rising 11 m to 12 m above the normal river level (Figure 1).

The slopes are 2H:1V except for the upstream face which was 10H:1V to ensure that the ice would creep up the slope and break up prior to reaching the island surface.

During break-up, ice jams may form downstream of the artificial islands, causing water levels to temporarily rise as high as 51 m elevation. Subsequent release of the ice jam causes rapid drawdown in the river level, with the possibility of excess pore pressures developing in the sand fill. The role of the geotextile is to prevent excess pore pressure buildup associated with a rapid drawdown and prevent the migration of sand fines during significant fluctuations in water levels. The geotextile was placed (a) between the hydraulic sand fill and the quarry run rock fill, both below the rip rap slope protection, and (b) between the sand fill and the inner slope of the rock fill dyke. A filter layer was also placed between the toe berm and any alluvium underlying the rock fill dyke.

The other alternative considered was a conventional sand filter. However, it was felt that the geotextile filter would perform better in the long term. Also, because of the current in the MacKenzie River, a geotextile would be easier to install than the sand filter layer.

CONSTRUCTION

The winter work involved cutting a trench through the ice and building a berm from the quarry run. The trench was in the shape of a "U" with the legs facing downstream to allow the ice to move from the centre of the "U" during breakup in the spring. The tops of the berms were made even with the ice.

The summer work involved closing off the berms, laying the geotextile filter and filling the centre with sand dredged from the river. The face of the slopes utilized two grades of armor rock. The first was 30 to 150 kg, and the second was 150 to 800 kg (see Figure 1). The borrow material had less than 10% silt (particles less than 75 μm in diameter) content by weight and no cobbles larger than about 150 mm in diameter.

GEOTEXTILE SELECTION

In order for geotextiles to function properly in filtration and related applications in artificial islands, they should:

(1)	Permit the passage of water without contributing to buildup of hydrostatic pressure.

(2)	Prevent piping of soil particles by establishing a stable hydraulic condition in which the soil, kept in place by the geotextile, maintains its structural integrity. Thus the soil particles do not move through the geotextile.

(3)	Have a specific gravity greater than 1.00 so as to sink into place.

(4)	Have high elongation to follow the contours of the irregular quarry stone and resist rupturing.

The nonwoven geotextile which was chosen was Texel 7613, with the following characteristics:

Polymer	Polyester
Specific gravity	1.38
Mass per unit area	400 g/m²
Thickness (CAN 2 - 4.2 - M77 Method 37) (ASTM D 1777)	3.8 mm
Tensile Strength at Break Elongation at Break (CAN 2 - 4.2 - M77 Method 9.2) (ASTM D 1682)	800 N 70 - 100 %
Burst Strength (Mullen) (CAN 2 - 4.2 - M77 Method 11.1) (ASTM D 3786)	2,800 kPa
Burst Strength (Ball) (CAN 2 - 4.2 - M77 Method 11.2) (ASTM D 751)	1650 N
Permeability (k)	2.6 mm/s
Equivalent Opening Size	70 - 125 μm

Photo 1. Inside of one island during backfilling.

Photo 2. High puncture resistance of geotextile.

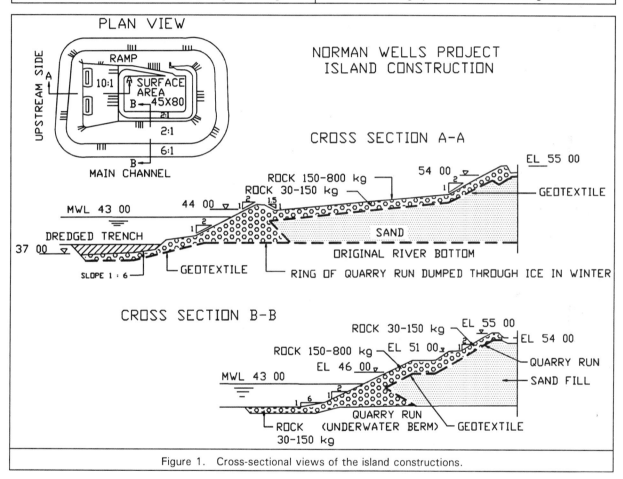

Figure 1. Cross-sectional views of the island constructions.

PERFORMANCE

The geotextile filter performance to date has been excellent with no apparent problems relating to rapid drawdown or unstable hydraulic conditions. This, combined with the ease of installation, makes the use of a geotextile in this application a wise choice.

REFERENCES

"Esso Resources Canada Ltd Norman Wells Expansion Project, 1980 Geotechnical Investigations", Komex Consultants Ltd, Calgary, Alberta, 1980.

"Esso Resources Canada Ltd Norman Wells Expansion Project, 1980 Geotechnical Investigations, Interim Data Report", Komex Consultants Ltd in association with Geocon (1975) Ltd.

"Subzero Weather is Contractors' Ally on Artificial Island, Pipeline Jobs", Heavy Construction News, February 18, 1985.

GEOTEXTILES FOR FOUNDATION MATTRESS IN BEACH EROSION CONTROL NORTH SEA COAST, GERMANY

F.F. Zitscher
University of Hannover
Hannover, Germany

The configuration of the north sea coast of Germany is shown in Figure 1. The northern part is confronted with the intense winds and the storm waves from the west.

Most of the coast line is protected by dikes. The narrow strip of land in front of the dikes must be stabilized by groynes. The sandy west coast of the islands left in their natural state retrogressed 1.0 to 1.5 m per year.

DESCRIPTION

The problems

For more than a 100 years coastal engineers have constructed groynes to stop, or at least to decrease, the retrogression. At first the construction elements were wooden pales, fascines and erratic blocks. Since about 1925 concrete pales have been used. These types of groynes, built as a vertical wall, have the disadvantage that the waves break abruptly. Since 1959 a new type led to a groyne with flat slopes, especially near the head of the groyne. This form results in a voluminous and expensive groyne body, filled by quarry stones. Such stones are expensive, since they are not available within a radius of about 500 km.

The solution by using geotextiles

The first use of geotextiles in coastal engineering in Germany is found in the following types of structures at the North Sea coast:

a. big bags, filled by sand from beach or dunes, to protect the head of small groynes (Project 1 and 2) and to fill out the inner part of the voluminous groynes (Project 4); and
b. mattresses to stabilize the base of a bag dam and furthermore a breakwater, constructed by Tetrapodes (Project 3).

The functions of the geotextiles are: (1) "to imitate stones or quarried materials" in the form of sand filled bags and (2) as an artificial foundation in the form of manufactured mattresses. The types of the geotextiles used can be characterized as follows:

- Plastic material: Polyamide 6 and 6.6
- Woven textiles: 840 and 1,000 dtex
- Special features: Manufacturing with double seam

FIRST ATTEMPTS

When the first attempts were made, the questions were: Could groynes be built or improved by packing sand from the beach or dunes into big bags? How would high strength plastic materials perform in the field?

The first test started in 1958. Its objective was to find out the best functioning layout. In 1959 about 130 bags, containing a volume between 0.1 and 1.1 m^3, corresponding approximately 180 and 1,800 kg/bag, were filled by ship during low water (Photo 1). This commenced the first test operation.

In detail, the different projects are as follows:

Project 1:

The first application was to stabilize the head of a groyne. The objective was to protect the flat land in front of the sea dikes against erosion (Photo 2).

Project 2:

Project 2 involved the building of a groyne to protect a sandy beach, situated between low and high water level, in the east of the island of "Amrum" (Figure 1 and Photo 1).

Project 3:

During a storm in Hamburg dikes were broken and large densely populated areas were flooded. After the storm, the river Suederelbe was dammed using 5,000 very big bags. The method for filling these very big bags was developed in 1962 and a funnel equipment was used. In addition the application of a geotextile mattress was developed to protect the foundation of the bag dam against erosion (Photo 3, foreground).

Project 4:

Project 4 was on the west beach of the island "Sylt" (Figures 1 and Photo 4). The beach was attacked by strong waves of more than 5 m height. The coast line had previously been protected (see "The problems"). The body of the voluminous groynes contained 8,000 m^3 of granite rock material of 0.6 to 1.2 t per piece. To decrease the costs, 1,000 bags, containing about 1.4 t of dune sand each, were used instead of rock material in the interior of the groyne body (Figure 2 and Photo 5). This method reduced the costs of the building materials to 50% per m^3.

CONCLUSION

Experience over 30 years has shown that design must ensure that the geotextile is protected against ultraviolet light and against driftwood and collision by

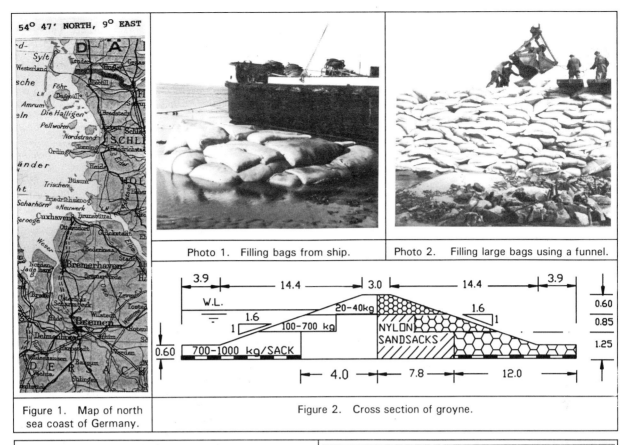

Photo 1. Filling bags from ship.

Photo 2. Filling large bags using a funnel.

Figure 1. Map of north sea coast of Germany.

Figure 2. Cross section of groyne.

Photo 3. Protection of flat land in front of groyne.

Photo 4. Protection for the beach at Sylt island.

ships. Bags with double seams were found to be strong enough to permit operating with a gripping claw. The 1,000 bags, used in the body of the groyne, are still in excellent shape, without any losses. This experience is important, because during the first developments problems occurred and were corrected. It allowed rethinking of the conventional methods of construction. It has resulted in the elegance of the new possibilities of using geotextiles in coastal engineering.

REFERENCES

Zitscher, F.F., "Kunststoffe für den Wasserbau", Bauingenieur-Praxis, Heft 125, Verlag W. Ernst & Sohn, Berlin, 1971, 225 p.

Photo 5. Bags used as part of groyne (see Figure 2).

GEOTEXTILE MATTRESSES FILLED WITH SAND FOR BANK PROTECTION
NIGER RIVER, NIGERIA

L.L.J. Kortsmit and W.H. Tutuarima
Zinkcon International bv
Papendrecht, The Netherlands

From 1981 to 1983, 300,000 m² of sandfilled geotextile (Profix system) were used as bank protection on two sites in the Niger Delta. The top layer of the mattresses was especially prepared to withstand the natural conditions.

DESCRIPTION

The Project

The project consisted of the construction of a flood and erosion protection. The new bank is a refill of sand above the old one. The average slope of the new sand bank is 5H:1V. The mattress length was 60 to 70 m from the crest down to the river bed. The width was 15 m, the overlap 1.0 m, the average thickness of the elliptical tubes was 130 mm.

Natural Conditions

In July, the water rises 6 to 8 m and the maximum current is about 2.5 m/s. In November, levels drop and an increasing amount of ground water seeps out of the bank. The yearly ultraviolet radiation energy per unit area is approximately 140 kcal/cm², maximum temperatures are around 35°C, and conditions are favourable for vegetation.

Construction Method

The folded pieces were spread, filled, with sand and pulled out in stages into the river. The filling was done pneumatically. For pulling, a special beam was used.

DESIGN

Overall Stability

For the analysis of the stability of the new embankment, worst site conditions were considered. A minimum safety factor of 1.25 was found for the most critical slip circle.

Permeability Criterion

The permeability of the mattress is larger than that of the subsoil (k = 0.37 μm/s). Clogging and blocking were not considered critical since coarse sand was used.

Retention Criterion

Due to limited hydraulic loads, design criterion of O_{90} < d_{90} was applied (d_{90} approximately 900 μm).

Tensile Strength

The required strength of the geotextile was 40 kN/m to ensure resistance to pulling forces during construction. Sliding down the slope in the final stage was prevented by anchoring the topside.

Hydraulic Stability

The hydraulic stability was calculated with methods developed by the Delft Hydraulic Laboratory [1981]. For the average mattress thickness, the critical flow velocity was calculated to be 4.2 m/s. Overlaps were placed in the downstream direction. A heavy tube along the down edge ensured a close contact with the river bed.

Resistance to Ultraviolet Radiation

The top fabric is directly exposed to the sunlight. Therefore the material selected was a nonwoven needlepunched polypropylene geotextile which was highly U.V.-stabilized. The procedure used to take into account the effect of the 140 kcal/cm² radiation is described in papers by Tutuarima et al. [1984] and Van Wijk et al. [1986].

Resistance to Thermo-oxidative Degradation

Due to the high temperature, special requirements had to be met to satisfy life time expectations. Special antioxidant systems have been developed in The Netherlands to lengthen the life time of geotextiles. So called heat-stabilized fabrics were used for the Profix mattress. The test requirements are described by Wisse et al. [1982].

GEOTEXTILE CHARACTERISTICS

Both bottom and top geotextiles were polypropylene woven fabrics. The main characteristics of the bottom geotextile are: type Amoco 6066/73; opening size 360 μm; hydraulic conductivity, k = 30 mm/s; tensile strength 75 kN/m; oven test, maximum 10% loss of strength in 7 days at 150°C. The main characteristics of the top geotextile are: type Amoco 6067/75/40; opening size 200 μm; k = 30 mm/s; tensile strength 50 kN/m; oven test, maximum 10% loss of strength in 2,000 hours at 150°C.

PERFORMANCE

Stability

During construction up to February 1988, some slides occurred, mainly on the first site at Otuokpoti during

| Photo 1. Growing of vegetation on the revetment. | Photo 2. Situation at Sagbama in 1988. |

the period from 1984 to 1986. The main reasons for these slides were:

- The sandfill technique applied.

- The flow of water from the village into the sandfill.

Most of the slides were of small magnitude, and the Profix mattress adjusted to the new profile. Two of the slides were more severe. These sections were repaired by the placement of a new Profix layer.

Deformations

The pneumatic filling system results in a low density for the sand in the mattress. However, due to natural conditions, the sand evolved into a higher density. The resulting change in shape of the mattress was limited. This became obvious after the first rainy season. Years later the situation remained stable.

Mechanical Damage on the Surface

The main activities directly affecting the surface of the Profix mattresses are: pedestrian traffic and transport of goods; stockpiling of goods; landing of boats (canoes, flyboats); bathing and washing; and laundry drying.

On the spots affected by those activities, the following was noticed: wearing off of the green felt layer and tearing of the top layer of fabric. Both damages are repairable and can be tackled by maintenance and control.

Vegetation

The settling of clay and silt particles in the felt layer caused a rapid growth of grass and plants in and on the revetment.

Durability

Tensile tests done in 1988 revealed that the strength of the top layer of geotextile was reduced to about 80% of the original value, and the strength of the bottom layer to about 90%. It is believed that the cover of silt, dust and vegetation is an important factor for the protection of the top layer.

CONCLUSIONS

The following conclusions can be drawn from this case history:

- The application of sandfilled mattresses in river delta areas as revetment type construction can compete with more traditional revetment type constructions based on stone, concrete and bitumen materials, especially at remote locations where the importation of stone, concrete or bitumen is costly.

- The technique of filling and placing of sandfilled mattresses has been evaluated in such a way that practically any desired surface (bottom or slope) can be covered.

- The geotextiles applied for this case performed satisfactorily regarding the mechanical and hydraulic conditions. Also with respect to the resistance against deterioration by ultraviolet and thermo oxidative processes, the reduction of strength from the time of construction up to now is as far as has been monitored, within expectations.

REFERENCES

Delft Hydraulic Laboratory, "Stability of Sandfilled Mattresses", Report R 1698, Delft, 1981.

Tutuarima, W.H. and Van Wijk, W., "Profix Mattresses - An Alternative Erosion Control System", Proc. Int. Conf. on Flexible Armoured Revetments Incorporating Geotextiles, ICE, London, 1984, pp. 335-348.

Van Wijk, W. and Stoerzer, M., "UV Stability of Polypropylene", Proc. 3rd. Int. Conf. on Geotextiles, Vienna, 1986, pp. 851-854.

Wisse, J.D.M., and Birkenfeld, S., "The Long-Term Thermo-Oxidative Stability of Polypropylene Geotextiles in the Oosterschelde Project", Proc. 2nd. Int. Conf. on Geotextiles, Las Vegas, 1982, pp. 283-288.

GEOTEXTILE FILTER USED IN A BANK PROTECTION
ROTTERDAM, THE NETHERLANDS

I.M. Veltman
Public Works Department
Rotterdam, The Netherlands

J.D.M. Wisse
T.N.O. Plastics and Rubber Research Institute
Delft, The Netherlands

In 1984 bank protection was required for the western side of one of Rotterdam's harbour basins. Above water the structure consisted of stone asphalt over sand asphalt, while below water there was a riprap covered revetment with a 4H:1V slope (see Figure 1). The revetment incorporated a geotextile filter which in addition to standard engineering specifications was required to have a life expectancy of 100 years.

DESCRIPTION

This was the first time that a specific life expectancy had been included in the specification. Although a standard for the determination of life expectancy was under development, no method was included in the specification. This study deals with the problems arising when an indication of quality, including a life expectancy, is specified without stating any method of determination.

When the work started, it was realized that there was no indication of the quality of the delivered geotextile. Samples tested in the usual way with regard to their being sandproof and permeable met the specifications. To prevent further delays a decision was taken to start the work using the geotextile, even though there was still no information relating to its durability. At the same time a sample of the geotextile was sent to T.N.O. to investigate its life expectancy.

TEST DEVELOPMENT

Samples of the polypropylene (PP) geotextile from 11 places in the revetment were submitted to the "ovenlife test". This test is used to determine the resistance of polymers to thermo-oxidative degradation. Samples are placed in a hot air oven at constant temperature, until they begin to display embrittlement (loss of mechanical strength). The time needed is a measure of the oxidation resistance of the PP. This test has now been adopted as a standard (NEN 5132). The results are shown in Table 1.

Sample 12 was a stock sample; sample 13 was a reference sample, put at the disposal of the PWD, Rotterdam. From the results, T.N.O concluded that the desired life expectancy of 100 years would not be attained. T.N.O. was therefore asked to investigate the range of life expectancy of sample 13, the weakest one.

ESTIMATION OF LIFE EXPECTANCY

Two series of ovenlife tests were then carried out on sample 13, at 120°, 100°, 80° and 60°C. The first series was executed on the geotextile as used and a second series on the geotextile after soaking in diethylether: by this means all the anti-oxidants present in the PP were extracted.

Comparison of PP with and without the addition of anti-oxidants indicates that the extracted unstabilized sample was only very slightly less oxidation resistant than was the original geotextile. Apparently the anti-oxidants present in the geotextile were only slightly active or were completely inactive.

In the calculation of the life expectancy it is assumed that a linear relation exists between the natural logarithm of the embrittlement time (ovenlife t_o) and the reciprocal absolute temperature: $t_o = A.\exp(\Delta H/RT)$, in which A is a constant, R the gas constant, T the absolute temperature and ΔH the activating energy of the thermo-oxidation reaction. In many cases this relation appears to apply only to a limited range of temperatures (ΔH is not truly constant); for unstablized PP geotextiles it appears that this relation is truly linear. Linear regression calculations produced the following:

No. 13	ΔH (kJ/mol)	Life expectancy in air at 10°C	Correlation Coefficient
As used	66.1	23 years	0.998
Extracted	64.6	18 years	0.993

To progress from the life expectancy in air at 10°C (as average ambient temperature, also in water) to the life expectancy in the underwater part of the revetment the following assumptions are made:

a) With permanent complete submergence in water thermo-oxidation proceeds four times more slowly than in air (lower oxygen pressure). In the harbour extra aeration of the water resulting from the action of ships' propellers must be taken into account. For this reason a factor three is taken.

Table 1. Ovenlife (140°C) in days. Samples from the revetment. (Required oven life 12 days.)													
Sample No.	1	2	3	4	5	6	7	8	9	10	11	12	13
Ovenlife	10	8	2	3	2	3	2.5	3	2	3	2	3	1

ISSMFE., Committee TC9 - Geosynthetics Case Histories.

Photo 1.   Construction of revetment.

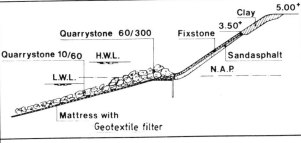

Figure 1.   Cross-section of the revetment.

b)   Even at ambient temperatures, metallic compounds (iron), which occur in the water and in the soil accelerate the thermo-oxidative degradation. This accelerates the degradation by a factor three.

What this amounts to is that for sample 13, a (minimum) life expectancy of about 20 years could be postulated. It could be assumed that the samples which had a longer ovenlife, would have a roughly proportionally longer life expectancy, always however shorter than required. In order to resolve the problem a practical solution via negotiation was adopted.

ADOPTED SOLUTION

The bank protection above low water was given an extra sand/gravel filter on the already sunken mattresses. Firstly, the coarsest riprap, 60-300 kg, was removed. The space between the remaining stones, 10-60 kg, was filled with coarse sand (0-7mm) to a level 250 mm above the geotextile. Above this 150 mm of coarse gravel (30-80 mm) was placed. Finally the (0 - 300 kg) riprap layer was replaced. This formed a structure which would meet the filter rules, even in the event of failure of the geotextile filter.

It was very much less simple to modify the part below low water level for which the following methods can be considered:

a)   Replacing the construction by one which meets the specifications. Theoretically a good solution, this is technically almost impossible. It would impair the stability of the bank and railway lying behind. Moreover, the quality of this solution cannot be checked: if all the riprap is not removed the new revetment may be damaged by stones which remain.

b)   Modification of the existing construction. For this there are a number of alternatives. The first is the application of a sand/gravel filter like that used above the low water line. Here also part of the riprap must be removed which will result in riprap damaging the underlying mattress. The stability of the bank may be endangered. Although the theoretical demands are met there are many practical drawbacks. The structure can also be modified without first removing part of the riprap if, for example, a layer of mining stone can be applied, which can then be covered by riprap. Alternatively a thick layer of steel-slag

can be applied to the existing riprap filling the space between the stones. Waves, currents and the wake of vessels will wash the slag further in between the riprap.

These solutions do not meet the filter rules nor the demand that a good closed filter and riprap layer must form over the entire surface. Although there are various application systems it is almost impossible to obtain a good closed layer.

A further method is to fill in the existing layer of riprap with a granular filter. First a layer of coarse sand is spread over the riprap. This will be washed between the riprap by waves and currents. Next a layer of coarse gravel is applied to keep the sand in place. This is the most satisfactory way to modify the existing structure. It is, however, almost impossible to check whether the sand and gravel have been sufficiently washed in and there is no certainty that the sand and gravel will not be scoured out again by the wakes of vessels.

c)   Periodic repair - solution which was finally chosen. The revetment will be repaired as and when this appears to be necessary in the future. This "must" need will be determined by regular monitoring. A financial arrangement has been made with the contractor relating to the future accelerated maintenance.

Where the geotextile filter no longer functions repairs can be made; for example, by filling up the riprap with mining stone, after which new riprap can be applied on top. It is anticipated that repair will first be required in those places where ships' wakes reach the banks. For these repairs it is not necessary to apply an even layer.

CONCLUSION

Although the problem was finally solved in this practical way, the lesson is clear. Firstly, it is important not only to include stipulations with regard to the properties of the geotextile filter in the specifications, but also the manner in which these properties can be determined. In the second place, research must be initiated to establish a simple relation between the test methods and the life expectancy.

REFERENCES

NEN 5132 "Plastic fabrics in hydraulic structures. Polypropylene yarns for fabrics. Requirements and test methods"; 1988.

Report No. 377/'84, T.N.O., Plastics and Rubber Research Institute.

Keuringseisen filterweefsel, Rotterdam, bestek 1-065-83 pt. 11.3 (Test requirements for filter cloth according to the specifications of Rotterdam).

GEOSYNTHETICS COMBINED WITH VEGETATION FOR SLOPE PROTECTION ALBPANORAMA URACH AND WORKSHOP CALW, GERMANY

U. Smoltczyk and K. Malcharek
Stuttgart Institute for Geotechnics
University of Stuttgart, Germany

Left uncontrolled the effects of weathering can lead to severe degradation of slopes. Slope protection is achieved most economically if the strength of the ground can be kept unaffected from weathering by covering the slope with membrane-like structures which consist of a reinforcing grid and vegetative soil fill. In terms of ecology, such techniques are preferable to conventional means as, for example, shotcrete facing.

CASE 1: SOFT GABIONS

Description

- Name of the structure: housing project Albpanorama Urach, Germany.
- Type of structure: membrane structure.
- Dimensions: h = 6 m, l = 35 m, slope 2H:1V.
- Role of the geosynthetic: slope protection against weathering to avoid deterioration of existing stability.
- Date of construction: autumn 1984.
- Special features of the structure: vegetation with cotoneaster plants.

Technical Considerations

The owner of the house at the top of the slope wanted to extend the house's terrace at very short notice. This could be realised at low costs by application of soft gabions made of a 400 mm thick layer of the HaTe geosynthetic filled with locally excavated stony loam. The HaTe geosynthetic used was type 50-145, which is a 225 g/m² PVC coated polyester fabric with an open, grid-like structure of 1.0 to 1.2 mm mesh size. Both the warp and weft directions have a tensile strength of approximately 38 kN/m and 15% elongation at failure.

Installation was completed within twelve days. Much of the time was spent in removing large volumes of soil to create a working space for small shovel loader. A breakdown of costs, which agreed well with earlier experience, showed roughly 12% of the cost was for providing the geosynthetic, 10% for the fill, with the remaining 78% for construction costs. The total costs per square metre were about 70% of those involved when using a gabion wall solution.

CASE 2: REINFORCED FILL

Description

- Name of the structure: Workshop, Calw, Germany.
- Type of structure: fill layers reinforced by geosynthetic.

- Dimensions: h = 5 to 9 m, l = 200 m, slope 1H:1V.
- Role of the geosynthetic: reinforcement.
- Date of construction: autumn 1984.
- Special features of the structure: grass cover.

Technical Considerations

Part of an area required to build an army workshop had to be raised by retaining excavated material from a hillside cut. Since a slope steeper than 1H:1V was not needed, a HaTe geosynthetic was used but was just laid out to reinforce the layers of fill without the need to protect the exposed face of the fill. The HaTe geosynthetic used was type 50-145, which is a 225 g/m² PVC coated polyester fabric with an open, grid-like structure, with a 1.0 to 1.2 mm mesh size. Both warp and weft have a tensile strength of approximately 38 kN/m and 15% elongation to failure.

The fill was placed with a 1 m extension beyond the edge of the geosynthetic reinforcing layers to protect them from displacement effects during the compaction of the fill. When compaction was finished, this metre of overfill was removed and the surface finished. Finally, an erosion control layer was pegged on the surface of the slope. For this, a newly developed wire netting with a 40 mm mesh size, made from an undulating wire of 1.4 mm diameter was used. This is spatially stabilized by transverse steel rods of 3 mm diameter which are inserted into the undulations of the 1.4 mm diameter wire and spot welded afterwards. This prefabricated mattress is unrolled on the surface of the fill slope and pinned to the ground using 16 mm diameter pins 500 mm long. The netting is available with a PVC coating; however, this was felt to be unnecessary since the protection afforded by the mesh is only needed until the vegetation is sufficiently developed on the slope to withstand erosion.

CONCLUSIONS

The examples given demonstrate the usefulness of combining various types of slope protection to gain the most appropriate solution in terms of both techniques and economy. For simple erosion control on slopes to be covered with grass only, synthetic matting (geomat) such as Enkamat would provide a sufficient protection system. Where reinforcement is to be used this can be provided using a geosynthetic reinforced fill combined with bushes or other suitable vegetation to provide long-term reinforcement. This system meets ecological requirements in a most favourable way.

Photo 1. Soft gabion construction.

Photo 2. Construction of geosynthetic reinforced fill.

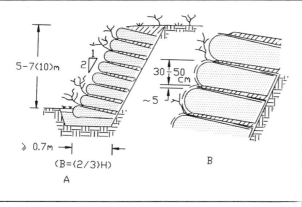

Figure 1. Slope protection by soft gabions (a) open type (b) closed type.

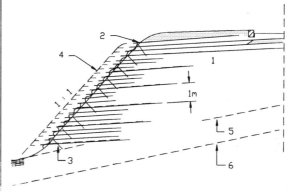

Figure 2. Geosynthetic reinforced fill combined with wire netting to prevent erosion (1) fill layers, reinforced by geosynthetics; (2) undulated mesh wire netting; (3) pins; (4) 1 m fill extension to allow for compaction; (5) natural ground surface; (6) preliminary excavation of soft top layer.

REFERENCES

Smoltczyk, U., and Malcharek, K., "Naturgerechte Sicherung von Steilböschungen", Geotechnik, Deutsche Gesellschaft für Erd - und Grundbau, No. 3/1984, pp. 117-129.

Smoltczyk, U., and Malcharek, K., "Slope Protection by Membrane Structures", Geotextiles and Geomembranes, Elsevier Applied Science Publishers, Vol. 2, No. 4, 1985, pp. 323-336.

Smoltczyk, U., "Neues Verfahren zur Sicherung von Steilböschungen mit Hilfe von Geotextilien", Proc. 23rd. Int. Man-Made Fibres Congress, Dornbirn, 1984, pp. 550-569.

Smoltczyk, U., "Lebendverbau an Steilwänden aus Tonmergel", Jahrbuch 2 (1985) der Gesellschaft für Ingenieurbiologie, SEPiA Verlag Aachen, pp. 170-177.

GEOTEXTILE FILTER AND GEOMEMBRANE LINER FOR SLOPES LUANMU RESERVOIR, CHINA

Z.Y. Liu
Water Conservancy Bureau
Hebei Province, China

S. Wang
Haihe Water Conservancy Committee
Tianjin, China

The Luanmu Reservoir is located on a tributary of the Dihe River in the Hebei Province of China. It was built in 1958-59. A terrace juts out into the reservoir between the main dam and auxiliary dam. Since the reservoir was built, no protection work has been made on its slope. An experimental project using a geotextile as a filter for slope protection and a geomembrane for seepage control was suggested and finished in 1985-86.

DESCRIPTION

The terrace between the main dam and the auxiliary dam is 50 m long and 9 m high with a slope of 3.5H:1V. It is composed of loess, sand, and gravel. During the performance of more than 20 years, the slope of the terrace was seriously eroded by wind and wave action. On its lower part, leakage of water through some continuous sand layers occurred during high water level.

TECHNICAL CONSIDERATIONS

Geotextile as Filter in Slope Protection

The experimental area is about 905 m^2. Four patterns of slope protection had been adopted for comparison (Figure 1).

Pattern A: The subsoil was covered with a needle-punched nonwoven polyester geotextile produced in China (mass per unit area: 450 g/m^2). On the geotextile a layer of 400 mm thick blockstone was laid. Metal pins were used to prevent the geotextile from sliding.

Pattern B: Same as Pattern A, except the mass per unit area of geotextile (in this case: 300 g/m^2); plus the geotextile was placed without sliding pins.

Pattern C: The subsoil was covered with the same polyester geotextile produced in China (mass per unit area of 300 g/m^2) adopted in Pattern B, but in this case, fixed with sliding pins. On the geotextile, layers of 200 mm thick gravel and 400 mm thick blockstones were laid.

Pattern D: A traditional sand and gravel system was adopted. It consists of 400 mm thick blockstone, 200 mm thick crushed stone, 200 mm thick gravel, and 300 mm thick sand.

Using the cost of Pattern D as reference the unit cost per m^2 of Pattern A was 57.4% lower, of Pattern B 70.4% lower, and of Pattern C 47.1% lower. It is obvious that the geotextile filter was much cheaper than the traditional sand and gravel filter.

Selection of Geotextile Filters

Design of the filters used the following criteria:

- For sand and gravel filters:
  Retention criterion: d_{15} filter $< 5 \times d_{85}$ soil
  Permeability criterion: d_{15} filter $> 5 \times d_{15}$ soil
- For geotextile filters:
  Retention criterion: O_{90} geotextile $< d_{85}$ soil
  Permeability criterion: O_{90} geotextile $> d_{15}$ soil

The above requirements were all satisfied, taking into account the following values of the hydraulic properties of geotextiles, measured in laboratory tests:

- For the geotextile 300 g/m^2:
  opening size : $O_{90} = 93 \ \mu m$
  coeft. of normal permeability: $k_g = 580 \ \mu m/s$
- For the geotextile 450 g/m^2:
  opening size: $O_{90} = 97 \ \mu m$
  coeft. of normal permeability: $k_g = 1,450 \ \mu m/s$

Geomembrane for Seepage Control

The experimental area was about 1,720 m^2. Two kinds of geomembrane (both produced in China) were chosen: calendered PVC geomembrane and bituminous geomembrane reinforced with glass fibre. The two patterns are:

Pattern E: Black PVC geomembrane (thickness of 0.8 mm) was set directly on the subsoil. On the geomembrane, three protection layers were laid, namely: 100 mm thick medium and coarse sand, 150 mm thick crushed stone and 300 mm thick blockstone.

Pattern F: Two layers of bituminous geomembrane bonded with hot bitumen were set directly on the subsoil. The protection layers were the same as in Pattern E except the thickness of the sand layer was 450 mm thick (instead of 100 mm thick).

The cost of the PVC geomembrane solution was 30.4% lower than that of an inclined clay blanket and the construction time for the geomembrane method was 38.0% less than that of the clay blanket.

Properties of Geomembranes

According to laboratory results, the tensile strength of the two geomembranes were as follows:

- For PVC geomembrane: $\sigma_f = 9.5$ kN/m
- For bituminous geomembrane: $\sigma_g = 14.8$ kN/m

Photo 1. Finished slope protection with geotextile (higher area) and geomembrane (lower area).

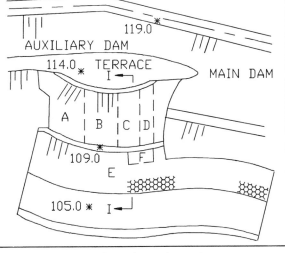

Figure 1. Plan of experimental area.

Observation Apparatus

- Piezometers: To observe the effect of filtration and seepage control.
- Thermometers: To compare the heat preservation effects of the different patterns.
- Displacement stakes: To observe the sliding of the protection and seepage control works along the slope of the terrace.
- Weirs: To measure the amount of seepage water.

Analysis of Observed Temperature Data Below Geotextiles

Air temperature and ground temperature were measured at Patterns A to D at 6 a.m. from December 1985 to February 1986, and from December 1986 to February 1987. The observed data are summarized in Table 1. From the observed temperature data we can conclude that:

- When the local air temperature is about -14°C, the geotextile filter of any one of Patterns A, B, and C, can protect the subsoil from freezing;
- On heat preservation the traditional sand and gravel filter is more effective than the geotextile filter;
- The effect on heat preservation of a layer of gravel in Pattern C is not obvious as compared with Patterns A and B;
- The observed data are obviously influenced by the variety of the direction and the duration of sunshine at different localities on the slope and the variation of air temperature before the observed date.

CONCLUSIONS

The placing of geotextiles and geomembranes in Luanmu reservoir was finished in November 1985 and July 1986, respectively. Since the amount of water stored in the reservoir was very small during the last years, no further observation data was recorded.

REFERENCES

Liu Zongyao, "Design of Geotextile Filters", Water Resources and Hydropower Engineering, No. 6, June 1987, pp. 23-28. (in Chinese)

Giroud, J.P., and Frobel, R.K., "Geomembrane Products", Geotechnical Report Fabrics, Fall 1983.

Wang, S., Zhang, Y., Zhao, Y., Zhao, D., and Liu, Z., "The Application of Geotextile and Geomembrane in the Experimental Project of Luanmu Reservoir", Proc. 1st. Chinese Conf. on Geotextiles, 1986, pp. 90-98. (in Chinese)

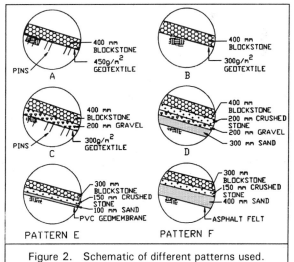

Figure 2. Schematic of different patterns used.

Table 1. Recorded Temperature Patterns.				
Patterns	A	B	C	D
Air Temperature	-14°C	-14°C	-14°C	-14°C
Subsoil Temperature Range	-1.1°C to 0.3°C	1.6°C to 2.0°C	0.3°C to 3.1°C	6.3°C to 10.1°C
Diff. between air temp. & temp. under 400 mm stone + gravel	7.7°C to 8.0°C	---	13.7°C to 15.6°C	---
Diff. of temp. above and below sand or geotextile	5.5°C to 6.4°C	5.5°C to 6.5°C	1.1°C to 1.5°C	3.0°C to 3.5°C

GEOTEXTILE AS FILTER IN DIKE WORK HEILONGJIANG PROVINCE, CHINA

Y.W. Hong
Heilongjiang Research Institute of Water Conservancy
Harbin, China

The Southern Division Work in Heilongjiang Province, China, was located in the west part of Heilongjiang, on the left bank of the Nen River. A filling reservoir was made up of 33 dikes. The water is being diverted from the Nen River (see Figure 1). The total length of the 33 dikes is 50 km. The filling water volume is 770,000,000 m^3. The earthwork was 10,454,000 m^3: the rockfill was 155,000 m^3; the concrete-lining was 587,000 km^2. A fishing area measures 20,000 km^2, and a reed area covers 37,000 km^2. The Division Work was begun in 1977 and completed in 1987.

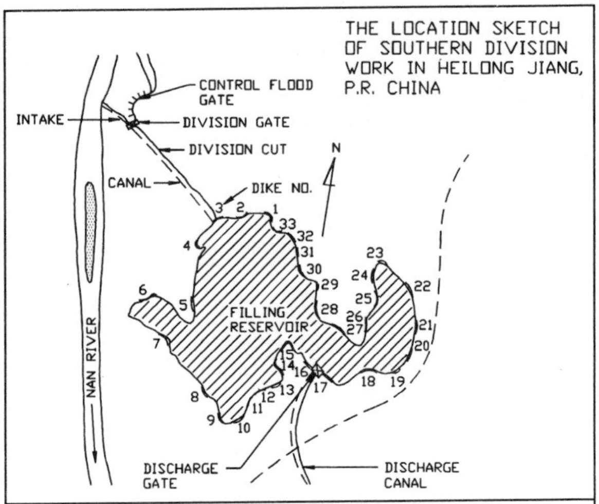

DESCRIPTION

The Dikes

The filling water reservoirs which consist of 33 dikes are located in a region with high natural moisture content soils. Some earth dikes (No. 2, 16, 17, 18, 19, and 21) were built with dispersive soil (high natural moisture content). During early construction, more than a hundred erosion pockets induced by rainwater were found. In this paper, three projects are described. The characteristics of these dikes are given in Table 1. Two of them are built with dispersive clay, one with fine sand.

The Dispersive Clay Characteristics

In order to study the erosion phenomenon on dispersive clay, tests were carried out. Many soil samples

Figure 1. General plan of Southern Division Work in Heilongjiang, China.

were obtained from the field and the following tests were carried out: normal physical tests; disintegration tests; collapse tests; chemical analysis of the porewater; clast tests; two-hydrometer tests; pinhole tests; lime-stabilized tests; sand filter tests; and geotextile pinhole test.

Through these tests it has been shown that the dispersive clay has poor erosion-resistance. It contained

Table 1. Characteristics of the three dikes projects in Southern Division Work described in the paper.			
Project Name	Red Soil Dike	Dike No. 16	Dike No. 21
Dike height (m)	5.5	4.0	4.0
Dike length (m)	400	400	838
Soil type	fine sand	clay	clay
Geotextile area (m^2)	6,700	4,200	12,000

Table 2. Properties of the dispersive soil.							
Grain Size (mm)				G_s	W_L	W_p	I_p
> 0.05	0.05-0.005	0.005-0.002	< 0.002		%	%	%
37%	28%	8%	27%	2.69	31	17	14

Table 3. Grain distribution (mm) for two samples of the fine sand used in Red Soil Mountain Dike.								
> 0.25	0.25 to 1.0	1.0 to 0.05	0.05 to 0.005	< 0.005	d_{60} mm	d_{10} mm	C_u	k_v $\mu m/s$
10.0	71.0	9.0	6.5	3.5	0.21	0.025	4.0	800
11.5	71.0	8.0	6.5	3.0	0.20	0.052	3.8	200

Photo 1. Constuction of Red Soil Mountain Dike, 1984.

Photo 2. Geotextile under rip-rap, 1984.

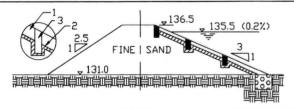

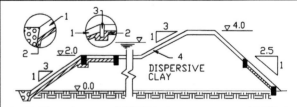

Figure 2. No. 16 dike section at Southern Division Work: 1. concrete slab; 2. geotextile; 3. concrete beam; and 4. grass.

Figure 3. The Red Soil Mountain Dike Section at Southern Division Work: 1. concrete slab; 2. geotextile; 3. concrete beam.

very high charged ions around the soil particles. The attractive forces between the soil particles, therefore, were very small. As the soil is saturated, the repelling force between particles become larger than the attraction forces. Then the particles begin to separate one by one on the soil surface. In still water, the clay soil particles go into suspension.

Some of the properties of the dispersive clay samples are given in Table 2. In addition the results of characteristic tests on the dispersive soils are as follows:

- Clastic test: white fog appeared after several seconds; grain scattered and suspended;
- Two-hydrometer test: dispersive degree D = 49%;
- Natural moisture content: 95.7%;
- Pinhole test: water head 50 mm; erosion occurred; pinhole enlarged to 30 to 50 mm over time; water muddy with suspended grains.
- Geotextile pinhole tests: no grain migrated from seepage area and the pinhole was not enlarged.

The Fine Sand Characteristics

The material used to build Red Soil Mountain Dike is fine sand; the characteristics are shown in Table 3.

GEOTEXTILE SELECTION

The geotextile pinhole test gave excellent results therefore it was decided to use a geotextile to prevent erosion of the dispersive clay. The same geotextile was also used as a filter in the red soil mountain dike project. The properties of the related geotextile (DS450-2) are given in Table 4.

DESIGN

The characteristics of the dikes built with dispersive clay are illustrated in Figure 2 for dike No. 16. It is very similar to dike No. 21. The characteristics of the Red Soil Mountain Dike are illustrated in Figure 3. In Table 5, the cost of the solution based on geotextile filters to prevent dispersive clay erosion, is compared with other systems.

Table 4. The properties of DS450-2 geotextile.

No.	Content	Value
1	Mass per unit area (g/m²)	450
2	Thickness (mm)	3.4
3	Strip tensile strength (kN/50 mm)	lati: 7.2 long: 7.8
4	Elongation (%)	lati: 67.8 long: 67.8
5	Puncture resistance (kg/20 mm)	120
6	Strip tensile strength after freezing and thaw (kN/50 mm)	lati: 7.0 long: 7.4
7	Permeability (μm/s)	62.0
8	Filtration opening (μm)	43 to 110
9	Material	PP
10	Manufactures process	Needlepunch
11	Name of company	Jia Mu Si

Table 5. Cost comparison of various measures of treatment of dispersive soil dike

Name of treatment measures	Relative Budget (Yuan)
Using non-dispersive clay to surround the dike	368
Throw down the lime to improve water of reservoir	802
Using $ALSO_4$ to improve the soil body	538
Using lime-soil at upstream and sandfilter at downstream	174
Using geotextiles instead of sandfilter to surround dike	100

REFERENCES

You-Wei Hong and Shou-Tain Sheng, "Behaviour of Dispersive Clay and its Treatment Practice in the West Part of Heilongjiang, China", Chinese Journal of Geotechnical Engineering, Vol. 6, No. 6, Nov. 1984.

Dian-Shi Qiao et al., "The Summary Report of Geotextile Application in the Slope Protection of the Earth Dam of Victory Reservoir in Heilongjiang", 1984.

GEOTEXTILES FOR CANAL BANK PROTECTION
CANAL DES DUNES, DUNKIRK, FRANCE

M. Schaeffner
Laboratoire Central des Ponts et Chaussées
Paris, France

In 1984-1986, a geotextile filter was used as part of the protection system of the banks of Canal des Dunes, Dunkirk, France. Test sections were constructed to compare several geotextiles and a granular filter.

DESCRIPTION

- Dimensions: The first stage of the work, described here, covers a length of 3,000 m.
- Area of geotextile used: $2 \times 3,000 \times 40 = 240,000 \ m^2$
- Role of the geotextile: To act as a filter between a fine sand and a layer of rip-rap while allowing large flow rates between the two materials.
- Date of construction and of geotextile placement: 1984-1986
- Special features: The Canal des Dunes is a maritime canal dug in a fine sand of uniform grading. Its banks are subjected to:
  - a tide having a daily range of about 7 m;
  - the wakes of ocean-going tugs and wave action that can be very violent;
  - currents in excess of 1 m/s when the locks are opened.

The above set of conditions is severe, especially with respect to the problem of filtering the sand, due to the large hydraulic gradients to which the sand is subjected.

TECHNICAL CONSIDERATIONS

Design of the structure and design of the geotextile application:

- The banks of the canal were cut to the following slopes (see Figure 1)
  - 5H:1V at the bottom, always under water (between levels 4.2 and +0)
  - 4H:1V in the middle portion, subjected to the daily tide (between levels +0 and +7);
  - 3H:1V at the top, under water only during equinoctial tides (between levels +1 and +8.7).
- The bottom part, always under water, needed no special protection.
- The middle and top portions of the banks are protected by a geotextile
- The rip-rap was delivered to the slope by dumpers and placed by hydraulic excavators that dropped it from a height often in excess of 1 m.

Discussion of Alternative Solutions

Given the technical and economic conditions of this project and existing experience of the use of geotextiles as filters for the protection of banks, no solution other than the one described above was considered. The project supervisor, however, decided to build a number of test sections at this site to compare the behaviour of the

		Nicolon 66550	Boussac St. F.	Bidim U_{34}	Bidim U_{44}
Identification characteristics	Nature of the geotextile	Woven polyethylene mono-filament U.V. protected	Woven polyethylene small banded U.V. protected	Nonwoven spunbonded polyester	Nonwoven spunbonded polyester
	Mass per unit area (g/m²)	220	305	270	340
	Thickness at 20 kPa (mm)	0.5	1.0	1.7	2.1
Mechanical characteristics	Tensile strength (kN/m)	warp: 60 weave: 30	warp: 58 weave: 54	warp: 23 weave: 23	warp: 26 weave: 26
	Elongation at rupture (%)	No measurements	13 12	40 40	40 40
	Tear strength (kN/m)	No measurements	0.5 0.5	1.0 1.0	2.0 2.0
Hydraulic characteristics	Permittivity (s⁻¹)	2.0	0.24	1.3	1.1
	Transmissivity (m²/s)	0.0	0.0	42×10^6	52×10^6
	Filtration opening (μm)	100	145	110	105

Table 1. Brand name type and properties of the geotextiles used.

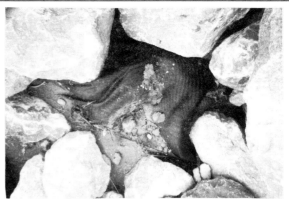

Photo 1. View of canal bank protected with 15/60 kg rip-rap placed on geotextile.

Photo 2. Detail of geotextile filter.

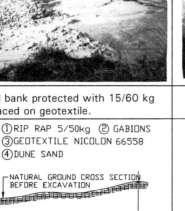

① RIP RAP 5/50kg ② GABIONS
③ GEOTEXTILE NICOLON 66558
④ DUNE SAND

Figure 1. Conventional filter design for canal.

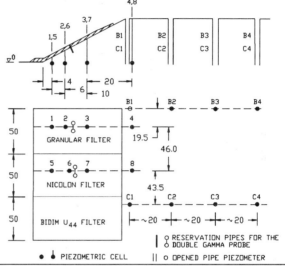

Figure 2. Instrumentation layout.

Nicolon 66558 geotextile filter selected with:

- a conventional granular filter designed as indicated in Figure 1.
- three other geotextiles (Bidim U34: Bidim U44: Boussac Saint Freres 30 DN).

INSTRUMENTATION

The above test sections were instrumented as shown in Figure 2. The purpose of the piezometers was to compare flow conditions under the two types of filter (granular and Nicolon 66558). The double gamma probe casings were to detect any internal erosion under the filters through a modification of the density of the sand in situ. In addition, the behaviour of the geotextiles, after several months use, was observed by removing the rip-rap, taking a sample, and measuring its residual mechanical properties.

GEOTEXTILE SELECTION

The hydraulic characteristics of the geotextiles were determined by applying the filter rules given in the document, "Recommendation pour l'emploi des géotextiles dans les ouvrages de filtration et de drainage". The mechanical properties of the geotextiles were determined by reference to similar structures mentioned in the literature, but there was no special design approach. This information is given in the Table 1.

CONCLUSIONS

More than a year after the canal was opened to the sea, it was found that:

- In the instrumented sections, the behaviours of the granular filter and of the Nicolon 88556 filter could

be regarded as equivalent.

- A number of settlements rapidly occurred in the slopes on which the Nicolon geotextile filter was used, some as much as 1 m deep. On removal of the rip-rap large tears were found (hundreds of mm long). These tears had manifestly been initiated by the falling stones during their placement.
- Tears were also found at other locations where no visible settlement occurred. They were, however, more common in the Nyicolon and Boussac Saint-Frères woven geotextiles. The nonwoven geotextiles, Bidim U34 and, more particularly, Bidim U44, had resisted perforation much better because of their high deformability.

REFERENCES

Book:

Recommandations pour l'emploi des geotextiles dans les systèmes de filtration et de drainage. Editions du CFGG.

Contract Report:

Josseaume, H. and Schaeffner, M., Comportement des filtres géotextiles utilisés sous enrochements: Convention STCPMVN-LCPC. Laboratoie Central des Ponts et Chaussées.

GEOTEXTILE FILTERS IN WATERWAY BANK PROTECTION CALARASI INLAND WATERWAY, ROMANIA

S. Andrei
Civil Engineering Institute
Bucharest, Romania

V. Strunga
Transportation Research and Design Institute
Bucharest, Romania

In 1978, to complete an inland waterway between the Danube River and the metallurgical complex plant in Calarasi (Romania), it was decided, after some preliminary tests, to use nonwoven geotextiles as filters in bank protection systems.

DESCRIPTION

The Calarasi inland waterway, constructed in the period 1982-1986, is 4.8 km long. Bank slope inclination is between 4H:1V and 5H:1V. The breadth of each slope bank is 70 to 80 m, from which 30 m is above the medium water level and the rest below this level.

Geotextiles were used below water level to make a protective mattress with fascines and above the water as a filter under concrete slabs (Figure 1). About 600,000 m^2 of nonwoven geotextiles were used.

The protective mattress (Figure 1.b), made of nonwoven geotextile type Terasin 800 and a fascine strand network (Figure 2) with 800 mm mesh, replaces a classical mattress consisting of three superposed fascine layers. First, geotextile strips were sewn together using synthetic thread, thereby ensuring suitable resistance. The resulting 8 x 40 m geotextile panels were stretched and sewn again to give 47 x 40 m panels. Finally the fascine network was installed on these panels, as is shown in Figure 2, to form mattresses.

The mattresses were transported to the site by floating and were sunk by ballasting with riprap. For the bank protection above water level, whose structure is shown in Figure 1.a, the filter made of Terasin 400 is placed on a 100 mm thick sand layer. A sheet of kraft paper was placed over the geotextile to prevent direct contact between geotextile and freshly poured concrete and to allow some movement of concrete slabs due to temperature changes.

TECHNICAL CONSIDERATIONS

The geotextiles used are made from different synthetic fibres reclaimed from the chemical industry and consolidated by needlepunching (Terasin 400) or by needlepunching and chemical bonding with acrylate (Terasin 800 impregnated).

The main characteristics of these geotextiles are given in Table 1. Other information concerning the properties and testing methods of these geotextiles are shown in a previous paper [Andrei et al., 1982].

The use of the 800 g/m^2 geotextile in bank

Table 1. Geotextile characteristics		
	Terasin 400	Terasin 800
Mass per unit area μ (g/m^2)	400	800
Force per unit width at failure a_f (kN/m)	2	12
Elongation at failure ϵ_f (%)	65	30
Breaking force in a tear test F_T (N)	160	500
Coefficient on normal permeability k_n (m/s)	0.0030	0.0020
Coefficient of permeability in the plane of geotextile k_p (m/s)	0.0025	0.0020

protection below water level resulted in the possibility to save three fascine layers having a thickness of about 600 mm.

The use of the 400 g/m^2 geotextile as a filter below the concrete slabs resulted in the possibility of eliminating a classical filter thus saving 200 mm of granular material.

PERFORMANCE

No damages or instability of slopes have been recorded. Inspection has shown that the geotextile is apparently in good condition. Laboratory tests have indicated that geotextile permeability was diminished by 5 to 10 times, but remained about 100 times greater than that of the protected soil.

REFERENCES

Andrei, S., Strunga, V., Antonescu, I., and Petrica I., "On Hydric Properties of Geotextiles", Proc. 2nd. Int. Conf. on Geotextiles, Las Vegas, 1982, pp. 121-126.

Strunga, V., "The Use of Geotextiles from Retrieved Fibres in Transportation and Telecommunication Ministry Activity", Constructii, No. 4, 1981, pp. 19-36.

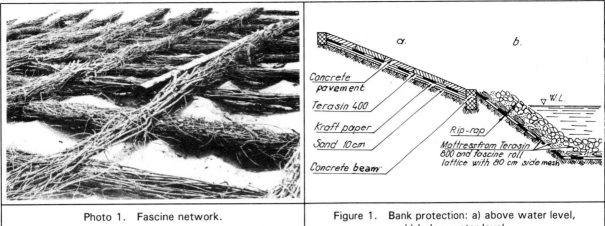

| Photo 1. Fascine network. | Figure 1. Bank protection: a) above water level, b) below water level. |

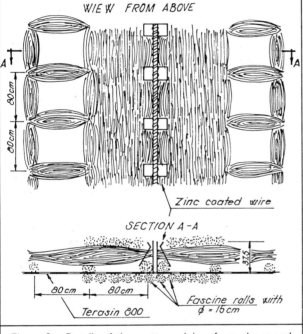

WIEW FROM ABOVE

Zinc coated wire

SECTION A-A

Fascine rolls with
∅ = 15 cm

Terosin 800

Figure 2. Details of the mattress (view from above and cross-section).

GEOTEXTILE FOR IRON-ORE/COAL TERMINAL
HUNTERSTON, UNITED KINGDOM

J.A. Hunt
Exxon Chemical Geopolymers Ltd.
Pontypool, United Kingdom

The construction of this coastal iron ore/coal terminal in 1974 provided civil engineers in the U.K. with an excellent opportunity to take advantage of a new construction material, a heat-bonded nonwoven geotextile ('Terram'). This product had already proved its worth on a small scale, in the construction of access roads, drains and erosion schemes. On this site, some 500,000 m² of 'Terram' 140 were used in separation, drainage and erosion applications.

PROJECT BACKGROUND

In the early 70's, the British Steel Corporation selected a coastal site on the Firth of Clyde in Scotland for the construction of a major terminal, for the importation of raw materials from its international supply sources.

In this area, steep hills extend almost to the sea, leaving only a very narrow coastal plain. At Hunterston, however, a narrow shelf of intertidal flats coupled with an area of low lying raised beach provided a location where landward excavation, and seaward reclamation, could provide a 566 hectare (1400 acre) development area. An existing coastal road, and railway line, provided excellent communications and transportation facilities. The industrial requirement was the construction of an iron-ore and coal unloading terminal and stock-holding facility capable of handling 350,000 tonne bulk carriers with an initial annual throughput of 4,000,000 tonnes for the steel manufacturing plant at Ravenscraig.

PROJECT DETAILS

The consulting engineers, Crouch and Hogg, of Glasgow were retained by the British Steel Corporation to design and supervise the project, which was divided into three parts:

Construct a causeway out to the deep water channel

This structure, 800 m in length, would be a fill causeway, from the end of which a 300 m pier would extend to a berthing platform.

Construct a large well-drained stock-holding area with handling facilities

This would comprise an area of approximately 900 m x 200 m which was fed from the unloading pier by 1.6 m wide conveyors onto stacking machines. The stacker would move on rails and would also act as a further conveyor system to a bunker terminal for train loading at the high level sidings.

Construct railway sidings and bunkers to transport the raw materials inland.

Some 350,000 m³ of clay and rock would be moved to create the necessary space adjacent to the main Glasgow/Largs railway line. Construction started mid-1974 and, in all, some 700,000 m³ of sand and gravel were moved across the low-level site. The excavations for the sidings yielded a further 550,000 m³ of which 290,000 m³, mainly rock, went into reclamation work with the balance being used for landscaping. Granular slag was brought in by road from an old ironworks some 21 km away.

The construction logistics were more complex than for a conventional site since much of the work was to be undertaken on intertidal flats with the preliminary structures being subject to wave action twice a day. In addition, the overall long term weather conditions at the site would be arduous and structure durability was of paramount importance. On both counts, the selection and introduction of a geotextile was to be extremely useful.

GEOTEXTILE APPLICATIONS

Separation

The geotextile was extremely useful in separating the granular fill material being placed on the soft subgrade of the intertidal area. It prevented 'punch-in' and also enabled the base layer of fill to be well-compacted without the intrusion of wet sand and mud.

Drainage

By protecting the horizontal drainage layer beneath the stockholding area, the geotextile at the basal and top levels prevented contamination of the free-draining zone.

CONSTRUCTION SEQUENCE

Stage 1 Causeway Construction

During low tide the geotextile would be rolled out over the sea-bed and the granular fill placed on it to build the causeway. The geotextile would extend outside each edge. Prior to the tide returning, the geotextile edges would be taken up the side of the embankment and anchored down with boulders. The geotextile would thus protect the embankment from marine erosion in the short term. To complete the causeway, the geotextile would be covered with a bedding layer of stone prior to placing the final armour along the side of the causeway. This armour would extend from the base to well above the highest recorded tide level.

Photo 1. Overall view of finished project

Stage 2 Seabed and Lagoon Construction

Wherever granular fill/slag was to be placed on the sea bed as part of the reclamation work, the geotextile was laid out first to provide a separator. The local water authority had placed strict conditions on effluent from this terminal finding its way into natural water. With such a large collection area, high volume discharges could be expected during heavy rain storms. To accommodate this excess water, lagoons were created lined with the geotextile, where the sedimentary 'wash-off' could settle. The geotextile would ensure the fine material was contained, and clean water could be piped away.

Stage 3 Stock-holding Area Drainage Blanket

The geotextile was used in the construction of a major area drainage blanket which extended beneath the total stock-holding area.   This drainage comprised permeable graded slag protected on each side by the geotextile. The object of this drainage layer was: (a) to relieve pore water pressure in the underlying laminated clays beneath the site, and thus accelerate overall settlement of the construction (the zone of beach sand within the underlying clays provided a path to the drainage blanket, thus assisting the rapid dispersion of pore water pressure); and (b) to allow the rapid transmission of precipitation run-off into major drainage channels and settling lagoons.

Stage 4 Stream Diversion and Drainage Channels

The diversion of an existing stream, and the construction of drains, was to be achieved using the geotextile-lining covered with coarse granular material. High peak flow rates could cause considerable scour in soft deposits; the geotextile would eliminate channel scour and bank undercutting.

CONCLUSION

This project introduced a geotextile into a major construction at a time when design criteria for its use was at a minimum. Nevertheless, the successful applications gave engineers confidence and experience: vital factors in extending the use of geotextiles into permanent constructions.

REFERENCES

Non supplied.

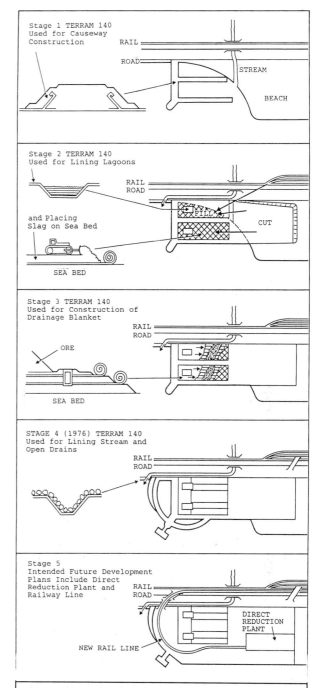

Figure 1.   Construction sequence for Hunterston Ore Terminal

GEOSYNTHETICS FOR EROSION CONTROL STRUCTURES ON SLOPES FRENCH ALPS, FRANCE

Y.H. Faure, J.P. Gourc
Irigm-UJF
Grenoble, France

A. Bechetoille
Cemagref
Grenoble, France

The case related in this paper is original in two respects. First, this a new application for geotextiles. Second, woven geotextiles were used, whereas French practice at that time tended to use nonwoven products.

DESCRIPTION

General Context

The dense geological formations in the Alps pose serious problems for the organisations responsible for soil conservation in mountain regions (organisations depending on the Ministry of Agriculture): bedded glacial and lacustrine clays and "black earths" which are in fact marls. Superficial landslides and mud flows caused by these formations are an extremely frequent phenomenon. Measures to control these erosion phenomena include both runoff control works (stabilisation of the surface layers of mountain slopes by wattling) and works to prevent the scouring of torrent beds (involving fixing the bed by means of torrent control weirs).

Geotextile Wattling

The Garguettes gulley, cutting through glacio-lacustrine clays, has very steep slopes without plant cover, which are thus very prone to erosion. This situation favours the generation of mud flows, which can be devastating downstream. Provision of plant cover on these slopes is possible by means of wattling. The conventional technique is to use plant fascines or wire netting. Works using geotextiles date back to 1977 on this steeply slopeing site (37° to 47°), which is at an altitude of 700 m. The wattling is provided in 19 horizontal rows forming steps down the slope, over a length of 90 m.

The retaining height h varies from 300 mm to 650 mm, and the spacing between the supporting stakes varies between 500 mm and 1.5 m. The width of the geotextile strip used corresponds to the retaining height h plus a horizontal fold back, to avoid loss of soil at the base of the wattling. The slope was then planted with species adapted to this harsh environment (willows, alders, hippophaï). The entire operation was completed in one day by a team of five labourers.

Torrent Control Weirs Using Geotextile Containers

The St. Aubert torrent is situated between 1300 m and 900 m altitude. It discharges into a tributary of the river Durance. The mean gradient of the torrent is 20%. During storms this torrent often carries a substantial bed load, although with relatively few large blocks. It cuts its bed through the "black earths". However, the surface horizons consist of clays, which make the side slopes of the torrent extremely unstable (active landslides).

In this sector, it was clearly necessary to build a torrential flow training weir to fix the bed of the torrent (and to stop the erosion-induced bed deepening process), thus stabilising the side slopes of the torrent. However, in this mountainous region, the construction of a conventional weir proved to be impracticable:

- no access track,
- presence of active lateral landslides, precluding the erection of rigid steel or concrete structures,
- insufficient stones available on site, precluding the construction of gabions.

It was in this context that it was decided to use, as a substitute for gabions, geotextile containers filled with compacted earth taken from the site. Construction dates back to 1982. The geotextile container configuration study was carried out at IRIGM by a trainee engineer from Engref (Perrin), and the structure was monitored by RTM and Cemagref.

The torrent flow training weir is made with stacked parallelepiped containers (width 1 m, height 800 mm and length between 3 and 5 m). The weir is 3.20 m high. Its foundation is made of gabions 500 mm high. The downstream facing is vertical, so as to avoid impact by bedload materials. It is protected by wire netting against impact by boulders carried by the torrent and against ultraviolet radiation.

The containers, made of geotextile sheeting sewed together, are filled from the top, and closed by lacing together the top flaps. This lacing operation also enables a certain tension to be applied to the geotextile, thus correcting possible compaction faults.

CHOICE OF GEOTEXTILES

Geotextile Wattling

The chosen geotextile is a woven three-dimensional polyester (C3X 171-Sarti), with a mass per unit area of 750 g/m². The single woven thread has a diameter of 220 μm and the weaving process allows holes to be provided in the sheet at regular intervals, to accommodate the wattle support stakes.

The tensile strength reaches a_f = 200 kN/m for a strain of ϵ_f = 12%. These characteristics are more than sufficient for the geotextile to withstand the soil thrust. The filtration opening size of the chosen geotextile was O_g = 300 μm.

Photo 1.   Geotextile wattling one year after construction.

Photo 2.   View of container.

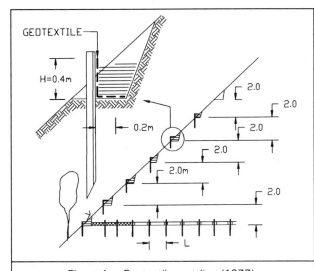

Figure 1.   Geotextile wattling (1977).

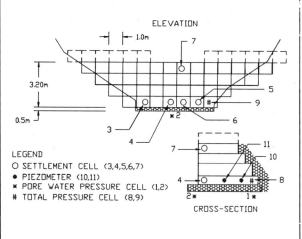

Figure 2.   Diagram of geotextile container weir (1982).

Torrent Control Weirs Using Geotextile Containers

The selected geotextile was a woven polypropylene product (PPD 420-Boussac St Frères) with a mass per unit area of 420 g/m². Its tensile strength is σ_f = 70 kN/m for ϵ_f = 30% and the tear strength is 0.75 kN in the machine direction (as per French standards). Particular care was taken with the seams of the geotextile strips.

The permittivity is 0.4 s⁻¹ and the opening size O_g = 100 μm. The soil used to fill the containers has poor mechanical properties. Particle size is as follows: 100% < 20 mm, 82% < 74 μm and 40% < 2μm. This justified the use of containers to prevent the fines from being carried away by water.

PERFORMANCE

Geotextile Wattling

The total cost of wattling can be broken down into 63% labour costs and 37% material costs and is about the same as other more conventional techniques.

As regards long-term behaviour, the only physico-chemical problem could have been its sensitivity to ultraviolet light: during the winter months, the geotextile is no longer protected by the plant cover. However, given the northeast orientation and the large diameter of the fibres (220 μm), the possible effect of the suns rays was limited. Moreover, a thin protective film of clay covers the

fibres. Ten years after completion, only a few local tears are apparent, where the textile contacts posts. Generally, the structure has behaved extremely well.

Torrential Control Weirs Using Geotextile Containers

As early as autumn 1982, the reservoir impounded behind the weir was completely filled by materials carried by floods and the structure had fulfilled its role of fixing the torrent bed over a length of 30 m.

Several measurement sensors were installed in the structure during the building stage. Interstitial pressure measurements under the foundations have confirmed the satisfactory operation of the drainage system. The most interesting measurements are the total stress values in the lengthwise direction (σ_L at depth h_L = 2.8 m) and in the transverse direction (σ_T at depth h_T = 3.6 m). The value of σ_L remains constant whereas, transversely, σ_T increases continuously as a result of lateral thrust from the unstable sides. The geotextile container structure has stood up to these lateral thrusts perfectly well.

REFERENCE

Faure, Y.H., Gourc, J.P., Giraud, A., and Bechetoille, A., "Applications des géotextiles à la protection contre l'érosion de formations instables (Alpes)"(Application of geotextiles to protect unstable formations from erosion (Alpes) - Proc. 5th. Int. Symposium on Landslides - Lausanne, 1988.

GEOTEXTILE TUBES FILLED WITH SAND FOR BEACH EROSION CONTROL NORTH SEA COAST, GERMANY

H.F. Erchinger
State Coast Protection Agency
Norden, Germany

On the German North Sea coast sand-filled flexible tubes of plastic fabrics for long-range or temporary coast protection purposes have been used since 1967. The paper describes various solutions used of such sand-filled tubes up to diameters of 1.8 m.

GENERAL DESCRIPTION

The Tubes

The skin of the first tubes was woven of small strips of black polyethylene (PE). This plastic web was almost impermeable; it became practically impermeable after pumping water and fine sand into the tube. The fine grains of the soil closed the remaining porosity.

The tubes were manufactured with a diameter of 1 m without any seam and with a diameter of 1.8 m out of 3 webs sewn together. Today they are made seamless up to 1.7 m diameter.

The geotextiles used have the characteristics shown in Table 1.

As the geotextiles type 3 and type 4 are slightly permeable, there is a thin geomembrane of PE laid as an inside impermeable skin.

Methods of Filling

Two methods of filling are usual:

a)   by hydraulic dredging; and
b)   with a hopper and sand, which is fed into a pipe with current water.

i)   On the silty and soft ground of the tidal flats the only way of filling the tubes is by hydraulic dredging. The sandy and coarse silty material near the building site will be obtained by a hydraulic dredger and transported into the tube through pipes. The sand settles in the tube, beginning at the inlet. Only a small "river" remains on top for the flow of the mixture of water and sand. The water flows out through a pipe at the other end of the tube. The pressure in the tube can be regulated by the height of the pipe fastened at the outlet of the tube. The outlet of this pipe is placed 300 mm to 1 m above the top of the tube.

Before rolling out the tube it is advisable to dig a small valley with a hydraulic excavator to prevent any displacement of the just blown-up and not yet sand-filled tube, e.g. by wind. Sometimes it is

Table 1.	Characteristics of geotextiles used in sand-filled flexible tubes.		
Type/Year	Raw Material	Tensile Strength (N/5cm)	Mass per Unit Area (g/m^2)
1 / 1967	PE	48	450
2 / 1971	PE	74	470
3 / 1971	80% PP, 20% PE	90	500
4 / 1975	80% PE, 20% PP	70	550
5 / 1986	PP/PE	90	450

favourable to stabilize the valley with a thin plastic membrane.

ii)   The method of filling with a hopper was developed in Denmark. To obtain a really impermeable tube from the start the type 3 and 4 geotextiles (Table 1) with an inside geomembrane are used. The sand is filled into a hopper and fed into a pipe at its bottom through which water is pumped into the tube by a small pump like a fire department pump. The pressure in the tube can also be regulated by the outlet pipe. As no heavy equipment is needed, this method is favourable for quick and cheap solutions and for emergencies.

DESCRIPTION OF THE EXAMPLES

Construction of Groyne on the Tidal Flats

On the tidal flats of the Eastfriesian coast rectangular sedimentation fields (100 x 200 m) are bordered by groynes. The groynes promote the reclamation of new foreland in front of the dikes, as they keep off currents and wave action and support siltation. In some cases the groynes are constructed with sand-filled flexible tubes of type 1. A small hydraulic dredger with 150 mm pipe diameter was used and the whole dredged fill material was fed into the tube, in which the sand settles. In 1967 the first tube groyne was built.

Retaining Dike in the Tidal Flats

On the tidal flats an artificial beach was created in 1971 in front of the sea dike and just beside a fishery harbour. The field has to be filled with sand by hydraulic dredging, bordered by a retaining dike consisting of a sand-filled tube after type 2, partly of 3 tubes like those presented in Photo 1.

The dredged material was portioned by a double junction so that if one part of the material was going into

Photo 1. Retaining dike in the tidal flats, one tube filled, the second on the right side prepared for filling, the third later on top.

Photo 2. Emergency dike of 6 tubes, in front the first two just being filled.

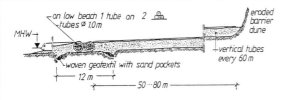

Figure 1. Tubes for a stabilization of a beach fill.

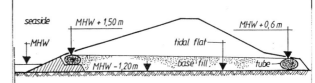

Figure 2. Fill of dike base in the tidal flats with a tube φ 1.7 m on each side as retaining dike.

the tube and the rest was falling into the field. With control valves each flow could be regulated. The length of single tubes was between 50 and 100 m and a tube of 50 m length could be filled in 2 to 5 hours depending on the grain size of the soil. After the field was filled with sand an embankment was built covering the tube.

Stabilization of Beach Nourishment

When the northwestern beach and the barrier dune of the island Langeoog were severely eroded in 1971, the sea defense had to be restored by beach nourishment. To keep off further erosion by the littoral drift, the beach fill was bordered and stabilized at the seaside by filled tubes (type 3). The 3 km long "wall" of tubes was built 60 m in front of the eroded dune toe. Further tubes were placed at right-angles to this wall, to hinder longitudinal currents. The tubes were filled with a hopper and then the fields by hydraulic dredging. For a number of years the tubes worked well. Meanwhile considerable parts of the tubes were sunk by the scouring effect of approaching swash channels and bars (Photo 1).

Dike Construction on the Tidal Flats

In order that a dike could be constructed on the tidal flats of the Leybucht, two parallel retaining dikes for the base fill had to be built (Figure 2). The dikes would resist currents and wave action even in wintry storm surges. These dikes were built of sand-filled tubes with a diameter of 1.7 m (type 5), at the front side on a base of stones from a mineral deposit. Scouring problems with the vertical joint between two tubes were solved by pulling the skin of the next tube over the preceding one and sewing them together on the work site (Figure 1).

Emergency Close of a Dike Breach

After some storm surges in 1973 sand-filled tubes were used for closing dike breaches on the island Borkum. The emergency dike has reached a height of 2.5 m with 6 tubes (type 3, Photo 2).

DURABILITY OF THE GEOTEXTILE

The webs of type 1, 2 and 5 were manufactured with an opening size of about 100 μm as the medium grain size of the soils were between 100 and 200 μm.

In 1979 geotextile samples were taken from several tubes: a) buried with soil since the construction; and b) exposed to sunlight all the time. It was found that for geotextiles protected from sunlight a reduction of less than 10% of the original tensile strength was measured for PE and PP/PE samples. For sunlight exposed samples the measured reduction of the original tensile strength was (a) for PE 46% (12 years) and 22% (11 years) and (b) for PP/PE 52% (8 years) and 17% (4 years).

CONCLUSION

The results show that such sand-filled tubes can be used favourably on a long-term basis when they are protected from sunlight. For temporary use, up to 1 or 2 decades, they are suitable unprotected, even near sea.

REFERENCES

Erchinger, H.F., "Land Reclamation and Groyne-Building in the Tidal Flats", Proc. 12th. ICCE, Washington D.C., 1970.

Erchinger, H.F. and Snuis, G., "Kunststoffgewebeschläuche im Küstenwasserbau", Wasser u. Boden, H. 1, Hamburg, 1972.

Heerten, G., "Geotextilien im Wasserbau - Prüfung, Anwendung, Bewährung", Mitt. d. Franzius Instituts, 52, Hannover, 1981.

Jacobsen, P.R. and Nielsen, A.H., "Experiments with Sand-filled Flexible Tubes", Proc. 12th. ICCE, Washington, D.C., 1970.

GEOTEXTILE FOR OUTFALL PIPELINE STABILISATION
CAPE PERON, PERTH, AUSTRALIA

P.J. de Geeter
Marecon Pty Ltd.
Perth, Australia

H.J. Dunnewind
Robusta Fabrics
Genemuiden, The Netherlands

In order to discharge the rapidly increasing quantities of sewage from the Perth metropolitan area in Western Australia, a large diameter pipeline was constructed in 1983 from Perth to Cape Peron, near the coastal town of Rockingham, approximately 30 km south of Perth.

At Cape Peron a 4.2 km extension into the Indian Ocean was required, in order to ensure proper mixing of the diffused sewage in water of sufficient depth, at an ample distance from coastal recreation areas. The outfall line with an outside diameter of approximately 1.7 m, was installed and stabilised in 1983/84.

DESCRIPTION

From shore point to approximately 1.2 km offshore the seabed consisted of fairly hard calcareous material which was trenched, with an average cross section as shown in Figure 1. Further offshore the pipeline was laid on the seabed without trenching, as shown in Figure 2.

To ensure stability of the pipeline under design wave and current conditions and in order to provide mechanical protection against damage by dragging anchors, the pipeline was covered with a layer of rock, dumped on a separation layer of geotextile.

DESIGN

The original design was undertaken by Binnie and Partners in Perth.

It provided for two rock layers to be dumped: first a (separation) layer with rock size ranging from 50 to 200 mm to be dumped directly onto the seabed around the pipe, followed by a top layer of armour rock, size 140 to 480 mm.

In a subsequent analysis, carried out by Marecon, it was found to be more economic to omit the lower rock layer and replace it by a separation layer of geotextile. The armour rock layer could then be dumped directly onto the geotextile. This would lead to considerable cost saving during installation.

Further advantages of the use of a geotextile with suitable strength would be, particularly in the soft soil areas offshore from the 1.2 km point outward:

- less subsidence of the fill body, reducing total fill volume required
- additional safety against slip circle failure of the subsoil (which could cause partial collapse of the fill body)

- no risk of undermining of the tie of the fill
- reduced rock wastage due to prevention of "in sinking" of rock pieces into the soft bed material

GEOTEXTILE SELECTION

Before selecting a suitable geotextile the functional requirements were formulated as follows:

- sufficient tensile strength to absorb the tensile force in the geotextile caused by (1) long-term differential settlements in the subsoil (if any) and (2) the downward force and weight of the armour rock dumped on the geotextile at either side of the pipeline (the tensile would be maximum at the top of the pipeline);
- sufficient puncturing resistance to prevent the free falling rock from piercing the geotextile;
- lasting permeability to minimize hydrodynamic lift forces, caused by overpressure below the geotextile during passage of the (trough) of the design wave;
- adequate durability in seawater;
- sand tightness;

Based on a safety factor of 2, it was found from rock weight and slip circle calculations that the required tensile strength would be in the order of 35 kN/m.

Allowing for non-homogeneous stress distribution it was decided to apply Robusta's woven polypropylene geotextile No. 500, which met the above listed design requirements (tensile failure strength in warp and weft direction: 80 kN/m; opening size (O_{90}): 240 μm; permeability 29 l/m^2/s at 100 mm head).

Durability in subtropical seawater, as calculated from tests carried out by Plastic and Rubber Research Institute TNO in the Netherlands, would well exceed the anticipated 50 years design life of the pipeline.

Punching resistance of the geotextile was tested by rock falling tests onshore (whereby the free falling height of the largest rock pieces was such that the impact energy was the same as for the same piece falling in water).

INSTALLATION

Geotextile was supplied folded on rolls with a length of 6 m. On site the rolls were unwound and the geotextile unfolded, after which the full width geotextile was respooled onto a large pipespool, as shown in photo 1.

For the inshore section (up to 1.2 km) the geotextile sheet width was 11.7 m. From 1.2 km outward the

Photo 1. Installation of geotextile on pipeline using a barge for unrolling.

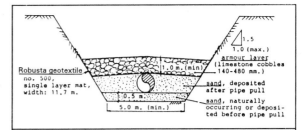

Figure 1. Backfill design profile of Cape Peron Outfall Line trenched section from 0.15 km to 1.2 km from shore.

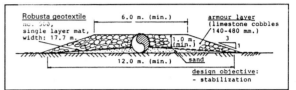

Figure 2. Backfill design profile of Cape Peron Outfall Line untrenched section from 2.6 km to 3.00 km from shore.

geotextile sheet was 17.7 m, due to the increased width of fill body in the untrenched section. Warp direction of the geotextile was at right angle to the pipeline, in line with the principal tensile stress direction.

The geotextile was installed by unrolling from the spool which was mounted on a barge, as shown in Photo 1. The geotextile coming off the spool was weighed by steel wire, which was hand-tied to loops in the geotextile at 2 m intervals.

Immediately after touchdown on the seabed, the geotextile was further pinned down by hand-dumped rock pieces, to prevent the geotextile from being washed away before arrival of the rock dumping vessel.

The whole operation of laying the geotextile and dumping the fill body took approximately 4 weeks.

Total area of geotextile used was in the order of 40,000 m².

REFERENCES

Bowles, J.E. "Foundation Analysis and Design", McGraw-Hill International, London, 3rd. edition 1982, p. 816.

Kroezen, M., Vellinga, P., Lindenberg, J. and Burger, A.M. "Geotechnical and Hydraulic Aspects with regard to Seabed and Slope Stability", 1982, 13 p. (publication No. 272 of Delft Geotechnics, The Netherlands).

Ogink, H.J.M., "Investigations on the Hydraulic Characteristics of Synthetic Fabrics", 1975, 42 p. (publication No. 146 of Delft Hydraulics Laboratory, The Netherlands).

Rankilor, P.R., "Membranes in Ground Engineering", John Wiley & sons, New York, 1981, 377 p.

Scott, C.R., "Soil Mechanics and Foundations", 3rd. edition, Applied Science Publishers Ltd., London, 1980, 406 p.

Antill, J.M. and Ryan, P.W.S., "Civil Engineering Construction", 5th. Edition, McGraw-Hill, 1982, 710 p.

GEOTEXTILE CONCRETE MATS FOR OFFSHORE PIPELINE STABILIZATION
SOUTH PEPPER-NORTH HERALD OILFIELD, AUSTRALIA

P.J. de Geeter
Marecon Pty Ltd
Perth, Australia

H.J. Dunnewind
Robusta Fabrics
Genemuiden, The Netherlands

Late 1987/early 1988 a total of 75 concrete mats (called "flexmats") were installed on a 600 mm diameter tanker loading pipeline in the South Pepper-North Herald offshore oilfield, located off the Northwest coast of Western Australia. The field is operated by Western Mining Corporation Pty Ltd. The flexmats consist of two rows of concrete blocks, precast on heavy-duty polypropylene fabric with inwoven loops.

DESCRIPTION

From shore point an uneven reef extends to approximately 700 m offshore. Beyond that point the reef ends abruptly with a drop from 8 to 14 m water depth over the next 100 m. Beyond that point the seabed consists of soft silty sand, sloping gradually downward to a water depth of 18 m at the tanker loading location, approximately 1.7 km from shore. The required design of the pipeline is 15 years under cyclonic conditions. This implies that the pipeline should be able to withstand a significant wave height at its most critical location (at the base of the reef) of 7.8 m. in combination with a steady current (1 m. above bed level) of 0.83 m/s.

Various stabilization options were considered, like trenching, rockdumping, anchoring, concrete cradles, and (extra) weight coat thickness.

Rock dumping, trenching, and anchor piling appeared uncompetitive because of the high cost of mobilization of equipment and vessel(s).

From the gravity options, the method of using concrete cradles was disregarded because of risk of undermining and subsequent tilt in the sandy offshore section of the pipeline and the risk of impact damage to the pipeline during lowering the cradles.

The use of weight coating (without supplementary stabilization) would have led to a required coating thickness of 110 mm. This would result in a very heavy pipeline with, as a consequence, increased cost of fabrication of coated joints as well as higher cost of transportation and pipelaying.

DESIGN

The required submerged weight of the concrete blocks in relation to the optimum spacing between blocks and hydrodynamically required shape of edge blocks (in order to minimize drag and lift forces) was determined by using a special, verified computer program.

This program took into account all relevant parameters influencing the potential overpressure that could be generated by a steady current and/or a design wave.

Parameters taken into account are: compressibility of bed material in relation to compressibility of water; elasticity modulus and tensile strength of geotextile; hydrodynamic drag and lift and inertia coefficients of edge blocks and inner blocks (as a function of block size and shape); long-term permeability of geotextile in relation to permeability of supporting bed material (a 50% reduction in geotextile permeability over time was assumed); and submerged weight and height of concrete blocks.

Cyclic flow velocity and particle acceleration at bed level was calculated by means of generally accepted Airy/Stokes wave theory.

Steady flow velocity at bed level was derived from flow velocity at l m above bed level by 1/10 exponent velocity profile above the boundary layer and 1/7 exponent profile within the boundary layer, in line with common practice.

Height, shape, and spacing of blocks were determined with the aim of minimizing drag and lift forces on the mats, so that added concrete weight would have maximum effectivity. For the same reason heavy concrete was used with density at least 2,600 kg/m^3. Mat design, as shown in Figure 1, was tested on a 1/10 scale model in the large flow channel of the Civil Engineering Department of the University of Western Australia. The tests confirmed the design calculations and showed that hydrodynamic coefficients assumed in the calculations were realistic.

GEOTEXTILE SELECTION

Selection criteria were: sufficient long-term permeability, durability in seawater, and strength to cope with dynamic loadings during installation and hydrodynamic loadings afterwards.

Sand tightness was not of significance, as insinking of the blocks into the seabed would actually reduce drag and lift and, therefore, enhance performance.

To meet above criteria it was decided to use Robusta's woven polypropylene geotextile 875 Special, with specially inwoven loops. During casting of the mats on vibration tables, these loops penetrated into the concrete and provided a strong bonding between geotextile and concrete blocks.

Calculations based on tests performed by Fibre

Photo 1. View of installed pipe.

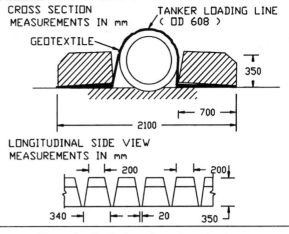

Figure 1. Typical sections through mats.

Research Institute of T.N.O. in Holland showed that in tropical seawater the expected lifetime of the geotextile would be at least 70 years, which is well in excess of design life of the pipeline (15 years).

INSTALLATION/COSTS

Concrete blocks were cast on the geotextile by a Concrete Company in Perth, after which the mats were transported by road train to Onslow, a small town with waterfront facilities, approximately 1,000 km north from Perth.

For handling and installation of the mats over the pipeline a simple spreader bar lift frame with straps was used.

Mats were loaded out onto a supply boat and ferried to the installation barge offshore. The mats were then installed over the pipeline, as shown in Photo 1, by means of a crane with one diver in attendance at the seabed.

Although heave action and currents were strong at times (the mats were installed during spring tide), the installation rate varied between 2 and 4 mats per hour, depending on the state of the tide and the amount of heave motion.

On the basis of contract sums and variations, the total cost of stabilization of the pipeline by means of the (patented) flexmat system was found to be highly economic, at least 30% less costly than weight coating stabilization (without mats) or other options. Saving in comparison to (quoted) cost of trenching was more than 60%.

REFERENCES

Bezuyen, A., Klein Breteler, M., and Pilarczyk, K.W., "Large Scale Tests on a Block Revetment placed on Sand with a Geotextile as Separation Layer", Proc. 3rd. Int. Conf. on Geotextiles, Vienna, Austria, 1986, pp. 501-555.

Koerner, R.M., "Designing with Geosynthetics", Prentice-Hall, Englewood Cliffs, N. J. 07632, 1986, p. 424.

Kroezen, M., Vellinga, P., Lindenberg, J., and Burger, A.M., ""Geotechnical and Hydraulic Aspects with regard to Seabed and Slope Stability", 1982, p. 13 (publication No. 272 of Delft Geotechnics, The Netherlands)

Ogink, H.J.M., "Investigations on the Hydraulic Characteristics of Synthetic Fabrics", 1975, p. 42 (publication No. 146 of Delft Hydraulics Laboratory, The Netherlands)

Veldhuijzen van Zanten, R., "Geotextiles and Geomembranes in Civil Engineering", Balkema, Rotterdam/Boston, 1986, p. 658.

GEOSYNTHETICS FOR PROTOTYPE TURBIDITY CURTAIN
WEST SIDE HIGHWAY IN NEW YORK CITY, USA

L.D. Suits
New York State Department of Transportation
Albany, New York, USA

A. Minnitti
New York State Department of Transportation
Albany, New York, USA

In the late 1970's and early 1980's the New York State Department of Transportation (NYSDOT) was involved in selecting geotextiles to be used in a turbidity curtain being designed by the consultant engineers for the Department's proposed replacement of the West Side Highway in New York City. The proposed designs involved dredging and placing landfill in the Hudson River over approximately a 4.5 km length. The landfill would extend approximately 488 m into the river. The project's Water Quality Certificate required that turbidity curtains be placed along the U.S. pierhead line totally isolating the areas of dredging and filling operations.

It was determined that the depth of the turbidity curtain required to comply with the Water Quality Certificate had never been used in a tidal estuary. It was therefore decided to develop a laboratory test program followed by the installation of a 180 m long prototype curtain on site.

DESCRIPTION

The purpose of the turbidity curtain was to isolate the area of dredging and filling operations from the main channel of the Hudson River. This was necessary in order to fulfil the requirements of the Water Quality Certificate, which were to protect the main channel of the river from becoming overloaded with material which might wash out into it from the dredge and fill operations.

The panels of the curtain consisted of two sections: a permeable geotextile, and an impermeable geomembrane barrier attached to the top of the geotextile.

The curtain consisted of: four panels 34 m long by 11 m high (including the 3.7 m high impermeable barrier), one panel 34 m long by 5 m high, and two closure panels 5 m long by 11 m high. The purpose of the half height panel was to determine if a full depth curtain was needed. The closure panels provided a means of access in and out of the area within the curtain.

Construction and installation of the curtain occurred between August and November, 1981. The curtain remained in place for 5 months during which time its performance was evaluated.

DESIGN CONSIDERATIONS

The criteria used in the design of the turbidity curtain were as follows: (a) approximate 1 m wave height; (b) 0.5 knot current perpendicular to the curtain; (c) 2 kN/m ice load; (d) ballast weight sufficient to keep the curtain on the bottom during the dredging and filling operations; (e)

flotation to be a minimum of 4 times the submerged weight of the ballast; (f) curtain height to be 1.5 times the mean high water depth to allow vertical billow to reduce stress of the curtain geotextiles; (g) 6.1 m horizontal billow from support centre lines; (h) differential head across the curtain of 63.5 mm; (i) a 3.7 m high impermeable barrier to be placed at the top of the curtain.

Seams within the geotextile materials were sewn with a minimum overlap of 75 mm and four lines of stitching. The seams in the impermeable panels were thermally welded with a minimum overlap of 37.5 mm.

GEOTEXTILE AND GEOMEMBRANE SELECTION

The minimum properties for the geotextiles were determined to be a minimum wide width strength of 175 kN/m in the weakest principal direction, and a minimum permittivity of 0.4 s^{-1}, as determined by the NYSDOT Soil Mechanics Bureau (SMB). Early in the design, a soil retention criterion based on a HYSDOT-SMB Soil Retention Test was included. The criterion was 75 percent retention of a slurry with 7.5 g of soil per 1000 cm^3 of Hudson River water.

The actual dilution expected at the site, based on tests performed, was 2.3 g/1000 cm^3 of water. The fact that the lower the dilution, the faster will be the particle fall, results in a lower percentage of material passing the curtain. Initial testing of the 7.5 g/1000 cm^3 produced results well within the 75 percent retention criteria. The lower dilution could only be better, so the test requirement was deleted.

Based on these criteria, the geotextile panels for the curtain were fabricated from Amoco Propex 1325 and 4557, Bradely Materials Filterweave 70-C, and Hoechst Trevira 1160. The geomembrane panels were made of Shelter-Rite 8028, a PVC coated polyester material.

PERFORMANCE

Monitoring the performance of the entire system was carried on as follows: (a) Tension in the cables was monitored with load cells, showing a maximum load in the natural environment of approximately 45 kN. Ice conditions did not produce loads exceeding this. (b) Structural tests involved running a tugboat at various speeds, at various distances parallel to the curtain to generate wave action. The loading in the cables was measured due to wave action, and due to propeller wash. The maximum load of 42.4 kN was produced by the propeller wash. (c) During stages of the structural testing, the curtain was visually inspected by a diver. Some of the

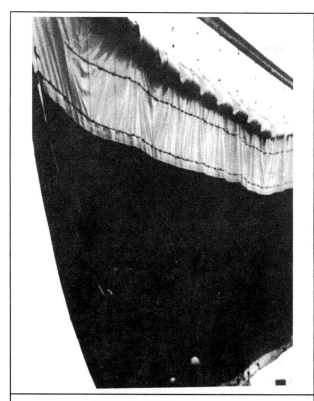

| Photo 1. Fabricated panel. | Photo 2. In-place turbidity curtain. |

grommets in the closure panels were seen to have been pulled out. (d) After four weeks, two panels were removed for visual inspection, and the laboratory testing of one panel. Overall, the panels showed little or no damage from the structural tests. There was a brown slimy coating over the curtain. Laboratory permittivity tests on one panel showed a reduction by a factor of ten in this property. (e) One of the removed panels was reinstalled. This along with the others remained in place for five months covering late fall and winter.

COST

The NYSDOT had estimated the cost of the curtain to be $454,380, including fabrication, structural support, and installation. The low bid received was $431,240.

CONCLUSIONS

Based on observations, the following conclusions were drawn concerning the turbidity curtain system: (a) a curtain could be fabricated and installed to meet the Water Quality Certificate requirements; (b) both the woven and nonwoven geotextiles performed satisfactorily; (c) Hudson River water in its natural environment quickly reduced the permittivity of the geotextiles tested; (d) ice had relatively little effect on the curtain and its support system; (e) the criteria for selection of the geotextiles are their permittivity and wide width strength properties.

RECOMMENDATIONS

Based on the results of this installation, several recommendations were made for the turbidity curtain proposed for use in the construction of a prototype fill on the project. Among these were: (a) reduction in width of the thermally welded seams in the impermeable barrier; (b) use of PVC coated fabrics for the closure panels instead of urethane coating (the urethane showed signs of

deterioration, and was significantly more expensive than PVC); (c) reduction of the ballast weight in the closure panel; (d) prohibition of the use of rolled microfilm for the flotation collar assemblies; (e) reduction of the vertical billow in the curtain.

COMMENT

The observations and conclusions reached in this installation were incorporated in the design of a smaller turbidity curtain in Upstate New York, and have also served as the basis for developing an approved list of geotextiles for general use in turbidity curtains.

REFERENCES

"West Side Highway Project Report on Prototype Turbidity Curtain," Mueser, Rutledge, Johnstone and DiSimone Consulting Engineers, New York New York, May, 1982.

"West Side Highway Project Evaluation of Test Results, Silt Curtain Fabrics," Mueser, Rutledge, Johnstone and DiSimone Consulting Engineers, and Woodward-Clyde Consultants Inc., New York, New York, Sept., 1983.

CHAPTER 5

TUNNEL AND HYDROELECTRIC APPLICATIONS

GEOSYNTHETICS USED IN DRY TUNNEL LINING SYSTEMS
ARLBERG TUNNEL, AUSTRIA

H. Posch
Civil Engineering Consultant
Innsbruck, Austria

G. Werner
Polyfelt Ges. m.b.H.
Linz, Austria

The Arlberg Tunnel, Austria's outstanding and most important road tunnel, was constructed in 1974-1978. The design methodology was the New Austrian Tunnelling Method (NATM), using three different types of lining systems for the tunnel waterproofing. Ten years after completion this almost classic example of the NATM has revealed remarkable results in terms of reducing crack formation in the concrete lining. A 40% reduction in crack formation has been found in the geotextile and concrete lined tunnel sections. In this section a geotextile is the separation and drainage layer between the shotcrete and inner concrete lining.

DESCRIPTION

The concrete lining of the Arlberg Road Tunnel is 13,972 m long. It was constructed in 12 m long ring sections of waterproof pumped concrete B30. The concrete consisted of 240-250 kg of Portland cement PZ 275, 40-60 kg of fly ash and aggregate with a maximum size of 32 to 60 mm.

The following three types of tunnel lining were installed (Figure 1):

I. A 300-400 mm thick concrete lining without any sealing measures or separation layers (34.3% of tunnel length).
II. A 300-400 mm thick concrete lining and 700 g/m² polypropylene needlepunched nonwoven geotextile, functioning as a separation and drainage layer (12.4% of tunnel length).
III. A 300-400 mm thick concrete lining and waterproofing system. The waterproofing system is a combination of a 1.5 mm thick PVC geomembrane and a 500 g/m² polypropylene needlepunched nonwoven geotextile protection and drainage layer (53.3% of tunnel length).

GEOTEXTILE SELECTION

The geotextile had to fulfil the following three criteria:

- Chemical Resistance: The geotextile has to resist all kinds of rock water, calcium hydroxide $Ca(OH)_2$, and other constituents such as the binding agents in concrete and grout.
- Mechanical Resistance: The geotextile must have certain minimum values for mechanical strength and elasticity. These are needed to absorb the stresses resulting from the installation and concreting pressures, the deformation of the inner lining of the tunnel due to load shifting and temperature

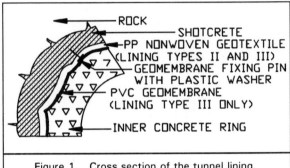

Figure 1. Cross section of the tunnel lining.

variations, and the joint water pressure increasing locally over time.
- Water Permeability in the Plane: Residual water, consisting of seepage and leakage, must be reliably drained in the geotextile plane to the bottom drain.

Based on the above criteria, a needlepunched polypropylene nonwoven geotextile of 700 g/m² (Polyfelt TS 008) with 3.6 kN puncture resistance (DIN 54307) was selected.

PERFORMANCE

Crack Formation

For a period of 9 years, all observed cracks in the inner concrete lining have been recorded, yielding the following results:

- 6.7% of the 7527 concrete ring segments, each 12 m long, failed to remain crack free.
- Out of a total of 918 observed cracks, 190 cracks were less than 0.2 mm wide. These are regarded as superficial shrinkage cracks. They do not penetrate the full concrete cross section. The remaining 728 cracks were actual penetrating cracks.
- The average number of cracks per ring segment was 2.32 for lining type I (concrete alone); 1.42 for lining type II (concrete and geotextile); and 1.18 for lining type III (concrete, geomembrane and geotextile).

These results show that the nonwoven geotextile acted (a) as a protection and drainage layer to a waterproofing geomembrane, and (b) by itself, significantly reduced the formation of cracks in the inner concrete lining.

The reason for this is that the geotextile acts as a stress relieving layer between the shotcrete and the

  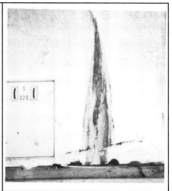

| Photo 1. Close up of the application of geotextile to the shotcrete surface. | Photo 2. Overall view of the application of geotextile. | Photo 3. Separation crack due to a change in concrete thickness. |

concrete lining. This allows free shrinkage deformation of the concrete during the setting process.

Leakage Areas

Localized leakage of water has been detected in 8 spots of the documented 6554 m² concrete tunnel surface. At 4 of these wet spots the water entering the cavity along the expansion joints was sufficiently small that it could be conducted to the bottom drainage. The remaining 4 cracks only exhibited signs of dampness without notable seepage occurring. They are expected to "seal" themselves through the sintering process. This happened for most of the cracks occurring immediately after constructing the inner concrete ring.

It was observed that the original leakage path of the rock water was altered in the transition area between insulated and un-insulated tunnel section. Once the tunnel was opened to traffic, the water was observed entering the cavity through separation cracks. Based on these experiences, a polypropylene needlepunched nonwoven geotextile, as a separation and drainage layer, was installed in the western tunnel section. This was done even in areas where no seepage of water was evident, or was expected at the time of construction. This measure reduced the crack formation in the inner concrete ring by 58.9% when compared with the sections of concrete lining without geotextile.

Geotextile Long Term Permeability

Geotextile samples were removed 12 years after construction, and the following results were obtained:

- The mass per unit area has increased by 9% due to sedimentation of fine particles.
- The coefficient of normal permeability was reduced from 5.72 to 3.25 mm/s.
- There was no indication of clogging caused by mineral precipitation.

CONCLUSIONS

A crack free concrete lining is the best guarantee for a waterproof tunnel. The use of a nonwoven geotextile as a separation and drainage layer significantly reduced the cracks of the inner concrete lining. This increased the cost of the concrete lining by only 9%.

The insignificant difference in the number of cracks in the geotextile lined section, compared with the

geotextile/geomembrane lined section, makes this design an alternative to lined waterproofing. Particularly as the use of a geomembrane increases the liner costs by 70%.

The water leakage path in the transition zone from the sealed to the unsealed area may change over time. Therefore, it is recommended that a geotextile be used as a separation and drainage layer. This applies even in those sections which do not show any immediate ingress of rock water during excavation of the tunnel.

In the limited area where cracks did occur in the geotextile lined section, effective drainage of moisture prevented seepage of water into the tunnel through the cracks. This was true even when drains at the floor of the tunnel showed seepage occurring behind the lining.

After 12 years the coefficient of normal permeability of the geotextile dropped by a factor of 1.76. This occurred without any indication of clogging.

REFERENCES

Springenschmid, R., and Breitenbücher, R., "Über das Vermeiden von Rissen am Beispiel der Innenschale von Tunneln", Zement und Beton, Heft 4, 1985.

Werner, G., "Sealing and Waterproofing with Geotextiles and Plastic Sheeting in Tunnel Constructions", Proc. of the Int. Conf. on Geomembranes, Denver, Colorado, June 1984, pp. 353-358.

Werner, G., "La Impermeabilización de Tuneles de acuerdo al Nuevo Método Austriaco de Construcción de Tuneles (N.A.T.M.)", 2º Encontro Nacional de Geotecnia, L.N.E.C., Lisboa, 1987.

GEOMEMBRANE WATERPROOFING OF WET HYDROELECTRIC TUNNEL
DRAKENSBERG HYDROELECTRIC TUNNEL, SOUTH AFRICA

P.L. Davies
Aquatan (Pty) Limited
Johannesburg, South Africa

In 1979, a geomembrane was selected for placement between the excavated rock and the concrete lining of the headrace tunnels of the Drakensberg pumped storage scheme. This was judged the most effective and least expensive method of preventing in-service erosion of the mudstone rock the tunnels ran through.

DESCRIPTION

The Project

The Drakensberg pumped storage scheme was built for the South African Department of Water Affairs and the Electricity Supply Commission, as a joint venture. The scheme provides peak-demand hydroelectric power and is also part of the large Tugela-Vaal water project. This project transfers underutilized water from the province of Natal to the Transvaal Witwatersrand, the industrial centre of South Africa. During the night, water is pumped through tunnels over the Drakensberg escarpment into Sterkfontein, the upper storage dam. During the day, this water flows back into Kilburn dam at the bottom of the escarpment, generating electricity as it does so.

The Tunnels

The scheme's two headrace tunnels are horseshoe shaped and have an equivalent diameter of 6 m. Each tunnel is 1.5 km long. Both are constructed in variable geologies that include mudstone, siltstone, and sandstone of the Beaufort series of the Karoo system. Standard tunnelling methods including drilling and blasting were used.

Need for Erosion Protection

The design idea for the tunnels is two fold. In-situ rock provides the support medium against internal hydraulic pressure. The concrete tunnel lining provides a smooth surface for the passage of water. The overburden pressures generally exceed the internal hydraulic pressure.

In the generating mode, each tunnel carries approximately 150 m³/s of water at a maximum head of 171 m. It was found that the mudstone is relatively impermeable, but is erodible by high-pressure water. Cracking of the concrete linings was considered inevitable under the support conditions encountered. The effect of water jetting through the cracks and impinging on the mudstone, and then returning through the cracks laden with the eroded tunnel support material, had to be closely studied.

Solution Chosen

Various alternatives were evaluated, including prestressing, steel lining and special reinforcement to concrete lining. The consulting engineers, Gibb Hawkins and Partners of Johannesburg, ultimately decided that a geomembrane liner would provide the most cost-effective solution.

THE GEOMEMBRANE

Choice of Geomembrane

The purpose of the geomembrane would be to act as a barrier between the probable powerful jets of water and the erodible mudstone. As both installation and service conditions would be severe, it was considered essential that the geomembrane be exceptionally resistant to tearing, puncturing, and abrasion. The consulting engineers investigated local and overseas materials. They ultimately chose a product especially designed for the project by Gundle Lining Systems (Pty) Limited of Johannesburg (now renamed Aquatan (Pty) Limited).

The Product

The product was a combination of three geosynthetics consisting of (a) a 2.5 mm thick Ethyl Vinyl Acetate (EVA) geomembrane, trade named Hyperlastic (now Hyperliner), which acted as the primary barrier, (b) a protective blanket of continuous filament needlepunched polyester nonwoven geotextile (Bidim U44) and (c) a layer of 0.5 mm thick Low Density Polyethylene (LDPE) geomembrane, tradename Driline. The composite product was successfully joined together by a process of radio high-frequency welding. The result of this combination was a composite geomembrane, 4 mm thick and 5.8 m wide by 38 m long, tradename Hypershield.

Product Properties

Tear strength of 104 N, tensile strength of 14.5 MPa, elongation of 1100% before loss of integrity and easy workability between -40° C and +60° C rendered Hypershield an appropriate geomembrane for its purpose. Reluctance to ignite and lack of toxic fume generation when burning were also considered to be extremely important. This was because tunnel construction was carried out under fiery mine conditions. Besides the above, the product was light in colour and thus contributed to better lighting conditions during construction. The exceptionally wide sheeting allowed for a minimum number of on-site joins, thus contributing to the ultimate integrity of the completed lining.

Photo 1. Construction of geomembrane lining.

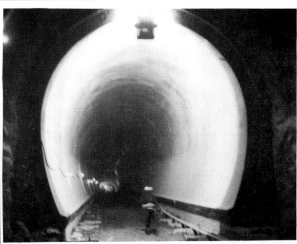

Photo 2. Main concrete tunnel lining.

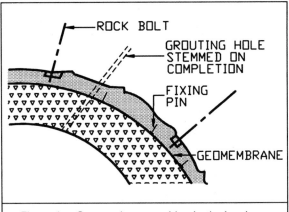

Figure 1. Geomembrane position in the headrace tunnel.

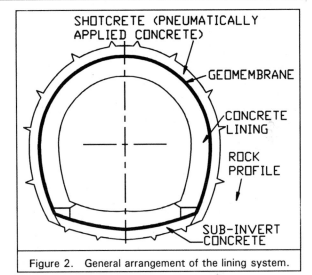

Figure 2. General arrangement of the lining system.

Product Design Considerations

The complex construction of the chosen geosynthetic satisfied the following requirements: (1) that the EVA geomembrane, acting as the primary barrier, should be waterproof and extremely resistant to the powerful jetting forces expected to be exerted by water under the full operating head; (2) that the sandwiched geotextile should serve as a cushion to the primary geomembrane when this membrane was forced against the supporting shotcrete layer by the pressure of the full operating head; and (3) that the secondary LDPE geomembrane would serve as a slip plane between the supporting shotcrete layer and the grout mixture that would be injected under pressure between the shotcrete and the main concrete tunnel liner. The purpose of this grouting was to ensure that no void existed between the main tunnel liner and its supporting structure.

Some phases of the construction are illustrated in Photos 1 and 2, and tunnel cross-sections are shown in Figures 1 and 2.

CONCLUSION

The tunnels have now been in service for seven years and the expected cracks in the concrete lining have formed. There has been no adverse concrete liner reaction and it can be assumed that the composite geomembrane is performing its design function.

REFERENCES

Drakensberg Energy Battery, published by the Communications Department, Escom, Johannesburg, South Africa, Nov. 1986, 8 p.

Editorial feature, "Waterproof Plastic Lines Drakensberg's Tunnels", Tunnels and Tunnelling, Construction Press Ltd., Vol. 12, No. 11, December 1980, pp. 41 - 42.

Lever, I.A., Personal Communication, Johannesburg, South Africa, 1987.

GEOSYNTHETIC WATERPROOFING OF DRY URBAN TRANSIT TUNNEL
WASHINGTON D.C. METRO TUNNELS, SECTION B-10A, USA

R.K. Frobel
Geosynthetics Consulting Engineer
Evergreen, Colorado, USA

In 1984, the Washington Metropolitan Transit Authority (WMATA) approved a Value Engineering Cost Proposal (VECP) for the use of the New Austrian Tunnelling Method (NATM) with geosynthetic waterproofing on section B-10a of the Washington Metro, Washington, D.C., USA. The winning contractor was ILBAU of America. They provided the VECP which included the use of a nonwoven polypropylene geotextile and PVC geomembrane as the waterproofing element. The B-10a Section was completed in 1987. It was the first major use in the United States of the NATM which included a waterproofing on a tunnel system. The contract won the 1987 award for the best civil engineering project from the National Capital Section of the American Society of Civil Engineers.

DESCRIPTION

The NATM is a tunnelling method by which the surrounding rock or soil formations of a tunnel are integrated into a general ring-like support structure. Thus, the formations themselves are part of this support structure [Meggl, 1982]. A shotcrete initial lining is placed over the excavated surface. This provides a smooth surface for the geosynthetics. In addition the rock surface is supported by the shotcrete immediately after excavation so that the radially acting forces can be accepted adhesively [Wagner and Hinkel, 1987].

The contract for Section B-10a of the Washington D.C. Metro included the driving of two 2500 m long tunnels from Forest Glen Station toward Wheaton, Maryland; excavation of the 210 m long Wheaton Station with twin station tunnels, passenger walkways and escalator shaft; and a 60 m long track crossover chamber with a 15 m clear span and 10 m rise. Five ventilation and fan shafts were also included on the B-10a contract. In addition to the recommended NATM redesign, the general engineering consultant, De Leuw, Cather and Co., and Section B-10a designer, Baker Engineers, also recommended approval for the use of geosynthetics waterproofing in Section B-10a. This recommendation was based on historical maintenance problems experienced by WMATA due to ground-water leakage into subway tunnels and stations constructed before 1983. The WMATA subsequently approved the use of geosynthetics waterproofing with the NATM VECP.

GEOSYNTHETICS WATERPROOFING SYSTEM

An integral part of the WMATA NATM design is the incorporation of a waterproofing and drainage system composed of two geosynthetic sheet materials, a nonwoven needlepunched polypropylene geotextile and a polyvinyl chloride (PVC) geomembrane. The geosynthetic system must provide watertight integrity for the life of the tunnel. It must withstand different kinds of stress and strain both during installation and after construction. And it must withstand variable and aggressive chemical environments. Fortunately the rapid increase in tunnelling worldwide has resulted in the NATM becoming a technically matured waterproofing system. The system effectively resists chemical environments and mechanical stress and deformation, thus guaranteeing permanent tunnel waterproofing. Plastic geomembrane sheet sealing with a protective nonwoven geotextile drainage layer has become the predominant sealing system worldwide. It has predominated over the conventional sealing methods such as asphalt membranes or spray applied glass fibre reinforced plastic or bitumen-latex based products [Meggl, 1982]. The geosynthetic system developed for NATM and the WMATA specifications not only meets the demands of rapid tunnelling rates, but also the demands for rough construction treatment. The requirement for absolute watertight sealing puts high technical demands on the system in which the protection of the loosely laid geomembrane is of paramount importance.

It should be noted that the staging of construction activities is such that the installation of the geosynthetics is a separate and continuous operation. The operation efficiently takes place at a time that minimizes interruption of other tunnel construction activities [Leonard, 1986].

Shotcrete Surface

The loose laying of a geomembrane presupposes a backing of sufficient non-deformability and natural strength. A shotcrete layer with a minimum thickness of 200 mm was specified for the backing, to serve as attachment for the fasteners (nails) of the fastening plates. The surface condition of the backing is of special importance at the time of concreting [Wagner and Hinkel, 1987]. The geomembrane sheeting should lie against the shotcrete as solidly and as flush as possible. This should be achieved without excessive stressing and damage. So that this is possible, the shotcrete must be used to smooth the excavated surface and to cover any metal protuberances. Besides providing a smooth surface over the excavation, recent investigations show that the rock surface is supported by shotcrete immediately after excavation. This support is increased by the placement of rock bolts, steel arches or reinforcing wire mats. The WMATA specifications called for a depth/width ratio of shotcrete recess to be restricted to 1/10 (i.e., 100 mm depth maximum over a 1 m span).

Nonwoven Geotextile

The nonwoven geotextile performs not only a protective function but also a drainage function, and,

Photo 1. Tunnel after geomembrane installation.

Property	Minimum Specifications	ASTM
A. GEOTEXTILE (non-woven polypropylene)		
Thickness (mm)	4.0	D1777
Mass per unit area (g/m²)	500	-----
Grab strength (N)	1150	D1682
Elongation (%)	80	D1682
Trapezoid tear strength (N)	440	D2263
Burst strength (kPa)	2760	D751
Chemical resistance (pH value)	2 to 13	N/A*
Flammability	Self extinguishing	D568
B. GEOMEMBRANE (PVC-soft)		
Thickness (mm)	1.5	D374
Ultimate tensile strength (kPa)	7600	D638
Ultimate elongation (%)	300	D638
Brittleness temperature	± 7°C	D1790
Flammability	Self extinguishing	D568
Dimensional stability 6 hr @ 80°C (%)	2	D1204

TABLE 1. Geosynthetic properties according to WMATA's specifications [Gnilsen, 1986]

*N/A = not available

therefore, it is important for the effectiveness of the total sealing system. The existing technical demands on the nonwovens in tunnelling are a result of the various kinds of stress and strain during the construction stage as well as in-service conditions.   It is only possible to claim a permanent mechanical protection function of the nonwoven when it is effectively and permanently inert to acid and alkali attack [Frobel, 1988]. The technical requirements for the nonwoven geotextiles used in Section B-10a specifications are shown in Table 1. General requirements call for a nonwoven polypropylene geotextile.   The geotextile was unrolled and positioned from a mobile scaffold in a radial manner and fixed to the shotcrete with fixing discs and nails.   Once in place, the 4 m wide geotextile strips were thermally welded at the overlaps.

The Fastening System

The nonwoven geotextile and the geomembrane sheets were installed with the help of a special scaffold. As a first step, the nonwoven geotextile was fastened to the shotcrete (gunite) by means of PVC plastic discs (plates) and fasteners (nails). As a second step, the PVC geomembrane sheeting was secured to these discs by means of hot-air welding. On average, four fastening points per square meter were required to fasten the protective geotextile layer to the tunnel wall. The fastening disc is designed in such a way that if the geomembrane sheet is overstressed and deformed at a weld, the failure will always occur in a certain plane of weakness inside the fastening disc, never in the geomembrane sheet itself [Meggl, 1982]. Thus it was possible to avoid excessive stress and distress of the geomembrane sheet during installation.

Geomembrane

The geomembrane sheet material specified in the

WMATA B-10a specifications was 1.5 mm thick polyvinyl chloride-soft (PVC). This is the most commonly specified material used in tunnel lining applications [Frobel, 1988]. PVC is also very flexible, workable and easily welded, even in the commonly specified thickness of 1.5 mm. The PVC sheeting was unrolled and positioned from a mobile scaffold in a radial manner. As it is supported below the crown, it is manually hot-air welded to the PVC fixing discs, thus providing required support for each 1.2 m wide PVC strip.   The individual strips were then thermally welded together at all overlaps and junctions, thus providing a continuous waterproofing system. Table 1 gives the minimum physical geomembrane properties required in the WMATA B-10a specifications.

REFERENCES

Frobel, R., "Geosynthetics in the NATM Tunnel Design", Proc., 1988 ASCE Spring Convention - Session on Geosynthetics for Soil Improvement, Nashville, Tennessee, 1988.

Gnilsen, R. and Rhodes, G.W., "Innovative Use of Geosynthetics to Construct Watertight Washington D.C. Subway Tunnels", Geotechnical Fabrics Report, Vol. 4, No. 4, 1986.

Leonard, G., "Control of Groundwater as Employed by the New Austrian Tunnelling Method", Proc., 1986 ASCE Annual Convention, Boston, Massachusetts, 1986.

Meggl, A., "Abdichtungssystemmit PVC Weich-Dichtungsbahnen fur bergmannisch erstellte Tunnel", Strasse und Tiefbau, Nov 1982.

Wagner, H. and Hinkel, W., "The New Austrian Tunnelling Method", Proc., Tunnel/Underground Seminar, ASCE, New York, Feb 1987.

GEOMEMBRANE WATERPROOFING OF DRY TUNNEL UNDER TWO RIVERS LYON METRO TUNNEL, FRANCE

J.P. Benneton
Lrpc
Lyon, France

J.L. Mahuet
Semaly
Lyon, France

J.P. Gourc
Irigm-UJF
Grenoble, France

This case history describes the first use in France of a PVC geomembrane for waterproofing a completely submerged tunnel.

DESCRIPTION OF PROJECT

Construction of Line D of the Lyon Metro included a tunnel section under the rivers Saône and Rhône. The tunnel was driven through sandy-gravelly alluvium having high permeability (up to 10 mm/s). Tunnel overburden averaged 5 m under the two rivers. Water levels above the tunnel invert varied between 5 m and 25 m.

The tunnel was constructed between 1984 and 1987. A mud-pressure shield technique was used over the total distance of 1250 m. The nominal diameter of the tunnel was 6.5 m. Waterproofing started in November 1986 and was completed in early 1988.

WATERPROOFING SYSTEM

Use of PVC Geomembranes in Tunnels

Since 1970, when the Fourvière motorway tunnel in Lyon made use of PVC geomembranes, waterproofing of underground facilities in France has undergone considerable development:

- road and rail tunnels (600,000 m²),
- cut-and-fill trenches (600,000 m² including 500,000 m² for the Lyon Metro system).

Since 1979, translucent PVC has been used at many underground facilities such as the European Nuclear Research Centre (CERN) in Geneva (135,000 m²), where the permanent head reaches 25 m in places, many drilled tunnels, and many cut-and-cover trenches.

Geomembrane Properties

PVC has advantageous mechanical properties for such applications:

- Strain at rupture, ε_f = 270%
- Tensile strength (for a sheet thickness of 1.5 mm), σ_f = 18 kN/m.

A material with these properties can absorb without difficulty the various stresses involved in concreting the final tunnel ring, along with the possible subsequent movements of the concrete structure.

As in many other underground facilities, the PVC used is translucent. The translucency does not affect the mechanical and physio-chemical properties:

- Behaviour in water (loss of plasticiser - test at 60°C for ten days): loss of weight < 1%,
- Resistance to microorganisms (NFX 41514 standard):
    - edibility: 0
    - mycostatic effect: 0 or 1.

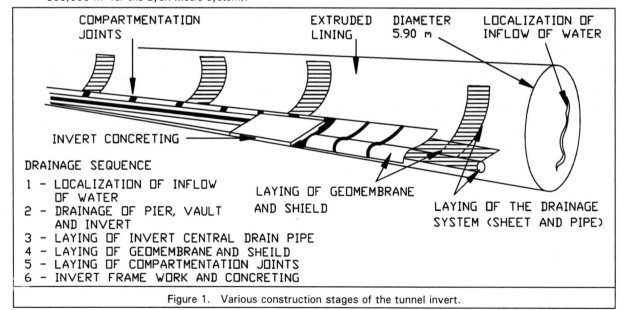

COMPARTMENTATION JOINTS   EXTRUDED LINING   DIAMETER 5.90 m   LOCALIZATION OF INFLOW OF WATER

INVERT CONCRETING

DRAINAGE SEQUENCE
1 - LOCALIZATION OF INFLOW OF WATER
2 - DRAINAGE OF PIER, VAULT AND INVERT
3 - LAYING OF INVERT CENTRAL DRAIN PIPE
4 - LAYING OF GEOMEMBRANE AND SHIELD
5 - LAYING OF COMPARTMENTATION JOINTS
6 - INVERT FRAME WORK AND CONCRETING

LAYING OF GEOMEMBRANE AND SHIELD

LAYING OF THE DRAINAGE SYSTEM (SHEET AND PIPE)

Figure 1. Various construction stages of the tunnel invert.

Photo 2. View of a cut-and-cover trench with geomembrane waterproofing.

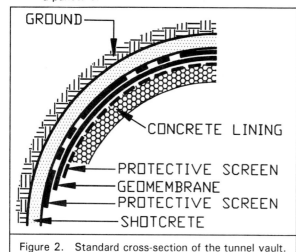

Photo 1. General view of the waterproofing placed on the vault.

Geomembrane Installation

The PVC geomembrane is placed automatically by means of a gantry equipped with a roll dispenser. The sheets are welded together by automatic heating devices. This allows the sheeting to be placed at a high rate.

With translucent PVC, the continuity of the welds can be checked instantaneously and efficiently, i.e., any defects (absence of a weld or carbonized zone due to overheating) are clearly apparent. For opaque geomembranes, electrical or pneumatic test procedures must be used. These are not easy to do underground.

Installation stages included:
- Extruded concrete coating placed by the tunnelling contractor.
- Grouting to stop inflowing water:
  Fissures with a high inflow rate are grouted. Then the flow on the tunnel side is drained off through cellular sheets linked to a central drain that were later placed on the invert.
- Preparation of waterproofing support:
  All rough points on the support surface are removed and a protective screen (geotextile or reclaimed PVC sheet) is installed to protect the geomembrane from a puncture.

- Application of the geomembrane:
  An important feature of the scheme is the partitioning system. A protruding strip of PVC is placed across the tunnel axis every 25 m and welded to the lower face of the geomembrane. This enables water leaks to be isolated, sector by sector, thereby optimizing subsequent grout repair works. The waterproofing is first placed horizontally on the invert then on the vault. Nearly all the heat welds are made automatically using a Leister 84 machine.
- Protection of waterproofing before concreting:
  A protective shield (3 mm thick PVC) is spot-bonded to the geomembrane before concreting the tunnel lining.
- Additional seals: these are placed at concrete restart points and consist of an expansion product (eg. butyl bentonite).

PERFORMANCE

During tunnel construction, nearly 90% of leakage flow was stopped by grouting. Since completion of the works no anomaly of any importance has been reported. It should be emphasized that, in view of the risk involved, inspection procedures during construction were extremely stringent. These procedures were done independently by the contractor and by the Engineer.

Of particular interest here is the number of heat-weld tests made: 22 weld samples were taken in situ so as to carry out 124 peeling tests. The average peeling force was measured at 10.34 kN/m (standard deviation of 1.21 kN/m, with a range of 6.80 to 12.80 kN/m). This is well above the recommended value of 4 kN/m.

REFERENCES

Mahuet, J.L., "Etanchéité de la traversée sous-fluviale de la ligne d du metro de Lyon", Tunnels et Ouvrages Souterrains, No, 82, July-August 1987.

Mahuet, J.L., "Etanchéité du L.E.P. au CERN à Genève", Tunnels et Ouvrages Souterrains, July-August 1988.

Mahuet, J.L., "Etanchéité du Métro de Lyon", Le Moniteur Review, 24 October 1987.

Mahuet, J.L., AITES congress - Subject "Tunnels and water", Madrid, June 1988.

Reith, J.L., "Utilisation des membranes plastiques pour l'étanchéité des ouvrages souterrains en France", 2nd International Symposium: Matières Plastiques et Caoutchoucs dan l'Etanchéité des Constructions de Génie Civil, Liège, 1984.

Figure 2. Standard cross-section of the tunnel vault.

GROUND
CONCRETE LINING
PROTECTIVE SCREEN
GEOMEMBRANE
PROTECTIVE SCREEN
SHOTCRETE

CHAPTER 6

RAILWAYS AND ASPHALT PAVEMENTS

GEOTEXTILE FOR RAILROAD BRANCH LINE UPGRADING
KANSAS, USA

G.P. Raymond
Queen's University
Kingston, Ontario, Canada

Much of the midwest North American continent consists of fertile clay terrain with very little or no outcropping of rock or coarse granular material suitable for aggregate subballast or ballast material. Numerous little-used branch lines exist. Occasionally a railroad company will negotiate or rationalize its traffic such that one of these branch lines has to withstand a considerable increase in traffic. The branch line then normally requires upgrading, preferably prior to the increase in traffic. Due to financial restrictions, however, such upgrading is often deferred until the profits from the increase in traffic are realized. When the decision to defer upgrading is made, it is not uncommon to experience considerable subgrade pumping and subgrade failures. Described herein are the procedures that were used on one such branch railroad line.

TYPICAL SUBGRADE FAILURE PRIOR TO UPGRADING

The conditions associated with a typical subgrade failure area prior to upgrading generally involve subsidence of the ties a considerable distance into the ballast. The ballast becomes badly fouled with pumping fines from the subgrade material to the extent that it bridges between the ties as the track is elevated. After rainfalls, the ballast is so fouled that water ponds around the ties, including when voiding exists below the ties.

METHODOLOGY OF TRACK SUPPORT RECONSTRUCTION

Examination of the fouling fines within the ballast and comparison with the subgrade soils indicated that the ballast contamination was due to penetration of the highly plastic clay subgrades. These subgrades softened on wetting and became weak during any sustained rainfall. Track support rehabilitation had to take this factor into account. Thus the track support needed to be reconstructed in such a manner that the plastic clay fines would be prevented from penetrating the ballast in future times of heavy rainfall. The normal method of dealing with this situation is the placement of a well-graded granular subballast having a top size not less than 12.5 mm and graded down to between 7 and 12% passing the 75 μm sieve (No. 200) in which the fines sizes are non-plastic and have a high permeability. In the Midwest, such graded granular material can be costly and is always scarce. One of the purposes of 'engineering' the track support is to use, where available, local materials that are readily available at a lower cost. These materials would have to function as effectively as those used in the more classical engineering approaches. The track support technique in combination with such materials was therefore used here.

Tests from a variety of sites in Kansas were already available using the minus 2 mm (No. 10 sieve) size of each of two readily available granular soils. One was a quarry waste and the other was being sold as a filter sand. These tests clearly indicated the desirability of using the quarry waste sand rather than the so-called filter sand. The importance of not being misled by a name is clear. The local non-plastic rock quarry tailings were available at a cost of $1.1/tonne. This material graded from a size of 420 μm (No. 40 sieve) down to 5% passing the 75 μm (No. 200 sieve). The deficiency of material over 420 μm would result in the quarry tailings material being vibrated, under traffic, into the voids of a coarse-grained, basically single-sized ballast. In order to prevent such migration of the very fine and fine sand-size particles, some technique of maintaining separation was necessary. The recent introduction of geotextiles to the railroad industry afforded such a technique and was the method used on this branch line upgrading. One modification to the commonly available geotextiles had to be made, and this was a stipulation of a lower equivalent opening size that is often available. An equivalent opening size of 75 μm (No. 200 sieve) or preferably less was considered necessary and used to retain the fine sand.

It should be noted that the more common method using geotextiles is to place the geotextile directly on the subgrade. Manufacture of geotextiles having equivalent opening sizes less than 75 μm (No. 200 sieve), which is the upper limit for silt-sized material, is extremely difficult; thus silt-size material is allowed to pass through the geotextile if subjected to sufficient vibratory or repetitive loading. While the geotextile would retard the rate of infiltration of the subgrade clay, it would not eliminate such infiltration. Consequently, contamination of the ballast would eventually occur. While it is not economically feasible to test more than a few selected samples, laboratory testing indicated that the fine granular sand-sized quarry tailings material was sufficiently fine grained that it had a high probability of acting as a filter and separator to the underlying plastic clay materials of the general region. A nonwoven, well-needlepunched geotextile with an equivalent opening size in the range of 75 μm (No. 200 sieve) or less should, in turn, act as a separator to the sand and prevent it from vibrating upwards into the ballast material while remaining, on a long term basis, free draining. To reduce cost, resin treatment of the geotextile was not specified but would have been desirable since it would increase abrasion resistance and longevity of a low equivalent opening size.

RECONSTRUCTION

The reconstruction was undertaken using a track sled and two track-mounted, self-propelled, hydraulic track jack liners, or more specifically, Geismar RVD Laborsavor

Photo 1.　Water in tie imprint.

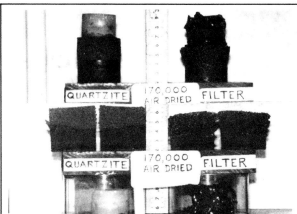

Photo 2.　Laboratory tested samples.

Photo 3.　Sledding of sand subballast.

Photo 4.　Installation of geotextile.

power jack liners having a 900 mm track jacking stroke and a 200 mm throw. In areas where the subgrade failed, a 3.6 m wide geotextile, delivered in rolls of 90 m, was incorporated into the track upgrading program by placement on the quarry waste. The sled was pulled by the high rail mounted vehicle via two high strength steel cables running parallel to the rails and attached to the ends of a 3.6 m long steel tube placed close to the vehicle and across the tracks. The cables then converged on the rear central towing hook of the high rail mounted vehicle. The two self-propelled track jacks were positioned an appropriate distance apart, usually about 30 m; the track vehicle was positioned ahead of the track jacks facing in the direction in which the sled was to be pulled. After the track was elevated about 600 mm, the sled, which was initially positioned adjacent to and in front of the rear jack pointing in the direction of sledding, was pulled to the second jack. The track jacks then moved forward to repeat the process.

The sand-sized quarry tailings were delivered in ballast cars to the closest siding where reconstruction was being undertaken. These ballast cars were then available as required. When needed, they were hauled to the reconstruction site from the siding using a high rail mounted track vehicle, and the sand was unloaded directly onto the track to fill the cribs and area between the rails. The track was then re-sledded to level the sand. The geotextile was unrolled directly on the sledded sand surface. This resulted in a sand layer about 3 m wide covered by a 3.6 m wide geotextile. The ends of the geotextile were thus about 100 mm lower than the central portion of the geotextile and would act as a sink for any water movement in the plane of the geotextile.

Ballast delivery and placement was made in a similar fashion to that of the sand subballast material. The ballast was delivered in ballast cars to the closest siding and brought to the site using the motor power of the high rail track vehicle. The ballast was deposited on the track that rested on the geotextile, after which the track was raised and lined without any tamping using the hydraulic track jack liners. In general, 300 mm of ballast was placed in 150 mm lifts. The track jacks were used to raise the track after each lift without any tamping being done. Lifts greater than 150 mm cannot be attained unless bags filled with ballast are placed under the ties, since the ballast cannot be allowed to cover the rails. Should ballast cover the rails, nothing could move along the rails. Once the track had been brought to final elevation, crib ballast was placed, and finally tamping and lining was undertaken.

ACKNOWLEDGMENTS

The construction work described was performed under the direction of Mr. Keith Pottorff, district engineer, and Mr. Leroy Draper, division engineer. Their cooperation is gratefully acknowledged, as is the permission of the Atchinson Topeka and Santa Fe Railway Companies permission to publish this article.

REFERENCES

Raymond, G.P., "Geotextile Application for a Branch Line Upgrading", Geotextiles and Geomembranes, Vol. 3, 1986, pp. 91-104.

Raymond, G.P., "New Options in Branch Line Rehabilitation", Progressive Railroading, Vol. 27, Mar 1984, pp. 71-74.

GEOTEXTILES FOR RAILWAY SWITCH AND GRADE CROSSING REHABILITATION
MARITIME PROVINCES, CANADA

G.P. Raymond
Queen's University
Kingston, Ontario, Canada

In the presence of excess water, fines contained within the subgrade, subballast or dirty ballast, subject to repetitive wheel loads, are pumped and migrate upwards through the track structure. Where this has occurred and is continuing to occur, the installation of geotextiles in track during rehabilitation at hard to maintain and drain areas such as grade crossings, track switches and the like has been found to be of immense value. Switch and grade crossing geotextiles in Canada's Maritime Provinces are prime examples of the beneficial use of track rehabilitation geotextiles.

DRAINAGE IMPROVEMENT

Since pumping generally occurs in the presence of water, drainage improvement (whether the improvement of side-ditch drainage, or the lowering of the ground water, or internal track drainage) is always the first and most essential item in any track rehabilitation involving ballast replacement or the cleaning of fouled ballast. Geotextiles are therefore installed to facilitate drainage from the load bearing area of the tracks to the ditch. This dictates that the geotextiles in-plane cross-sectional drainage has a sink that is, at all times throughout the geotextiles useful life in track, at a lower elevation than the rest of the geotextile.

When undercutting long lengths of track, special attention is directed to the removal of the fouled shoulder material so as to allow water to escape and prevent construction of a "canal" effect, or on flat and marshy land, to the use of French drains. Similarly French drains are used over short lengths of undercut track such as grade crossings, stations and the like that suffer from the disadvantage of lacking longitudinal ditch drainage. Geotextiles are never used as a substitute for good drainage. Indeed, when geotextiles are installed without the ability to drain and discharge by gravity to the side ditches or French drains, they are found to facilitate the retention of water within the load bearing area of the track. Such retained water is found to provoke the pumping phenomenon and, during cold weather, frost heave.

BASIC FUNCTIONAL REQUIREMENTS OF GEOTEXTILES

In general, when dealing with track rehabilitation problems, the track has been in existence for some time and excessive subgrade settlements have ceased. The use of a geotextile's strength for subgrade reinforcement has not, under these circumstances, been found to be a major consideration. Rather, the geotextile needs to be highly abrasion-resistant and durable to withstand the harsh environment of ballast particle movement on ballast or subgrade aggregate. On undercut, ploughed, or sledded track in which the rail remains in place during rehabilitation, the prepared surface to receive a geotextile will contain ballast particles either lying on the surface or protruding from the surface. Although raking may remove some of these protrusions, the prepared surface remains rough and any geotextile placed on it has to be abrasion-resistant, and also have the ability to elongate around such protrusions without puncture or tear. If punctured or worn through, the geotextile is found to lose some of its ability to filter and separate. The deficiency of the inability to elongate is found to be particularly apparent in all excavations made where woven and woven/nonwoven composite geotextiles were installed directly on the undercut surface. The normal specification requires a resin bonded needlepunched geotextile of 1000 g/m^2 when installed directly on the undercut surface.

The ability to transmit water within the plane of the geotextiles has been observed on a number of installations during the passage of a train. When an axle or group of axles passes a location, the track support compresses. If the soil is saturated or near-saturated, water will escapes along the path of least resistance. Geotextiles with in-plane permeability offer such a path of least resistance even when placed in sand or broadly graded gravel layers. They are installed to permit water to drain into the side ditch and not back into the load-bearing area of the track.

In summary, the basic functional requirements of geotextiles in Canadian railroad bed rehabilitation technology is:

- To drain water away from the track roadbed (on a long-term basis, both laterally and by gravity) along the plane of the geotextile without buildup of excessive hydrostatic pressures;
- To withstand the abrasive forces of moving aggregate caused by the tamping and compacting process during cyclic maintenance, tamping during initial compaction, and by the passage of trains on a frequent basis;
- To filter or hold back soil particles while allowing the passage of water;
- To separate two types of soils of different particle sizes and grading that would readily mix under the influence of repeated loading and of water migration; and
- To have the ability to elongate around protruding large angular gravel-sized particles while resisting rupture or puncture.

DEPTH OF INSTALLATION

One of the contributing factors to a geotextile's performance in-track is the depth at which it is placed

| Photo 1. Undercut surface showing protruding ballast. | Photo 2. Installed geotextile. |

below the base of the ties. To assess the effect of abrasion with installation depth, data were obtained from several sites installed with a needlepunched resin-treated geotextiles all having a mass per unit area between 450 and 510 g/m^2. After excavation, the estimated damage to each geotextile obtained from each location was established by measuring the percentage of completely worn-through areas in the worst 300 x 300 mm square section (generally below the intersection of the rail and tie). These results ranged from 0.3 percent at a depth of 350 mm to 4.1 percent at a depth of 175 mm. Below 250 mm, the amount and rate of change in damage was small.

The results show that a ballast placement depth of about 250 mm is preferred as a minimum depth of ballast on the installed geotextile prior to any ballast tamping.

TRANSITION ZONE

On short lengths of rehabilitation track where geotextiles are installed it has been observed that, if the geotextiles are laid to the end of the undercut, a major change in track modulus occurs at the transition. In order to minimize this sudden transition, a 3 m to 6 m length of undercut track without geotextile is used between the track rehabilitated with geotextile and the non-rehabilitated track.

REHABILITATION GEOTEXTILE SPECIFICATION

- Needlepunched with > 80 penetrations/cm^2.
- Fibre linear density < 0.7 tex.
- Fibre tenacity > 4 mN/tex.
- Yarn length > 100 mm.
- Filtration Opening Size < 75 μm.
- In-plane permeability > 50 μm/s.
- Elongation at failure > 60%.
- Mass per unit area > 1000 g/m^2.
- Abrasion resistance: > 200 kPa on 102 mm dia. burst after 5000 revolutions of H-18 stone each loaded with 1000 grams (ASTM D-3884).
- Fiber bonding by >5% to <20% low modulus acrylic resin or other suitable non-water soluble process that leaves geotextile pliable.
- Width and length without seaming to be specified by client.
- Colour must not cause "snow-blindness".
- Packing: Waterproof, black, and identified at both ends with manufacturer, width, length, type, and date of manufacture.

SUMMARY AND CONCLUSIONS

Canadian railway track that was constructed with a deficiency of a suitable separation layer, or whose drainage is poor, or is impacted at discontinuities of the rail such that segregation of fines from within the separation layer occurs are being rehabilitated so they incorporate drainage improvement and, often, a heavy geotextile.

Particular attention is being paid to improving internal track drainage. This involves the sloping of interface layers or undercut surfaces toward drainage ditches or French drains. Proper and adequate perpendicular drains to prevent water accumulating in the track structure or in French drains are often used in the rehabilitation work. In addition the discharge end of any geotextile is installed below the level of the undercut load-bearing area.

A minimum depth of 250 mm of ballast on a geotextile is required before the tamping is performed when a geotextile is installed. Where practical, a 300-mm ballast depth is used.

For geotextiles installed directly on the undercut surface a 1000 g/m^2 resin bonded nonwoven needlepunched geotextile made from fibres with a linear density less than 0.7 tex and a tenacity greater than 4 mN/tex is recommended.

REFERENCES

G.P. Raymond, "Research on Geotextiles for Heavy Hall Railways", Canadian Geotechnical Journal, Vol. 21, 1984, pp. 259-276.

G.P. Raymond, "Subgrade Requirements and the Application of Geotextiles", Proc., Conference on Track Technology for the Next Decade, Thomas Telford Ltd., London, England, 1984, pp. 159-166.

G.P. Raymond, "Installation Factors Affecting Performance of Railroad Geotextiles", Rail Track Structures, Transportation Research Record 1071, Transportation Research Board, Washington, D.C. Jan. 1986, pp. 64-71.

G.P. Raymond, "New Options in Branch Line Rehabilitation", Progressive Railroading, Vol. 27, March 1984, pp. 71-74.

GEOSYNTHETICS FOR RAILROAD TRACK REHABILITATION
ALABAMA, USA

J.C. Walls
Inter Sol Engineering Inc.
Milton, Ontario, Canada

J.E. Newby
Newby Soils Inc.
Reno, Nevada, USA

This paper describes the first use of polymer geogrids to reinforce railroad track ballast in North America. The project involves the use of a geotextile for separation and polymer grid for reinforcement in the repair of a problem section of track in Alabama.

DESCRIPTION

In 1976, a 2000 m long section of track, which is owned and operated by CSX Transportation, was relocated from its original site along a bank of the Tallapoosa River to its present location approximately 365 meters to the east. Most of the new track section was situated in a deep, wide cut through interbedded sand and weak clay layers and at an elevation which was about 7.5 m below the original phreatic surface. The cut section had 2H:1V side slopes and was benched at 7.5 m intervals.

Although deep side ditches had been constructed to provide drainage for the large runoff that was anticipated, erosion of the side slopes and benches soon filled the trenches with sediment and blocked drainage. As a result the trackbed became saturated and unstable. Heavy rail traffic then caused the subgrade soil to become plastic resulting in progressive shear failure of the embankment and pumping of soil fines into the ballast, further reducing the stability of the track structure.

Due to the combination of excessive deformation and fouled ballast, track realignment and resurfacing was required every two to four weeks. Furthermore, train speeds had to be permanently reduced to 8 km per hour through this short section of track in order to prevent derailments.

Since the installation of a major drainage system in the slopes and trackbed was cost prohibitive, several alternative remedies were attempted, but none were successful. One such effort was a commonly used method whereby rail piles are driven vertically at the end of the ties to strengthen the roadbed.

In May 1983, the track was inspected by railroad personnel and consultants who identified several problems that needed to be corrected, namely: increase the bearing capacity of the subgrade soil, prevent the contamination of the ballast with subgrade fines and dissipate the high pore water pressures built up by cyclic train loading. Since geosynthetics have been used separately to solve each of the above problems, a combination of geotextiles and geogrids was considered to maximize the benefits of the two products in the following ways.

- Geogrid to provide tensile reinforcement and shear resistance to increase the effective bearing capacity of the subgrade.

- Geogrid to interlock with and confine the ballast, increasing its resistance to both vertical and lateral movement.

- Geotextile for separation and filtration to prevent contamination of the ballast and provide quick relief of pore water pressures.

Although two other stabilization alternatives were proposed, it was decided to use the geotextile/geogrid combination because of its relatively low cost and the proven performance of geogrids in other reinforcement applications such as pavement base layers. In addition, large scale tests simulating tie-ballast loading at the Royal Military College of Canada had shown that the number of cyclic loads to cause 50 mm of permanent vertical deformation could be increased by up to a factor of 10 with geogrid reinforced ballast over very weak subgrades.

DESIGN

The design called for the removal of the fouled ballast to a depth of approximately 0.30 m below the base of the tie. Rather than disposing of the old ballast, it was to be placed along the edges of the embankment to widen the existing shoulders. Next a 380 g/m^2 nonwoven geotextile was to be placed on top of the remaining subballast followed by a geogrid placed directly on top of the geotextile, and 0.30 m of new ballast. The specifications for the geotextile required that it be a nonwoven needlepunched engineering grade fabric comprised of polyester fibres with a linear density of 0.8 to 1 tex per filament. The minimum fibre tenacity was to be 4 mN/tex and the minimum fibre length was to be 150 mm. The geotextile selected for this project was Quline 160 manufactured by Wellman Quline.

The geogrid specified was Tensar SS2 geogrid manufactured by The Tensar Corporation. Although no other polymer geogrids were in the market-place at the time, the important properties of the Tensar geogrids that made it suitable for ballast reinforcement were open grid geometry for interlock capability, high junction strength to resist lateral deformation of the grid cross members and high tensile modulus to reinforce at low strain levels.

Although the design thickness of ballast was selected arbitrarily at the time, recent developments in geogrid design technology for railroad trackbed indicate that about 600 mm of reinforced ballast and subballast would be required for a weak subgrade having a CBR value of

| Photo 1.   Condition of track prior to rehabilitation shows sediment blocking drainage ditches and fouled ballast. | Photo 2.   Placement of geotextile/geogrid combination under raised track. |

approximately 1.0% compared to 1.0 m of unreinforced ballast and subballast. However, since the actual depth of existing ballast and subballast was considerably greater than 300 mm, it is reasoned that the remaining ballast and subballast provided enough support for the new reinforced ballast while fulfilling the total reinforced thickness requirement to prevent overstressing of the weak subgrade.

As stated previously, two other alternatives were rejected in favour of the geotextile/geogrid solution. The first was to relocate the track at an estimated cost of $570,000. The second alternative was to remove the fouled ballast and excavate the shoulders from the near end of the ties outward to a depth of 300 mm below the ballast base and replace with free draining material. An 810 g/m² geotextile would then be placed on top of the existing subballast and new ballast added to a depth of 300 mm.

CONSTRUCTION

Construction of the geogrid reinforced track was carried out in December, 1983. Since geotextiles have been used extensively in trackbed construction over the last 10 years, no special equipment of procedures were required to install both the geotextile and the geogrid.

PERFORMANCE

Following, an initial observation period of approximately 3 months in which it was determined that the reinforced track structure was performing satisfactorily, it was decided to gradually increase the allowable speed up to 56 km/h and ultimately to 80 km/h. The rehabilitated track has now been in service for four years without any reoccurrence of stability problems and only routine track maintenance has been required.

CONCLUSIONS

The geotextile/geogrid solution was successful in achieving the required track performance for just one sixth of the estimated total cost of the relocation alternative. Furthermore, the project supports the results of large scale laboratory tests on tie-ballast loading that geogrids can increase the life of ballasted track between maintenance cycles, particularly over weak subgrade soils.

CONCLUSIONS

The geotextile/geogrid solution was successful in achieving the required track performance for just one sixth of the estimated total cost of the relocation alternative. Furthermore, the project supports the results of large scale laboratory tests on tie-ballast loading that geogrids can increase the life of ballasted track between maintenance cycles, particularly over weak subgrade soils.

REFERENCES

Bathurst, R.J. and Raymond, G.P., "Geogrid Reinforcement of Ballasted Track", Paper presented to Transportation Research Board 66th Annual Meeting, Washington, D.C., January 1987.

Walls, J.C. and Galbreath, L.L., "Railroad Ballast Reinforcement Using Geogrids", Proceedings, Geosynthetics '87, Vol 1, New Orleans, LA, 1987, pp. 38-45.

Newby, J.E. and Walls, J.C., "Railroad Track Structure Stabilized with Geosynthetics", Geotechnical Fabrics Report, Vol 5, No. 6, Nov. 1987.

The Tensar Corporation, "Design Guide for Tensar Geogrid Reinforced Ballasted Track - Draft", Dec. 18, 1987.

GEOTEXTILE TO PREVENT SHRINKAGE CRACK OF RIGID PAVEMENTS
PARIS, FRANCE

G. Colombier
Laboratoire Régional des Ponts et Chaussées
Autun, France

France has been using for more than 20 years in an intensive way material treated by hydraulic binders to construct rigid pavements for use in highways with high or medium traffic densities. Such structures show technical and economical advantages.

Observations are proving that, for the French climate and for the binders considered, rigid pavements treated with hydraulic binders are susceptible to a cracking caused by an unavoidable thermal shrinkage. Such cracking is transmitted to the bituminous surface course and appears on the road surface in the form of transverse cracks. The spacing of the cracks is between 5 and 10 m. The width of the cracks is limited to a few mm depending upon the existing temperature.

As soon as 1977, trials to delay or prevent the transmission of such cracks in bituminous courses were undertaken using geotextiles impregnated with bituminous binder.

The purpose of this paper is to describe the field trial undertaken.

The experimental field trials were conducted on National roads in the Paris area of France.

Date of the works was June 1982

The length treated was 115 m in one way. Sixteen transverse cracks were repaired.

CHARACTERISTICS OF THE EXPERIMENTAL SITE

The highway RN 20 is a 4 way high road. It has a daily traffic of about 1000 heavy trucks in the direction considered to be the most important traffic. This high road was reinforced in 1971 by 250 mm of slagbound materials and 60 mm of bituminous concrete.

Before work commenced the high road had a regular pattern of transverse cracking with a spacing of about 7 m. From a mechanical point of view the road was in good condition with small (unimportant) deflexions.

TRIAL DESCRIPTION

In the area where the layer of 60 mm bituminous concrete was placed, the bituminous concrete was placed on a 115 m length of geotextile that was asphalt impregnated. The geotextile was located under the new bituminous concrete.

Characteristics of Geotextile

The geotextile is a needlepunched polyester nonwoven fabric with a mass per unit area of 240 g/m². During manufacture the geotextile is hot pressed. This lowers both its flexibility and compressibility. The width of the geotextile roll is roughly 2 m.

Characteristics of the Impregnation Binder

Cationic bituminous emulsion with 68% of bitumen, pH 2.8 and quick breaking was used for impregnation.

Method of Placing

The impregnation binder was spread at about 1 kg/m² that is 700 g of asphalt per m².

The geotextile was unrolled by hand (Photo 1) on broken emulsion. A minimum 400 mm of recover was specified (i.e. distance from crack to geotextile edge).

The bituminous concrete was placed with a finisher in a 60 mm thick layer compacted by both vibrating roller and rubber tyre roller.

FINDINGS AT THE PLACEMENT

The geotextile stuck well to the road surface if placed as soon as the emulsion broken.

The geotextile's loss of flexibility resulting from being hot pressed during manufacture made it difficult to place without folds.

BEHAVIOUR OF THE EXPERIMENTAL FIELD TEST

All the cracks present in the old road were noted before the field trial started. All reflection cracks were recorded for several years.

The behaviour of the experimental section has been compared with the traditional section without geotextile. After four winters, the recorded observations are as given in Table 1.

CONCLUSIONS

Five years after starting the trials, the following conclusions may be drawn:

- The reflection of cracks were clearly delayed by the geotextile. They were not, however prevented.

ISSMFE., Committee TC9 - Geosynthetics Case Histories.

| Photo 1. Geotextile unrolling near a crack. | Photo 2. End of unrolling of first strip. |

- Inversely, tightness seems to be guaranteed by the geotextile even in places where cracks where clearly apparent.

- a larger efficiency could have been obtained by the use of a bituminous binder having little or no thermal susceptibility.

REFERENCES

Colombier, G. Astesan, and A. Goacolou, H. "Using a geotextile to prevent shrinkage crack of rigid pavements." Proc., 2nd. Int. Conference on geotextiles, Las Vegas, 1982.

Colombier, G. et al., "Shrinkage crack of rigid pavements: Synthesis report". Bulletin de liaison des laboratoires des Ponts et Chaussees, France No 156 et 157.

	Table 1. Field observations			
Structure	Numbers of cracks			
	Before field	after 2 winters	after 3 winters	after 4 winters
without geotextile	30	3[1]	5[1] 5[2] 6[3]	6[1] 4[2] 7[3]
with geotextile	16	0	6[1]	4[1] 1[2] 1[3]
[1] beginning of crack [2] discontinuous crack [3] complete crack				

GEOTEXTILE FOR REINFORCEMENT OF SURFACE DRESSING ROAD 138, FRANCE, AND ROAD 2, FRENCH GUYANE

G. Colombier

Laboratoire Régional des Ponts et Chaussées
Autun, France

The use of geotextiles for reinforcement of surface dressings is being studied in France to achieve two distinct goals:

- Elimination of the effects of cracks rising to the surface of pavements treated with hydraulic binders.
- Improving the behaviour under traffic of surface dressing on low cost highways.

CRACK RESISTANT SURFACE DRESSINGS

Description of the Technique

An "Armaco" licensed technique was created and developed in France since 1985.

Surface dressing "Armaco" is constructed with a special geotextile and several layers of polymer modified bitumen.

A nonwoven geotextile polyester or polypropylene, depending on the case under study, with a mass per unit area ranging between 100 g/m^2 and 150 g/m^2, is hot pressed on one face. The geotextile is laid in strips 500 mm or 1 m wide.

The binder used is a fluxed bitumen with the addition of polymeric material "Styrelf 103".

Characteristics of the Field Test Site

- National Road 138
- Department: Indre et Loire, France
- Date of the works - July I 1987
- Surface treated: 10,000 m^2

The National road 138, Tours-Le Mans, is a two lane road bearing a traffic of about 500 heavy trucks a day. This road, reinforced with hydraulic materials, has many transverse and longitudinal cracks.

Description of the Test

The field tests were constructed in the following way:

- Placement of a tack coat Styrelf 103 750 g/m^2.
- Placement of geotextile in strips, of width 500 mm or 1 m, by a mechanical unroller.
- Spraying 1.4 kg/m^2 of Styrelf I03.
- Blending 10.0 l/m^2 chipping 10/14 mm.
- Spraying 0.8 kg/m^2 of Styrelf 103.
- Blending 6.0 l/m^2 chipping 4/6 mm.

Compacting was made by rubber tyred roller and smooth roller.

Performance

All the cracks present in the old road were carefully noted before the work started. This field work was permanently supervised.

In December 1987 no incorrect construction was recorded and the road's behaviour after 6 months of traffic was excellent. It is important to note that, on field trials using the same technique in 1985, surface tightness was perfectly maintained even when the prints of the cracks were apparent on the surface.

REINFORCED SURFACE DRESSING FOR LOW COST HIGHWAYS

Characteristics of the Field Test Site

- National Road 2 - Department of French Guyane
- Date of works: October 1985
- Surface treated: 1650 m^2 in reinforced surface
- Dressing and 350 m^2 in reinforced surface
- Dressing and 350 m^2 in traditional surface
- Dressing as a type section

Site Characteristics

The National Road 2, in the treated part, is an unpaved road in laterite soil of good quality.

The road width is about 7 m. The average daily traffic is 150 vehicles with 10% of heavy trucks. It should be noted that there is an important downwards slope of about 10%.

The Geotextile

The geotextile used was "Nader", a nonwoven with little needlepunching and hot pressed on one face. It has a mass per unit area of 120 g/m^2. The width of the rolls is 1.78 m.

Description of the Test

The placement of the surface dressing was made in the following way:

- Sweeping of lateritic soil.
- Impregnation with 0.9 to 1.0 kg/m^2 of cut back.
- Drying during 24 hours to 48 hours.

ISSMFE., Committee TC9 - Geosynthetics Case Histories.

| Photo 1. Field trials at National Road 138. | Photo 2. Field trials at Guyane - National Road 2. |

- Placing of geotextile in four strips with overlaps of about 100 mm.
- Spreading of 1.5 Kg/m² of anionic emulsion.
- Blending of 11 l/m² with chipping 10/14 mm.
- Compacting with smooth roller.
- Blending of 11 l/m² with chipping 4/6 mm.
- Compacting with rubber tyred roller.

Performance

From the beginning of the works, the field trials have been regularly observed.

In October 1986, after one year of traffic, which included a wet season, the behaviour of the reinforced surface dressing was considered excellent. Several other field trials have been made in Guyane in 1987 using the techniques described herein.

REFERENCES

Khay, M., Morel, G., and Perrier, H. "Use of geotextiles in construction of low cost highways: an experiment", Proc., 3rd. Int. Conference on Geotextiles, Vienne, 1986.

De Garidel, R., Morel, G., and Negre, J.P. "The use of geotextiles in surface dressing: reinforced surface dressings", Conf., on Routes et Developpement, Paris, 1984.

GEOTEXTILE STRIPS FOR PAVEMENT REPAIRS
LOGAN INTERNATIONAL AIRPORT, BOSTON, USA

A.J. Craven and M. Marienfeld
Fay, Spofford and Thorndike
Lexington, Massachusetts, USA

Massachusetts Port Authority's (MPA) Logan International Airport, Boston, constructed on land recovered from the bay, is subjected to unusual pavement stress. The paved surface is asphalt cement to take advantage of asphalt's relative flexibility compared to PCC pavement.

Nevertheless, paving repairs need to be routinely performed to keep runways, taxiways, and aprons in good condition. Work is generally carried out at night to avoid any interruptions in the airport flight schedule.

As part of this routine maintenance, an $8,000,000 paving project (contract MPA #1374) was awarded to John McCourt Company of Boston. The project involved runway, taxiway, and apron repair.

DESCRIPTION

Logan International Airport pavements have been plagued by cracks which occur due to settlement in the weak foundation soils underlying the airport. These cracks have been effectively treated in recent rehabilitation projects by crack filling and subsequent application of a paving geotextile interlayer system.

A paving geotextile interlayer strip product called Petrotac®, manufactured by Phillips Fibers Corporation, is used to cover each crack in the old pavement prior to overlay placement. The Petrotac® product consists of a nonwoven polypropylene geotextile coated on one side with a rubberized asphalt modified with additives to make it self-adhering to the old pavement surface and coated on the other side with a paving grade asphalt tack coat. This product is applied to provide waterproofing and stress absorption. The strips were used as opposed to full coverage of the pavement because the cracking in the old pavement was distinct, limited cracking due to settlement over the weak foundation soils. The coverage of a limited number of cracks with a precoated paving geotextile as Petrotac® can be more economical than full-coverage.

CONSTRUCTION

Construction took place in May 1987. It was all done at night with 120 to 180 m of the pavement being rehabilitated each night. The work consisted of: 1) milling, 2) identifying and cleaning cracks, 3) sealing the cracks, 4) covering the cracks with Petrotac®, 5) applying the tack coat, 6) laying down the surface course, 7) cutting the safety grooves, and 9) painting.

The cold-planing was the first step. This was done by milling the old pavement surface to various depths in an effort to level the surface at the proper grade. The milled surface was cleaned, and the cracks were cleaned.

Next, all cracks greater than 22 mm wide were filled with a fiberized crack-filling asphalt. The crack filler waterproofs and helps resist reflective cracking by providing a better surface on which to apply the Petrotac®.

On this project, 305 mm wide rolls of Petrotac® were unrolled over the cracks by hand by a two-man crew. The 33 m long rolls were easily applied by removing the release paper as the self-adhering product was applied to the milled surface. A 150 mm overlap is recommended along each side of the covered crack. For many projects an 460 mm wide product is needed to compensate for wide cracks or crack wandering.

For this application over a milled surface it was necessary to use a pneumatic roller over the Petrotac® to achieve a more complete bond to the rough surface. The strips were also extended approximately 150 mm past the end of each crack.

Finally, an asphalt emulsion tack coat of approximately 0.37 l/m² was applied to the whole area, over the strips and over the milled surface prior to overlay placement. Depending on area and final grade, 50 to 88 mm of bituminous concrete was placed. Following overlay placement, safety grooves were cut across the runway, and the necessary paint was applied.

The design engineers for the project were Fay, Spofford and Thorndike, Design Engineers of Lexington, Mass. The general contractor was Trimount Bituminous. The owner is the Massachusetts Port Authority.

PAVING GEOTEXTILE

The Petrotac® strip product was developed as a simple way to apply a paving geotextile interlayer without getting involved with full-width geotextile application and special asphalt tack coat application. The functions of the full width and the strip applications are the same. The primary function is waterproofing. On the Petrotac® strip, the rubberized asphalt coating is waterproof and when adhered to the pavement the crack in the pavement is capped and sealed. By keeping water from running down the crack, the subgrade is protected from getting wet, softening and pumping. The paving geotextile interlayer also provides a stress-absorbing layer, breaking the hard contact from the old pavement to the overlay and allowing for some slight movement and dissipation of stress. This stress dissipation helps retard reflective crack development.

Photo 1. Cold planing the runway.

Photo 2. Petrotac being place by hand to seal the cracks.

CONCLUSION

The performance of Boston's Logan International Airport's pavements which have received this rehabilitation treatment has been excellent. Previous attempts of overlaying without the paving geotextile interlayer strip treatment resulted in a rapid development of reflective cracks in the new overlay. As of the date of this writing overlays which incorporated the paving geotextile strip treatment have been in place and performing excellently for over five years.

REFERENCES

Non supplied.

Photo 3. 'Band-aided' runway section.

Photo 4. Bituminous concrete being placed on tack coat.

GEOTEXTILE BEHAVIOUR CONCERN IN ASPHALT RECYCLING
SYRACUSE, NEW YORK, USA

J.W. Dykes
Philips Fibers Corporation
Greenville, South Carolina, USA

R. Christman and L.T. Gray
Pavement Resources Managers Inc.
Newington, Connecticut, USA

Increased concern in the USA to conserve energy consumption and natural resources while still providing quality transportation systems has broadened the use of nonwoven geotextile applications in transportation paving maintenance and construction activities. Over the past 20 years nonwoven geotextiles have been used extensively and successfully in repair and maintenance of asphalt concrete overlays to provide waterproofing and to arrest distress cracking in aging pavements.

Recycling of pavement materials likewise has been accepted as a maintenance rehabilitation alternative which saves project costs, energy, and virgin materials while providing equal or greater structural properties. In the USA, many states, thanks to the effort of the Federal Highway Administration, are actively engaged in recycling using either in-place, surface, central plant, or combination thereof.

CONCERN AND INVESTIGATION PROGRAM

There has been some concern about road maintenance programs involving recycling pavements containing paving geotextiles. Can such pavements be recycled? Will the paving geotextile reduce to a workable size during pavement recycling? Will bituminous recycling plant stack opacities turn from snow white plumes to dark opaque clouds? Can bituminous concrete mixtures produced from recycled pavements with geotextiles meet specifications?

In an effort to provide answers to these important questions, the manufacturer of Petromat®, Phillips Fibers Corporation, contracted with Pavement Resource Managers, Inc. (PRM) of Newington, Connecticut, to investigate the recycling of bituminous concrete pavements containing Petromat®. The objectives and work plan of the research program were as follows:

1 Investigate, using field trials, the relationship between the protective paving geotextile Petromat® and pavement recycling;
2. Investigate, using laboratory testing and mixtures, any structural relationships between the paving geotextile Petromat® and pavement recycling;
3. Develop recycled bituminous concrete mixture designs using the paving geotextile Petromat® incorporated within a bituminous mixture.

FIELD TRIAL

Site Description

A 240 m long, 7.2 m wide pavement test site was located in Syracuse, New York, on an access road leading to the city's department of public works yard. The pavement was subdivided into three sections, the control section, the test section (106 m long) and the experimental section (33 m long). The paving geotextile Petromat® was installed in both the test section and the experimental section. The experimental section was used to evaluate:

a. Mandrel upcut, downcut, and rotation velocities of the forward speeds;
b. Cold milling machines production capabilities at various forward speeds;
c. Material gradation characteristics throughout each manoeuvre; and,
d. The visual Petromat® characteristics obtained when varying production depths and forward speeds.

This work was performed with a Gallon RP-60 and a CMI PR 275 RT.

Paving Geotextile and Overlay placement

The paving geotextile Petromat® was installed in the test and in the experimental section on an RS2 emulsion sprayed with a residual asphalt content of 0.75 l/m². The entire pavement was then overlaid with a 44 mm thick N.Y. DOT Type 6 surface course.

Recycling

The first section milled was the experimental section. This section was subdivided into 15 separate operation and sampling sites to study the effect of milling gradation versus cold milling equipment, production speeds, depth of cut, mandrel tooth contamination or wear, and type of mandrel tooth.

Based on the results of the investigation performed in the experimental section, the milling was done at a rate of 3 to 4.5 m/min with chisel teeth on the mandrel and milling at a uniform depth of 63 mm on the control and test sections. The material milled in the experimental section was wasted and not used in any further work. The materials milled from the test and control sections were stockpiled separately for feeding into the dryer drum plant.

Use of Recycled Material for Paving

At this phase of the program, PRM developed a prototype mixture design using the actual pavement millings removed on the project site. Fifty percent of the "not-so-good" pavement millings were combined with 20% stone screenings, 10% coarse aggregate # 1, 3% AC-20 and no reclaiming agent. The combination results in a mix

ISSMFE., Committee TC9 - Geosynthetics Case Histories.

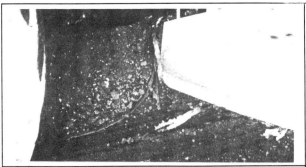

Photo 1. Under cutting previously installed Petromat®.

Photo 2. Side view of adjoining undercut section.

Photo 3. Milled asphalt including milled Petromat®.

Photo 4. Repaving operation.

that is 50% recycled material, and 50% new material (50/50 recycled mix). It was the decision of P.R.M. not to add reclaiming agent at this point since the majority of asphalt in the milling stockpile was still quite new and "lively". Past experience by P.R.M. has shown that the virgin 3% asphalt cement should combine well with the "aged" asphalt cement to form a good binder.

The paving operation began at station 0 + 00 (stations in feet = 305mm) at a planned depth of 63 mm in one lift using the control recycled material. This mat was placed uniformly with a Blaw-Knox paver and 4.5 litre 9 t dual steel drum roller terminating at station 4 + 00. The recycled material containing the paving geotextile Petromat® was then placed from station 4 + 00 to station 7 + 00 using the same placement equipment. The remainder of the project (station 7 + 00 to 8 + 00) was overlaid with various materials not used for further study. Mixture temperatures did not vary appreciably from plant output to laydown due to the close proximity of the project to the plant; perhaps only 300 m at the farthest distance. Both paving materials could be placed with comparable ease with no noticeable difference by PRM or the equipment operators.

Short Term Evaluation

Two months later, fifteen pavement cores were removed from the control section and the test section, respectively. Each core was analyzed for:
a.   gradation of the mineral aggregates;
b.   bitumen content;
c.   compaction characteristics;
d.   field air voids;
e.   Abson test properties of the asphalt film;
f.   bond.

Also, concurrent with the core removal operation, a condition survey was undertaken. The test properties of the cores were compared between control and test sections. The study of the data indicates that the asphalt cement, in either case, has undergone normal aging after

exposure to the plant mixing and heating, hauling, laydown, and compaction. Abson test properties of penetration at 25°C, ductility at 25°C, and absolute viscosity at 62°C are consistent and normal for either case.

No differences could be noted at this time between the standard test properties of the recycled mixtures containing Petromat® and those that contain no geotextile.

Laboratory Program

A laboratory program was designed to evaluate several different conditions. Information from this program supported the field data earlier described.

CONCLUSIONS

The work described provided the following conclusions:

•   Milling bituminous concrete pavements containing the paving geotextile Petromat® does not pose any problem to the milling operations. The smallest geotextile pieces, 19 mm in width and 48 mm in length, were obtained using the RP60 with chisel tooth design at 3 m/min. The other method used produce pieces varying in width from 25 mm to 75 mm and in length from 50 mm to 480 mm.
•   The presence of the paving geotextile Petromat® within the recycled paving mixtures at a 50/50 blend using non melted geotextile pieces of varying size and weight proportions under controlled laboratory conditions has no detrimental effect on the mixture properties.
•   The presence of the paving geotextile throughout the entire study had no effect on the asphalt film properties of the recycled paving mixtures, including those mixtures formulated with varying types of rejuvenating fluid.

REFERENCES

Non supplied.

GEOGRID FOR ASPHALT REINFORCEMENT
TRONDHEIM, NORWAY

J. Paul
Netlon Limited
Blackburn, United Kingdom

Research work carried out at the University of Nottingham in England from 1980 to 1984 identified substantial increases in life for asphalt pavements reinforced with a high tensile strength polymer geogrid.

Large scale use of the geogrids began in 1984, although the earliest installations were carried out in 1982.

DESCRIPTION OF THE PROJECT

The Project

In August 1984 a geogrid reinforced asphalt was used in a structural overlay to a heavily-trafficked industrial estate road on the outskirts of Trondheim in Norway. The involved road length was 550 m and the width was 6.5 m.

Road Condition Before Overlaying

Over part of the road length there were ruts up to 75 mm deep with evidence of plastic deformation both laterally and longitudinally. No longitudinal frost cracks were present, but two trench cuts crossed the full width of the road. Extensive crazing was present in the rutted areas.

Deflection testing was carried out using a Falling Weight Deflectometer which gave maximum deflection readings varying from 0.3 mm to 0.7 mm. Analysis of the data, taking account of traffic volume, showed a maximum permissible axle loading of 14 t. Allowing for the reduction in bearing capacity experienced in the spring thaw period the estimated permissible axle weight in springtime was 8.4 t.

Function of the Overlay

The asphalt overlay was required to perform a number of functions:

1. Permissible springtime axle loadings were to be increased to 10 t (equivalent to around 16.5 t in summer).

2. Rutting of the new pavement surface was to be controlled.

3. Reflection cracking from the trench cuts and crazed areas was to be controlled.

TECHNICAL CONSIDERATIONS

Testing Program

All of the potential failure mechanisms had been investigated in the testing program at the University of Nottingham.

In fatigue tests, geogrid reinforced asphalt showed a tenfold increase in life when compared with unreinforced asphalt.

A threefold increase in life was observed with respect to failure by rutting.

The reflection cracking test program showed no development of cracks in the reinforced specimens [Brown et al., 1985].

The polymer grid was therefore used in a 50 mm thick overlay of asphaltic concrete to provide extended fatigue life, control rutting and control reflection cracking.

An alternative solution would have been to reconstruct part of the road providing a stronger base and thicker asphalt layers.

A significantly thicker overlay could have been designed, but was rejected on grounds of cost, compatibility with adjacent levels and lack of control of reflection cracking.

Geogrid Reinforcement

Geogrid reinforced asphalt is a standard mix incorporating a layer of polymer geogrid Tensar AR1. This geogrid is produced by stretching a punched sheet of polypropylene in two orthogonal directions. The stretching is carried out at carefully controlled temperature and strain rate to produce an oriented polymer geogrid with rectangular apertures approximately 50 mm x 70 mm having high tensile strength and tensile modulus.

The oriented polypropylene is sufficiently temperature stable to permit its use within layers of hot rolled asphalt or asphaltic concrete.

Installation

Half of the road width was closed over a length of 400 m. Prior to installing the geogrid the deeper ruts (> 25 mm) were filled with hot asphalt. The 50 m long rolls of geogrid were trimmed to 3.3 m wide and laid out along the edge of the road (Photo 1). The end of the first roll was fixed to the existing road surface using masonry nails and washers; two rolls were joined together using hog rings on overlapping longitudinal filaments, then the free end of the second roll was attached to a tensioning beam. The beam was used to stretch the geogrid to ensure that all wrinkles

| Photo 1. Geogrid installation. | Photo 2. Bitumen emulsion and stone chipping placing. |

and undulations are removed and the geogrid lies flat on the existing surface, not to pre-tension the system. Whilst maintaining the tension, the geogrid is fixed in position (using masonry nails and washers as before) and the beam is then removed.

Moving on to a long straight, four rolls were connected together and to the end of the second roll then the full 200 m section was tensioned and fixed. The remaining two rolls were then installed in a similar manner.

Of the 550 m length of overlay, polymer geogrid was included over the 400 m in worst condition. The remaining 150 m received an unreinforced overlay of equal thickness.

When the geogrid was fixed over the full length of one lane, the geogrid was dressed with a chip seal layer using K1-60 bitumen emulsion at 1 l/m² and 10 mm stone chipping at 7 kg/m² (Photo 2).

Immediately after rolling the lane was re-opened to traffic with a speed restriction in operation.

Exactly the same procedure was then adopted on the second half of the road.

The following morning the chip sealed surface was brushed to remove any loose chipping and paving took place using standard equipment and techniques. The asphaltic concrete overlay was 40 mm thick over the chip sealed area giving a total overlay thickness of 50 mm.

One lane width of 1320 m² was laid by three men in 2 hours - i.e. 220 m²/man hour.

A typical installation cost was:

Geogrid (including contractors profit)	= £1.50/m²
Labour in fixing	= £0.10/m²
Chip seal	= £0.90/m²
	£2.50/m²

In Norway the cost of laying 50 mm asphalt was £7.70/m², therefore the additional cost of geogrid reinforcement is equivalent to around 16 mm additional thickness of overlay.

At least 40 mm additional overlay thickness would have been required to meet the design requirements for the project.

CONCLUSIONS

A substantial saving was achieved by using a reinforced asphalt overlay and after four years of heavy traffic the road is still in excellent condition and is performing as expected.

The short section of unreinforced overlay is already showing signs of rutting even though it is on an area where few problems were present in the existing pavement.

REFERENCE

Brown, S.F., Brunton, J.M. and Hughes, D.A.B., "Polymer Grid Reinforcement of Asphalt", Association of Asphalt Paving Technologists, San Antonio, Texas, 1985.

GEOSYNTHETICS FOR CONCRETE PAVED MOTORWAY
A26 MOTORWAY, NORTHERN FRANCE, FRANCE

G. Bordonado and J.Y. Buffard
Scetauroute
Lille, France

J.P. Gourc
Irigm-UJF
Grenoble, France

Construction work has been underway since 1983 on the A26 motorway in Northern France, using an original design of carriageway, based on a thick concrete slab placed on a drainage geotextile layer.

DESCRIPTION

Thick Concrete Slab

Several advantages are to be obtained by designing the carriageway as a single thick concrete slab. Firstly, construction is simplified, requiring a single machine and a single pass. It is also relatively inexpensive, as a result of the use of limestone aggregates that are in abundant supply locally, and in the decreased use of bituminous products.

The main technical difficulty to be overcome in a concrete carriageway structure relates to circulation of water between the concrete slab and the foundation soil, even though, in the case of a thick slab, the mechanical consequences of such water circulation are minimized by the inertia of the carriageway.

If the water trapped at the interface between the concrete slab and the foundation soil cannot be drained off, it will be under pressure when vehicles pass ("beating" the concrete slab). This causes erosion of the foundation soil, the formation of cavities and deposits of fine soils, all factors of instability.

Drainage Under Concrete Slab

In Northern France, the foundation soil forming the subgrade is generally a fine, loamy soil, which is erodible. The drainage system initially selected for the A26 motorway involved placing, between the foundation soil and the concrete slab, a 100 mm thick drainage layer, using untreated limestone aggregates graded 5/40 mm or 6/20 mm.

Although satisfactory results were previously obtained for this solution, the solution presented certain drawbacks: movements of construction equipment on this material are delicate, the solution is relatively costly, and its long-term performance is short of perfect. It was thus decided, in 1983, to replaced this drainage layer by a thick geotextile. The chosen product was designed to fulfil the following functions:

- low compressibility under traffic loads,
- efficient long-term drainage,
- freedom of movement of the concrete slab, without friction, under the effect of thermal gradients.

GEOTEXTILE

Description

The project engineers selected a specific geotextile called Drainatex, a nonwoven, needlepunched, polypropylene product supplied in 4 m wide rolls, with a draining part and a filter part, bonded together in the manufacturing process. The draining part has a mass per unit area of 600 g/m^2, and is made up of short fibres, about 100 mm long, 60% of the fibres with 140 μm diameter and 40% with 30 μm diameter.

Mechanical Behaviour

The geotextile's tensile strength is $\sigma_f = 3$ kN/m and the strain at failure is $\epsilon_f = 110\%$ in the roll direction. It should be noted that the low tensile strength is not a handicap in the present case. On the other hand, the large strain facilitates adaptation of the geotextile to the deformation of the supporting soil.

Stress measurements made under the slabs on the completed motorway have shown that the passage of a heavy goods vehicle (130 kN axle loading) is equivalent to a compression of 40 kPa (including the weight of the slab). A sample of the geotextile was subjected to a traffic load simulation in the laboratory by applying alternately the traffic load (40 kPa) and the static load without traffic (10 kPa = weight of the slab). The resulting measurements of thickness of the geotextile are given in Table 1.

Hydraulic Behaviour

A safe assumption was adopted for design purposes. It is assumed that water situated upstream of the longitudinal carriageway joint infiltrates entirely under the concrete slab. The daily rainfall of annual frequency is considered, i.e., 25 mm of rain in 24 hours. Under these conditions, the draining layer must have a minimum transmissivity of $\theta = 20 \times 10^{-6}$ m^2/s (discharge to be drained off: 150 l/linear m/h).

Table 1. Compression and transmissivity test on geotextile vs. number of loading cycles.

Number of cycles	Thickness T_g (mm)	ΔT_g (mm) (between 10 and 40 kPa)	Transmissivity θ (m^2/s)
0	6.5	25/100	85×10^{-6}
10,000	3.73	2/100	-
40,000	3.71	1/100	26×10^{-6}
160,000	3.71	1/100	26×10^{-6}

Photo 1.   Construction of the carriageway.

Photo 2.   Thick concrete slab.

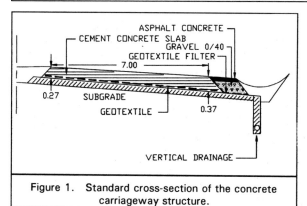

Figure 1.   Standard cross-section of the concrete carriageway structure.

Table 2.   Application of geotextiles in different sections of A26 motorway.

Year	Section of A26	Length of Carriageway
1983	Nordausques-St Omer	400 m
1984	Cambrai-St Quentin	7,500 m
1985	Cambrai-St Quentin	20,700 m
1986	St Quentin - Laon	25,000 m
1987	St Quentin - Laon	9,100 m
1987	Laon-Reims	10,750 m
1988	Laon-Reims	36,925 m

The transmissivity measurements given in the table show that even after 160,000 cycles, the measured transmissivity remains acceptable ($\theta = 26 \times 10^{-6}$ m²/s).

However, it was important to check that there would be no risk of clogging. Tests were thus performed under real site conditions, and showed that there would be no risk of clogging by laitance from the concrete.

On the other hand, there is a risk of clogging due to the fine particles in the foundation soil. The geotextile draining layer has a filtration opening size $O_f = 80$ μm on the foundation soil side. This filter is needlepunched in the factory on to the draining geotextile.

PERFORMANCE

A first experimental strip 400 m long was built in 1983 in the St. Omer-Nordausques section of the motorway, with the thick concrete slab + geotextile structure. After one year in service, it was interesting to observe that the slab "beating" values were lower with this technique than for sections built with a draining interface of granular materials (less than 5/100 mm with geotextile, and more than 15/100 mm with granular materials). These encouraging results led to widespread adoption of this technique (110 km of carriageway completed with geotextiles by 1988), as shown in Table 2.

It is also to be noted that the winter of 1984/85 was particularly severe in Northern France (depth of frost: 0.70 m). Despite these conditions, no rise in carriageway level was observed in the sections completed with geotextiles. Core sampling made down to the draining layer confirmed the satisfactory overall behaviour.

CONCLUSION

In conclusion, this technique of drainage under a concrete slab, both easy to implement and economical, appears to be most promising. Nonetheless, it is advisable to wait until the long-term behaviour has been observed before making any final conclusions.

REFERENCES

Bordonado, G., and Buffard, J.Y., "Textile Drainant en structure de chaussée" (Draining Textiles in Carriageway Structures).

Poilane, J.P., Buffard, J.Y., and Deleurance, J.C., "Drainage Latéral et couche drainante sous chaussées" (Lateral Drainage and Draining Layer Under a Carriageway).

GEOTEXTILE FILTER UNDER A CONCRETE PAVED ROAD
NEAR THE SAMOTLOR LAKE, USSR

V.G. Leitland and A.G. Polunovsky
All-Union Highway Research Institute (Soyuzdornii)
Moscow, USSR

In 1976 a geotextile was for the first time used in an oil field road near the Samotlor Lake, in West Siberia. A geotextile filter was placed under the joints of a pavement composed of precast reinforced concrete slabs laid over a sand base. The function of the geotextile filter was to prevent sand pumping-out from the slab joints at the passage of heavy transport vehicles during periods when the base was saturated.

DESCRIPTION

The 6 m wide pavement was built of precast prestressed reinforced concrete slabs, 6 m x 2m x 140 mm in size. The road was placed over an embankment up to 2 m high made of fine uniform sand ($d_{60}/d_{10} < 2$). The road was designed for a traffic flow with a very high percentage of heavy vehicles of 10 to 13 t axle loads.

Due to a high level of precipitation along the road saturation of the base occurs during summer and spring-autumn periods.

TECHNICAL CONSIDERATIONS

Base Course Under Precast Concrete Pavement

At the passage of heavy vehicles on a thin and flexible reinforced concrete pavement laid over an unstabilized base, slab deflections, especially near the pavement joints, are very large (several mm). During the periods when the base is saturated, pavement deflections cause excessive pore pressures and pumping out of a water-sand mixture in the same manner as it is observed, though in a lesser degree, in the monolithic pavements.

Because of the short and humid summer in that region, treating the base with cement was impossible. Instead, it was designed to build the base using imported sand-gravels with a layer thickness of 160 mm and to place it over a 50 mm course of dry cement-sand mix. As an alternative, a proposal was made to place the slabs on a sand base with geotextile interlayer.

Some sections with a total length of 2 km were built with placement of the geotextile interlayers either across the whole width of the pavement, shoulders included, or in the form of strips. The strips were located under the pavement joints and edges; the width of the strips was equal to 30% of the slab width (see Figures 1 and 2); and extra lengths of strips extended on the shoulders and the embankment slopes.

Geotextile Selection

The geotextile interlayer was designed for retention of sand particles at the joints when water is squeezed out, for draining the sand base, and for lowering the pore water pressure in the sand at load application. Thus, the geotextile interlayer served both functions of filtration and transmission. These two functions could be accomplished simultaneously using a geotextile with justifiable filtration properties and considerable longitudinal permeability. The selected geotextile was a needlepunched nonwoven short fibre (length of fibres about 90 mm), with a mass per unit area of 550 g/m² and a nominal thickness of 5 mm: the commercial name of the product was Dornit. The geotextile opening size was about 100 μm and this ensured the reliability of the use of the selected geotextile as a filter even under pressures of the order of 100 to 200 kPa.

The efficiency of the geotextile filter is explained by the peculiarities of its structure resulting from the fact that the material is made of synthetic fibres differing both in thickness and the kind of polymer. Before the beginning of the service, the selected geotextile had a water permeability of 500 μm/s, a tensile strength of 7 kN/m, and a strain at failure of approximately 100%.

Work Execution

First, the sand fill surface was graded to ensure two-sloping profiles with a 2% slope. Then, after marking the joint positions, the geotextile strips were laid. In the subsequent practice a more reliable continuous geotextile interlayer was used. After laying the pavement slabs, shoulders with 4% crossfalls were filled up with sand or sand-gravel.

Performance

Observations of the text sections were carried out over 10 years. The program of observations included visual inspection of pumping-out, instrument evaluation of the evenness of the precast pavement on test and control sections, checking the condition of the joints between the slabs, and evaluation of the condition of the base under the slabs by means of lifting separate slabs.

As observations showed, the geotextile interlayer (for a daily traffic intensity up to 1,500 vehicles with 10 t axle loads) provides the required level of the pavement performance and may be used along with mechanical (gravel addition) and chemical (cement treatment) methods of sand base stabilization. Evenness of the pavement on the sections including geotextile was practically identical to that of the pavement laid on the sand-gravel base.

Photo 1. Installation of the precast slabs over the geotextile strips.

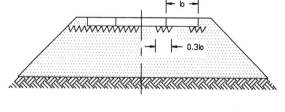

Figure 1. Cross section of the precast concrete paved road with continuous geotextile interlayer (left) and geotextile strips (right).

Observations have shown that the geotextile interlayer successfully performed the functions of drainage and filtration. On the sections with the geotextile the moisture content in the upper part of the sand layer, decreased rapidly due to the permeability of the geotextile. Although pumping-out of water from the pavement joints was not avoided in the initial stages of overwetting, for instance during a rainfall, the filtration function of the geotextile prevented sand particle loss. Only at separate places where the fixation of the geotextile strips was insufficient (less than 300 mm) bulging of the geotextile into the joints was observed with subsequent tearing under the action of vehicle wheels. Tests were carried out on geotextile samples taken from the geotextile interlayer under the middle of the slab and near the joint after 5 and 10 years of service. It was found that during the service life some changes occurred in the geotextile: its thickness decreased from 5.0 mm to 2.0-2.5 mm; some clogging of the material took place resulting in lowering its permeability from 500 to 300 μm/s; its strength decreased by 20 to 25%; and its strain decreased by 15 to 20%. It should be noted that the changes in geotextile characteristics were the same for samples taken after 5 and 10 years of service, that is the change in properties occurred essentially in the first years. This suggests a satisfactory durability of the geotextile interlayer in this application.

CONCLUSIONS

The following main conclusions can be drawn from the above example of the use of geotextiles: The geotextile interlayer successfully performed the function of filter under the joints of the precast pavement and prevents the sand loss through the slab joints.

- Multiple load application does not impair the geotextile performance.

- After 10 years of service the evenness of the pavement was similar to that of the control sections.

- A reduction of the strength and permeability characteristics of the geotextile was observed. However, this reduction was of an acceptable amount and took place during the first years of the structure operation.

REFERENCES

Nguen Cong Phu, "Hydraulique du pompage des chaussées en beton. Premier bilan de l'approche théorique et des résultats de mesure en laboratoire et sur autocontrole", Bulletin de liaison des Laboratoires des ponts et chaussées, Numéro spécial VIII, July 1979, pp. 15-31.

Polunovsky, A. "The use of Geotextiles in Road Construction", Automobile Roads, 1985, No. 4, pp. 11-13.

GEOMEMBRANE USED IN AIRFIELD PAVEMENT
BUOCHS, NEAR LUCERNE, SWITZERLAND

M.R. Hausmann
University of Technology
Sydney, Australia

J. Huder
Swiss Federal Institute of Technology (ETH)
Zurich, Switzerland

In 1962 the Swiss Department of Military Airfields (DMP) constructed an airfield in Buochs, near Lucerne, central Switzerland using a polyethylene membrane as a partial replacement of a traditional sand filter layer in the pavement structure. The Swiss Federal Institute of Technology, through its Institute for Hydraulic Research and Soil Mechanics (now Institute für Grundbau) was consulted for this project and involved in compaction tests of various trial profiles. Also involved in the project were Blum Consulting Engineers.

DESCRIPTION

The base course of the airfield pavement was composed of a layer of aggregate on a layer of sand. A thin plastic membrane (we would say today a geomembrane) was placed at the interface between the sand and the clayey silt subgrade (Profile C in Figure 1). Roll width of the polyethylene membrane was 5 m; an overlap of 500 mm was applied in the construction.

The standard profile envisaged a 500 mm thick gravel aggregate layer underlain by a 50 to 150 mm thick sand layer where a weak subsoil was encountered. Weak zones consisted of clayey silt on which pressures of 50 kPa produced failure in the plate load test.

ECONOMIC CONSIDERATIONS

The economic justification for using a membrane was simple: cost savings could be achieved by reducing the thickness of the sand filter layer placed on the clayey silty subsoil before building up the aggregate layer. In 1962, costs of sand were as given in Table 1.

Table 1. Aggregate costs in 1962	
Item	Cost (SFr)
Sand 150 mm thick layer	1.50 per m^2
Sand off quarry wall	4.50 per m^3
Sand, washed	11.00 per m^3
Natural sand	10.00 per m^3
Transport (1,500 m)	4.50 per m^3

Compared to the sand, the approximate costs of the 0.1 mm thick plastic sheeting was as given in Table 2.

Table 2. Geomembrane costs	
Membrane (material only)	0.55 SFr/m^2
Membrane placed on site	1.00 SFr/m^2

TECHNICAL CONSIDERATIONS

Plate load tests on top of the compacted aggregate layer were interpreted by means of the M_E value, calculated according to:

$$M_E = \frac{\Delta p . D}{\Delta s} \quad (kPa)$$

where Δp = pressure increment
(in this case 150 to 250 = 100 kPa)
Δs = settlement increase for the above pressure increment
D = plate diameter.

For flexible pavements, design criteria adopted for this project required the base course to achieve an M_E value of 80 MPa; for concrete surfaces, the minimum allowable M_E value was 40 MPa.

As Figures 1 and 2 illustrate, these design criteria were not satisfied in the trial section and the aggregate thickness had to be increased for the actual project.

Figure 1 presents the plate bearing test results for four different profiles after four passes of a multiplate vibrator. Figure 2 shows the effect of the number of passes on the M_E value for three of the profiles tested, two of them incorporating a membrane.

PERFORMANCE

The described pavement structure has proved its suitability during the past 30 years, and only had to be strengthened due to the increase weight of modern aircrafts. The good performance of the described construction resulted in the successful application of plastic sheets in similar airfield projects.

REFERENCES

Non supplied.

Photo 1. Geomembrane placing.

Photo 2. Granular material placing.

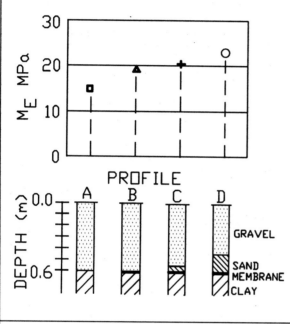

Figure 1. M_E-values achieved with four passes of a multiplate vibratory compactor.

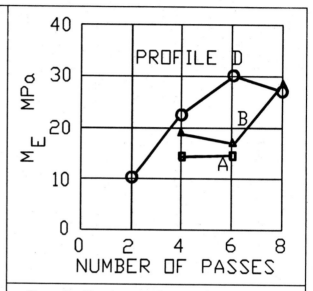

Figure 2. M_E-values as a function of the number of passes for three different profiles.

GEOSYNTHETIC REINFORCEMENT FOR PAVED EMBANKMENT OVER PERMAFROST
BONANZA CREEK, ALASKA, USA

T.C. Kinney
University of Alaska Fairbanks/Shannon and Wilson, Inc.
Fairbanks, Alaska, USA

R.L. McHattie
Alaska Department of Transportation and Public Facilities
Fairbanks, Alaska, USA

The Parks Highway between Fairbanks and Anchorage, Alaska crosses Bonanza Creek at MP 330. The road at this location traverses warm, ice-rich permafrost terrain on a high fill. The permafrost has been rising under the centre and degrading under the toe of the embankment. Differential movements caused by changes in the surface of the permafrost have caused severe distress in the road. Several test sections using various stabilization techniques were used in the original design. In spite of this, the road performance was poor and the decision was made to reinforce the area with several layers of geotextile.

DESCRIPTION

The Parks Highway is the most heavily travelled route between Fairbanks and Anchorage, Alaska. About 40 km south of Fairbanks the road crosses Bonanza Creek on a fill that is between 6.7 m and 7.6 m high. The fill is underlain by 300 mm to 600 mm of muskeg overlying ice-rich silt. A 300 m section of that embankment has undergone severe settlement and cracking since construction in 1972. Maintenance has been required several times a year to keep the road safe.

The fill has changed the foundation thermal regime. Ten years of temperature data indicate that the surface of the permafrost (permanently frozen ground) was lowering at the rate of about 300 mm per year under the embankment toes and raising at about the same rate under the centre of the fill.

The centre of the road has been settling at the rate of about 25 mm per year. The slopes were moving outward at between 100 mm to 200 mm per year and downward at a slightly greater rate.

The ice-rich silt has gravimetric ice contents between 30% and 380% with an average of about 100%. Thawing of this material caused two problems. First, it created a plane of very wet and weak material along the thaw front. The thaw front was sloped, causing the potential for embankment instability and cracking of the road as shown in Figure 1.

The second consideration is one of shoulder settlement. Settlement of the thawing permafrost was highly variable but averaged about 50% of the thawed thickness. The shoulder settlement caused the embankment to split apart at the top, leaving differential settlement and cracks in the road as shown in Figure 1.

Additionally, some lateral spreading may have been caused by creep of the warm ice-rich materials beneath the embankment. There was also evidence of surficial

sloughing caused by seasonal frost action.

As originally constructed, the embankment contained experimental design features intended to limit permafrost thawing in the toe areas. These experimental features concentrated on heat flow and did not contain any form of structural reinforcement of the road embankment. Thawing was reduced, but the road performance was extremely poor.

In 1987 the entire Bonanza Creek fill received extensive repair and reconstruction. Part of this reconstruction consisted of using geosynthetics to form a long-term solution to the continual maintenance problem. The paved portion of the road was excavated to a depth of 4.3 m and reconstructed using seven layers of woven slit film geotextile, each separated by 600 mm of fill as shown in Figure 2 and Photo 2. In essence, the design consisted of two back-to-back buried retaining walls.

TECHNICAL CONSIDERATIONS

When building roads over ice-rich permafrost in the interior of Alaska, engineers have learned to expect some differential movement, and motorists have become quite tolerant of this movement. Neither the engineers nor the motorists have come to accept longitudinal cracking gracefully. Several hundred millimetres of vertical differential movement over several meters is usually acceptable as long as the deformation is not abrupt and the pavement is not cracked excessively.

The design concept was to create a block of material in the centre of the fill that might deform vertically to some extent but would not spread laterally more than a few tens of millimetres.

The side slopes were reconstructed for aesthetics and safety, and to help support the reinforced portion of the fill, thereby reducing the stresses in the geotextile. Experience has shown that the slopes will probably be unstable and move away from the reinforced portion of the fill. The backfill material was cohesionless so that the cracks in the slopes will be of limited depth and the slope materials will collapse into the cracks, providing some lateral support.

Two critical times were considered in the design process. The first is late summer, when the most rapid movement occurs. At this time, the embankment is thawed and can deform with the foundation. As the embankment deforms, there can be stretching of the geotextile and relative movement between the geotextile and the fill material.

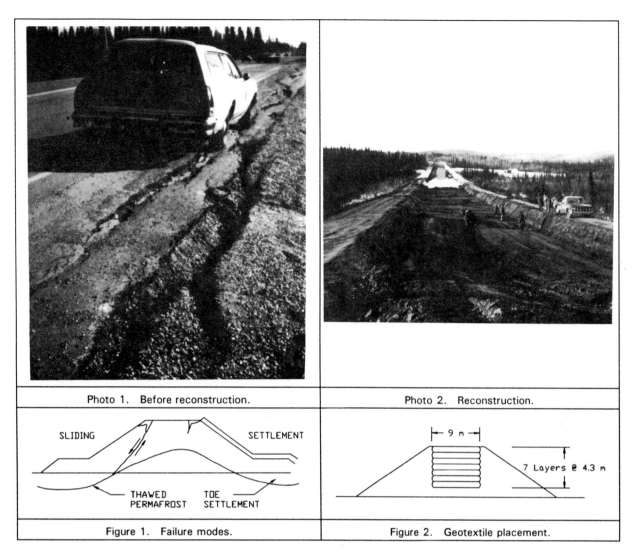

Photo 1. Before reconstruction.	Photo 2. Reconstruction.
Figure 1. Failure modes.	Figure 2. Geotextile placement.

The second critical period is in the late spring. At this time, foundation movements are minimal but the embankment materials with the geotextile inclusions are frozen. There is virtually no opportunity for slippage between the geotextiles and the fill material. If cracks form, either because of low temperatures or movements of the foundation materials, the geotextile must either resist the movement or comply with the movement and strain over a fairly short distance.

INSTRUMENTATION

Instrumentation included: survey points for measuring horizontal and vertical surface displacements, inclinometer and settlement casing for measuring 3-dimensional displacements within the fill, and thermocouple strings for recording soil temperatures. Initial measurements were made in the fall of 1987. To date (March 1988) there has been no measurable deformation of the embankment or cracking of the road surface.

REFERENCES

Esch, D., "Evaluation of Experimental Design Features for Roadway Construction over Permafrost", Proc., 4th. Int. Conference on Permafrost, Vol. 1, Fairbanks, Alaska, USA, 1983, pp. 283-288.

Koerner, R.M., "Designing with Geosynthetics", Prentice-Hall, New Jersey, 1986, 424 p.

GEOSYNTHETIC FIN DRAINS FOR HIGHWAY DRAINAGE
WROTHAM, UNITED KINGDOM

D.M. Farrar
Transport Research Laboratory
Crowthorne, United Kingdom

Geotextiles have been increasingly used in highway drainage in the last decade. In 1979, lengths of geotextile fin drains were laid experimentally in a side road in a Gault Clay cutting adjacent to the M26 Motorway at Wrotham, Kent, UK. In 1985, the performance and condition of these drains after six years in service was examined [Samuel et al., 1987].

DESCRIPTION

Two types of geosynthetics fin drains were used for this project: Filtram and Trammel. Filtram consists of a polyethylene mesh core with filters of polypropylene/polyethylene nonwoven heat-bonded geotextile attached to either side. Trammel also consists of a polypropylene mesh core with filters of woven polypropylene tapes and filaments on either side; the core and filters are assembled on site and pinned in place.

A cross-section of the 100 m length of verge drain incorporating a geotextile fin drain (Trammel type) is shown in Figure 1. The Filtram drain is similar, except that the lower edge is fed through a slot in the 200 mm diameter PVC collector pipe. There is also a 100 mm length of surface water drain incorporating Trammel (Figure 2).

PERFORMANCE EVALUATION

Measurements in 1979-80 and in 1985 showed that the water table was drawn down within some 4 m on either side of the drains, both in the verge and in the road formation, in accordance with expectations. The highest flows from the 100 m lengths were 3.6 and 2.4 litres/min for the Trammel and Filtram respectively in 1979-80, and 6.6 and 5.4 litres/min in 1985.

Exposures showed that the geotextiles in the verge drains had remained in contact with the trench walls, but that the upper edge had settled 100 to 250 mm below its intended position. Clay particles had entered and clogged the upper 100 mm of the Trammel; the manufacturer now recommends that this edge be protected by a filter wrapping. This had also occurred to a limited extent with Filtram. The lower part of the Filtram had settled (Photo 1) and become encrusted with a calcareous deposit, although water could still pass through it. The moisture content of the clay within 20 mm of the geotextile was higher than at a greater distance (43% as against 32-36%). The Trammel surface water drain still functioned, with no evidence of ponding of surface water, although clay particles and road detritus had entered it.

The results of in-situ and laboratory tests of transmissivity (flow in the plane of the drain) are summarized in Table 1.

The most noticeable feature of Table 1 is that transmissivity measured in-situ is much less than that measured in the laboratory. Water flow tests normal to the plane of the Terram gave values of 1 to 26 l/sec/m^2 (100 mm head) for recovered samples, which rose to 50 to 100 l/sec/m^2 after washing. The latter is higher than the published value in the manufacturer's literature.

Electron microscope examination showed no evidence of significant damage or deterioration in either geotextile, although there was a coating of clay particles.

CONCLUSIONS

Specifiers and contractors have gained experience since 1979, but clearly good specification, workmanship and supervision are essential to avoid problems such as the downdrag and exposure of the upper edge at this site.

The geosynthetic fin drains have proved effective both as verge and surface water drains since 1979, although in-situ flow is substantially less than would be expected from laboratory tests on clean samples. The high moisture contents in the clay near the geotextiles could be of concern as a potential slip surface in some applications.

Calcareous deposits were found in the Filtram, and clogging by clay particles in the Trammel. These problems did not seriously interfere with the performance of the drains, and could have been avoided by better installation techniques. Apart from these problems, there was no evidence of long-term deterioration.

TABLE 1. In-situ and laboratory test results		
Type of test	Transmissivity (litres/min/m)	
	Filtram	Trammel
In-situ	1.4, 1.1	1.6, 0.1*
Laboratory (TRRL)	11-18	10-12
Published value	23	43
(* Test on upper edge clogged with clay particles.)		

ISSMFE., Committee TC9 - Geosynthetics Case Histories.

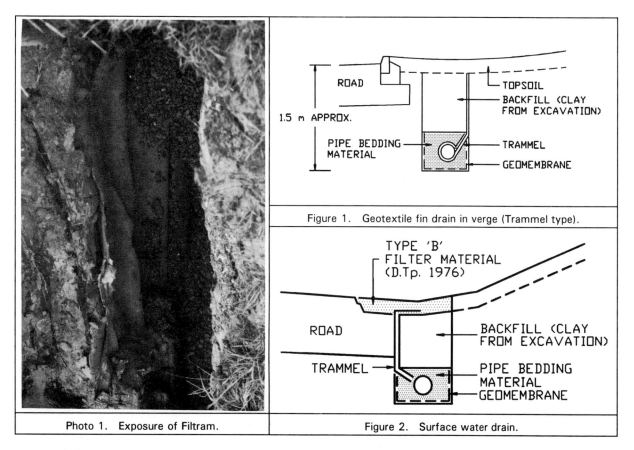

| Photo 1. Exposure of Filtram. | Figure 1. Geotextile fin drain in verge (Trammel type). |
| | Figure 2. Surface water drain. |

REFERENCES

Department of Transport, Specification for road and bridge works, 5th. Edn., Her Majesty's Stationery Office, 1976 (H.M.S.O.).

Samuel, H. R., Farrar, D. M., Jewell, R. A. and Wale, J.A., "Performance of fin drains in a road cutting", Proc. 9th ECSMFE., Dublin, 1987.

ACKNOWLEDGMENTS

The 1979 studies were carried out by the Dept. of Transport (S.E.R.O.), and the later studies by Binnie & Partners under a T.R.R.L. research contract. The work described forms part of the program of the Transport and Road Research Laboratory (now the Transport Research Laboratory) and is published by permission of the Director.

CHAPTER 7

DEEP FOUNDATION IMPROVEMENT

GEOSYNTHETIC VERTICAL DRAINS FOR DEEP FOUNDATION IMPROVEMENT
MOOLMAN EMBANKMENT, SOUTH AFRICA

C.H. Cleaver
Kaytech
Durban, South Africa

The Richards Bay coal rail line which came into existence in 1976 was upgraded in the late seventies as a result of the energy crises and high overseas coal prices. In order to increase the export quota of coal to over 44 million tons per annum the 501 km rail line required the upgrading of its track structure, 234 bridges and viaducts, 1094 culverts and 24 tunnels. One deviation at Moolman resulted in an earthfill embankment nearly 35 m high and was founded on very soft clay.

DESCRIPTION

The embankment which is part of the Richards Bay coal line is of national interest. The rail link is almost totally dedicated to coal export. Coal is South Africa's second largest foreign exchange earner after gold.

The site for the embankment resulted from a 7,7 km deviation which bypassed the existing Moolman station and particularly a 3 km section where the gradient was 66H:1V. The new track gradient is at least 160H:1V over the whole deviation.

The geology of the area consists of Basement Granites of the Swaziland Super Group which have weathered to a dense sand. This is overlain by cohesive and noncohesive alluvium to a depth of 5 to 10 m (see Figure 1).

The critical length of the embankment was 120 m. The fill material allowed a minimum base width of 140 m.

The clay layer, although not of great thickness, had a shear strength of less than 18 kPa.

Due to the proposed rapid rate of construction and the cost of removing poor subgrade, it was decided to install prefabricated vertical drains to reduce pore pressures and accelerate consolidation. In addition, a geotextile was used at the interface between the subgrade and sand drainage blanket (see Photo 1). This geotextile is a polyester needlepunched nonwoven (Bidim U44).

In order to reduce the back pressure as much as possible in the vertical drains, it was decided to slit the geotextile and pull the vertical drains through the geotextile. This way the drains could discharge directly through the geotextile into the sand layer (see Photo 2).

TECHNICAL CONSIDERATIONS

The speed of construction of the embankment was originally intended to be between 20 and 24 months. The construction time, however was dramatically reduced to about 7 months. Without the use of the drains this rapid construction would have led to high pore pressures in the subgrade and potential instability.

To reduce pore pressures, vertical drains were selected, based on the design proposed by McGown and Hughes [1981]. The drains were on a triangular grid with 1 m spacings. Alternatives considered were: removal and replacement of the subgrade, and sand columns.

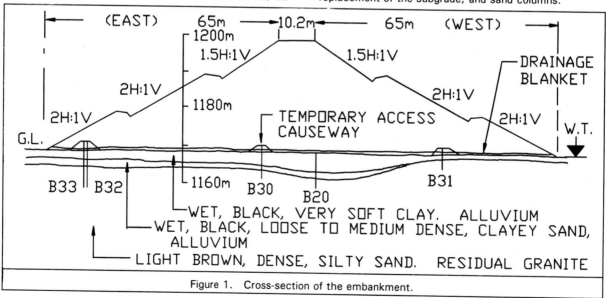

Figure 1. Cross-section of the embankment.

ISSMFE., Committee TC9 - Geosynthetics Case Histories.

| Photo 1. Installed vertical drains prior to covering by geotextile separation layer. | Photo 2. Vertical drains pulled through geotextile prior to covering by sand layer. |

Originally, 100 mm wide Mebradrains were specified and priced by the contractor. In October 1984 the rapidly depreciating local currency necessitated the search for a locally manufactured alternative.

Kaytech, manufacturers of polyester nonwoven geotextiles in Southern Africa, produced a 100 mm wide vertical drain using a polyethylene Netlon CE613 geonet as a core. This material is extruded in a 200 mm circumference circular tube. Mesh openings are about 2.5 mm square and the total thickness of two layers of the doubled net (i.e. flattened tube) is 2.5 mm.

The filter jacket consisted of needlepunched nonwoven geotextile (Bidim U14) wrapped around the core and glued. It passed the filter requirements of the specifications. However, tests had to be conducted to ascertain whether the drains were "capable of transmitting at least 0.1 cm³/s along their lengths, per unit of hydraulic gradient, in conditions of lateral soil pressure up to 600 kPa".

A testing apparatus had to be hastily constructed to supply the correct information on time. A further point requiring investigation during testing was that "kinking" of the vertical drain did not pinch off the flow as was noted with some of the other alternative products.

CONCLUSIONS

Over 100 km of vertical drains were installed at a rate of over 2500 m per shift. The readings on the 14 piezometers installed show low to extremely low pore pressures (see Figure 2). The latter readings may be due to vertical drains linking small sand layers.

As noted by Hanbury (1985):

"the drains are proving much more effective than designed, probably since the overall permeability of the clay is influenced by sand lenses which are now penetrated by the drains."

REFERENCES

Hanbury, R., "Pore Pressures in Embankment 3 at Moolman", SA Transport Services Internal Report, Foundation Section, August 1985.

McGown, A. and Hughes, F.H., "Practical Aspects of the Design and Installation of Deep Vertical Drains", Geotechnique, 31, No. 2, 1981, pp. 3 - 17.

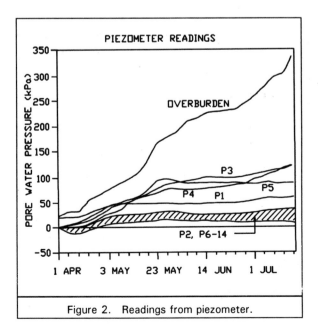

Figure 2. Readings from piezometer.

GEOTEXTILE-GRAVEL SYSTEM FOR DEEP FOUNDATION IMPROVEMENT
ALLHAU BYPASS EMBANKMENT, AUSTRIA

Hazivar W.K.
Geotechnical Consultant
Wien, Austria

The B50 feeder road to the A2 motorway was planned in 1982. It is located in the southern part of the Burgenland province. As part of the Markt Allhau bypass, a stream with its adjacent swampland of approximately 300 m width had to be crossed by an embankment up to 18 m high. Earthworks were completed in May 1988. Geotextiles were an integral part of the site stabilization scheme.

DESCRIPTION

Embankment

The embankment has an overall length of about 400 m. The fill is made up by alternating layers of sandy silt and fine gravel. The slopes are inclined by 2H:1V, with a 4 m bench at mid-height. Near both ends of the embankment, but still on the swampland, two culverts are embedded partly in the fill, partly in the subsoil. Through one of them also runs a regional sewer with a gradient of only 0.4%.

Subsoil Conditions

The top most 8 to 10 m of the subsoil consists of very soft sandy silts and loose sands. The soil tests showed water contents of up to 37%, organic content 8.5%, plasticity index (I_p) 24%, consistency index (I_c) 0.53, and compression modulus 6.5 MPa. The groundwater table is very close to the ground surface. Below this soft zone are stiff clayey silts and medium dense sands.

DESIGN AND CONSTRUCTION

It was decided to leave the subsoil in place as it was. The ground surface layer could not be removed since it was impossible to enter the swampland with heavy equipment. A surface horizontal drainage layer was built to form the base of the embankment.

A layer of geotextile (polypropylene needlepunched nonwoven Polyfelt TS700) was laid out perpendicular to the road axis. This orientation was to avoid sewing the geotextile in the direction across the main tensile stress. A layer of 800 mm of fine gravel was placed on the geotextile. This served as a working surface for the equipment used to install the subsoil improvement measures. After these measures were implemented, and after the two culverts were erected, the gravel layer was completed to 1 m thickness and another layer of the same type of geotextile was laid out in the same manner.

The measures to improve the subsoil consisted of placing prefabricated vertical drains (Mebra drains) in a 2 m by 2 m grid, to depths up to 10 m. In the zones beside and under the culverts, rammed gravel piles (650 mm diameter) were placed instead. The gravel piles are situated in a 1.5 m triangular mesh under and near the culverts. To avoid sharp differential settlements that might lead to additional load on the culverts by uphanging caused by the relatively rigid structures, this grid is gradually enlarged to 5 m away from the culverts. The outmost two lines of gravel piles are overlapped by the plastic drains. Both drains and gravel piles penetrated the geotextile without difficulty and without tearing uncontrolled holes.

Due to the rammed gravel piles, the excavations for the culverts could be made without sheet piling. The flanks stood free almost vertically in one case to 3 m high; in the other case they were inclined 1H:1V (7 m high). Both withstood flooding of the excavation during the winter of 1986-87 without problems.

ALTERNATIVE SOLUTIONS

The boundary conditions imposed by the subsoil and by the task of placing two embedded culverts at the embankment base led to the dismissal of consideration of other conventional methods for erecting embankments on soft ground.

Full excavation and replacement would have required moving some 300,000 m³. It was dismissed because of the high ground-water table and interlayed unstable sands of high permeability.

Displacement methods such as blasting or displacing by wedge-shaped fill were considered unreliable for founding the culverts or, if carried out after culvert construction, could severely damage the new structures.

GEOTEXTILE SELECTION

The geotextile requirements were:
- filter characteristics adequate for a wide range of soil particles due to the heterogenous subsoil;
- tensile strength;
- resistance against tear propagation after puncture;
- high local deformability to follow the shape of crushed rock.

The selected needlepunched nonwoven geotextile was found adequate to meet these demands.

MONITORING AND PERFORMANCE

Filling speed was limited to 600 mm per week. A network of porewater pressure gauges was designed, but

ISSMFE., Committee TC9 - Geosynthetics Case Histories.

Photo 1. Site conditions at the embankment base.	Photo 2. Filling fine gravel on geotextile.

unfortunately not approved by the authority. Six settlement gauges (double and triple type) were placed and are scanned once a week. Maximum settlement was 800 mm in February 1989 and 1.10 m in October 1989. Settlements are expected to finally reach 1.20 to 1.50 m. Strain hardening (decreasing compressibility) due to progressing consolidation could be observed as early as 1989.

Since filling speed could be increased in the final stages to 1.20 m per week additional surveillance was imposed. Four inclinometer borings were made. They were monitored weekly. The embankment base was geodetically surveyed weekly, a sight line on both sides was controlled daily. Lateral displacement suddenly accelerated in mid-February 1989 from 4.5 mm/week to 23 mm/week and the base survey showed the start of upheaval. Therefore, filling work had to be stopped. Since no deceleration of movement was observed after stopping filling works, additional stabilizing measures were carried out immediately. These consisted of a system of gravel drainage cuts at the embankment base: 4 m deep with a comb-like groundplan, laid out with geotextiles and filled with crushed rock. The embankment base was enlarged by 6 m horizontally and 4 m vertically, creating a second berm (Figure 1). Lateral displacement now amounts to a maximum of 150 mm in a zone up to 5 m below soil surface.

CONCLUSIONS

Earthwork was completed in May 1988. A total of 306,000 m³ of fill, 18,000 m² of geotextile, 19,300 m of gravel piles and 74,000 m of prefabricated vertical drains were used. Applying geosynthetics proved to be the only practical method to economically place an embankment of such height on such poor subsoil. As shown, alternatives had to be dismissed because of both technical and economical reasons.

REFERENCES

Chemie Linz AG, "Polyfelt TS - Design and Practice", Technical Design Manual, 1986.

Perfetti, J., "A Comparison Between Woven and Nonwoven Geotextiles", Geotextilien in der Geotechnik, 23. Internationale Chemiefasertagung, Dornbirn, 1984, pp. 138-160.

Wilmers, W., "Anforderungen an Geotextilien aus der Sicht des Straßenbaues", Geotextilien in der Geotechnik, 23. Internationale Chemiefasertagung, Dornbirn, 1984, pp. 652-658.

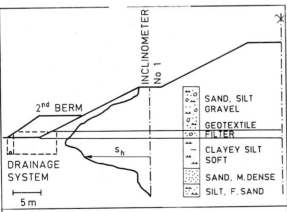

Figure 1. Embankment profile, additional stabilizing measures and characteristic displacements.

GEOGRIDS AND VERTICAL DRAINS FOR DEEP FOUNDATION IMPROVEMENT
COCHRANE BRIDGE EMBANKMENT, ALABAMA, USA

R.M. Mattox
The Tensar Corporation
Mobile, Alabama, USA

Using four different geosynthetic materials made possible the construction of a bridge approach embankment over soft soils without the need for stage construction. The four types of geosynthetics used on this project were: vertical strip drains, uniaxial geogrids, biaxial geogrids, and nonwoven geotextiles.

DESCRIPTION

The alignment of the new Cochrane Bridge required construction of the east approach embankment over the very weak marsh deposits of Blakely Island. Preliminary analyses indicated that a 5.1 m high embankment would cause approximately 1.4 m of settlement during an 11-year period. In addition, the low shear strengths of the marsh dictated the use of flat side slopes with stability berms and stage construction. These measures would avoid deep seated failures of the embankment during construction. The required construction schedule, however, made this conventional approach impossible.

SITE CONDITIONS

Soil borings revealed that three predominate soil types existed at the site. The surface stratum was found to be a silty to sandy clay with moisture content varying from 45 to 105%. The thickness of this stratum ranged from 2.7 m to 5.2 m. Liquid limits varied from a low of 32 to a high of 55 with the plasticity index ranging from 9 to 30. The results of unconfined compression tests showed shear strengths varying from a low of 8 kPa to a high of 11 kPa near the bottom of this stratum.

The second stratum ranged in thickness from 3 m to 7 m and consisted of silty to clayey sand. Standard penetration tests in this material showed blow counts ranging from 2 to 6 with moisture contents varying from 23 to 33%. The major fraction of this material was predominately sand, and the majority of the Atterberg limits showed the material to be non-plastic. Beneath this layer, a stratum of dense sand was found to depths of 18 m.

Undisturbed samples taken from the first stratum of silty clay revealed a large variance in the material. Void ratios generally fell between 1.0 and 2.0; however, some samples revealed void ratios as high as 5.0 with a significant organic content. Results of consolidation tests revealed that the average vertical coefficient of consolidation was 13.8 m^2/s. For purposes of the design, the shear strength profile of the upper stratum was assumed to vary linearly from 0.0 kPa at the surface to 10.4 kPa at the bottom of the stratum.

EMBANKMENT DESIGN

The project schedule did not allow sufficient time for stage construction of the bridge approach embankment. Cost estimates of several schemes showed that the use of vertical strip drains coupled with geogrid reinforcement provided the most economical approach.

Based on the tight construction schedule, only two months could be used to achieve 100% consolidation under the embankment. Analyses were conducted to determine the optimum spacing of vertical strip drains which would achieve an estimated settlement of 1.7 m beneath the maximum embankment plus 6.6 m of surcharge height within the specified time period.

It was determined that an embankment construction rate of 300 mm/day coupled with a 1.2 m triangular spacing for the vertical strip drains would produce a construction and surcharging period which fits the overall schedule for the project. Using this criteria, it was then possible to estimate the residual piezometric pressures which would exist within the marsh deposits at any time during the construction of the embankment. These estimates of the piezometric regime enabled the shear strength of the underlying soft deposits to be calculated at various times during construction. The shear strengths permitted stability analyses to be conducted to ascertain the amount of horizontal reinforcing required to achieve a minimum factor of safety of 1.20 for an embankment with 3H:1V slopes. The stability analysis showed that a primary reinforcing width of only 56% of the embankment base width was required to achieve this factor of safety.

Further analyses also showed that the vertical strip drain spacing could be spread to 1.5 m spacing for embankment heights up to 4.5 m and still achieve the desired degree of consolidation within the specified surcharging period. This was made possible due to the fact that this portion of the embankment would reach final surcharge height while the filling process was continuing on the higher portions of the embankment near the bridge abutment. Therefore, for this portion of the embankment, a longer period of consolidation time was available and a corresponding increase in vertical strip drain spacing used.

For these lower embankment heights fewer layers of horizontal reinforcing were required to achieve the required factor of safety of 1.20. The final design used one layer of Tensar SR2 uniaxial geogrid at the beginning of the embankment. Additional layers were added as the embankment height increased. At the bridge abutment, six layers were required. Details of the design are presented in a paper by Lockett and Mattox [1987].

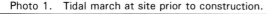

Photo 1. Tidal march at site prior to construction.	Photo 2. Completed embankment at surcharge grade.

EMBANKMENT CONSTRUCTION

Construction began in February, 1986. The first construction step was the installation of the sand blanket on the marsh surface. This was accomplished through the use of a lightweight nonwoven geotextile and the Tensar SS1 biaxial geogrid for reinforcement. The placement of the sand blanket was achieved with no mudwaving. Vertical strip drains were then installed to a depth of 6.10 m using an hydraulicly activated mandrel. The vertical strip drain equipment was mounted on a Cat 235 backhoe. No mobilization difficulties were encountered during the vertical strip drain installation. The subcontractor achieved a production rate of over 3,000 m of Amerdrain installed per eight hour shift.

After the installation of the vertical strip drains, the first layer of primary reinforcing was placed directly on top of the sand blanket. Truck-hauled embankment material was then spread and compacted until the next prescribed elevation for reinforcing was reached. Each layer of geogrid was precut to the design length, and field laydown was accomplished very quickly. The contractor reported that no difficulties were encountered with either the laydown operation or the spreading and compaction operation.

When the fill reached final surcharge elevation, four clusters of piezometers showed a rise in pore pressure which closely tracked the design prediction. Both the piezometer and the settlement plate data showed that 100% consolidation was achieved within the specified surcharge time frame. The surcharge was then removed. Construction of the balance of the project is still underway. Total settlements in the range of 1.8 m occurred in the areas of maximum embankment height. There was no evidence of embankment cracking, lateral spreading or shear displacements of the marsh.

CONCLUSIONS

The success of this project demonstrates the economic advantages that can be achieved through multilayer reinforcing provided by geogrids. For a given cross section, the primary reinforcing is placed only where needed, and the required anchoring length is optimized by placement of the geogrid in select material. Varying reinforcement requirements can be easily achieved through the use of multilayer reinforcing. In addition, the integrity of the reinforcement is not threatened by the installation of vertical strip drains.

The interfacing of vertical strip drains and geogrid reinforcement resulted in a savings of approximately $600,000 to the Alabama Highway Department.

REFERENCE

Lockett, L. and Mattox, R.M., "Difficult Soil Problems on Cochrane Bridge Finessed with Geosynthetics", Proc. Geosynthetics Conf. '87, Vol. 1, New Orleans, Louisiana, 1987, pp. 309-319.

GEOSYNTHETIC VERTICAL DRAINS IN ORGANIC SOILS FOR DEEP FOUNDATION IMPROVEMENT MARCY-UTICA-DEERFIELD EMBANKMENT, USA

L.D. Suits and F. Ariemma
New York State Department of Transportation
Albany, N.Y., USA

The Marcy-Utica-Deerfield (MUD) Interchange Project was undertaken to alleviate capacity and safety problems. The project was located adjacent to and between existing transportation corridors.

The project involved the construction of several embankments of varying heights up to approximately 11 m. The foundation soil for these embankments was a highly organic deposit having the consistency of toothpaste. Stability and settlement of these embankments were the major concerns during and after construction.

The use of vertical strip drains resulted in an estimated savings of $3,000,000 over the cost of other alternatives considered.

DESCRIPTION

Project Location

The project, which runs generally east-west through the area, was located in the East Central section of New York State. The area is densely populated and contains many commercial and industrial buildings along with shopping centres and schools.

The New York State Thruway, the Conrail System, the Mohawk River, and New York State Barge Canal all traverse the project area.

Geological History

As the latest glacier which covered New York State nearly 13,000 years ago retreated from this area, glacial Lake Iroquois was formed, occupying the present Mohawk Valley.

The Mohawk River evolved as the lake disappeared. The repeated action of flooding and receding waters caused deposits of highly organic soils to be formed.

Soil Profile

The typical soil profile in the area where the vertical strip drains were used was as follows: (a) 1.5 m of soft organic silt and peat with an average moisture content of 125%; (b) 2.4 m of very soft organic silt with an average moisture content of 400%; (c) 2.4 m of a mixture of soft silt, clayey silt, and organic silt with an average moisture content of 40%; (d) 9.2 m of sand and sandy silt with an average moisture content of 20%; and (e) a 15.2 m bottom layer of clayey silt with an average moisture content of 28%.

The Embankment

Of the several embankments constructed on this project, a 305 m long section varying from 6.1 m to 10.7 m in height is the subject of a detailed study assessing the performance of vertical strip drains.

Construction of the subject embankment was done in four stages between March 1985 and April 1986. The final required waiting period brought completion into May 1986.

TECHNICAL CONSIDERATIONS

Alternate Solution Considerations

During the course of the design, five different foundation treatments were considered. They included (a) lightweight fill; (b) berms; (c) slope flattening; (d) stage construction with vertical strip drains; and (e) a close sequence excavation and backfill technique. The lightweight backfill was rejected due to the lack of readily available material. The berm and slope flattening were rejected due to right-of-way limitations.

The cost analysis comparison made between the excavation and backfill technique and the stage construction option showed the excavation and backfill option to be about twice as costly.

Based on these considerations, the stage construction with vertical strip drains option was selected. This resulted in approximately a $3,000,000 savings on the project.

Vertical Strip Drain Selection

Based on the laboratory evaluation of vertical strip drains summarized in a report by Suits et al., [1985], criteria for acceptance of vertical strip drains were established. The criteria were: (a) the vertical strip drains must have an average equivalent sand drain diameter of 38 mm, and (b) the net volumetric core flow capacity, when taking into account reductions for crimping, lateral earth pressure, and frictional resistance to flow, must exceed the anticipated volumetric flow rate of water from the soil.

From the list of approved vertical strip drains, the contractor chose to use Alidrain™. The results of the laboratory test program had shown the Alidrain™ to have an average equivalent sand drain diameter of 49 mm and a net core flow capacity of 18 cm³/s.

Photo 1. Preconstruction view.

Photo 2. Vertical strip drains and drainage blanket.

PERFORMANCE

As previously mentioned, the embankment was constructed in four stages, with required waiting periods scheduled between each stage.

The vertical strip drains were installed to a depth of 7.6 m in a triangular pattern with a 1.2 m spacing.

Design analysis had predicted 1.2 m of settlement for the first stage of the construction waiting period of 97 days. Due to equipment breakdown, the actual waiting period turned out to be 142 days. Predicted settlement based on the 142 days was 2.1 m for the required 95% consolidation. Actual measured settlement was 2 m. Stage 2 of the construction had a predicted settlement of 460 mm over a 2 month waiting period. Measured settlement was 240 mm. Stage 3 of the construction had a predicted settlement of 370 mm over a 1.5 month waiting period. Measured settlement was 370 mm. Stage 4 of the construction had a predicted settlement of 150 mm over a 1.5 month waiting period. The measured settlement was 90 mm.

The predicted cumulative settlement for the four stages of construction was 2.95 m. The measured cumulative settlement was 2.6 m, equalling 89% of the predicted.

Based on this, the majority of waiting periods have been terminated. Portions of the MUD project area have been paved and opened to traffic.

It is believed that the reason for the difference in projected versus actual measured settlement was due mainly to soil preconsolidation, which was not taken into account in design. Soil preconsolidation was indicated in the laboratory consolidation test results but was not considered, allowing for a conservative design.

CONCLUSIONS

The primary conclusions made from this project are: (a) vertical strip drains, combined with stage construction, provided for the successful construction of the embankment; (b) the success of the installation was a result of experiences and geotechnical principles combined with extensive subsurface exploration and representative field and laboratory soil testing; (c) the reliability of field instrumentation was reaffirmed, providing more insight as to its effectiveness and limitations; (d) as a result of satisfactory time and settlement analysis, embankment stability was never a problem; and (e) there were additional cost savings which were not anticipated in the original cost analysis. This included a bid price of $1.96 per linear m of installed vertical strip drain compared to $6.56 per linear m estimated, and shortened pile lengths at abutment sites due to embankment preload and waiting periods.

REFERENCES

Ariemma, F., "MUD Case History - Stage Construction/Wick Drains", Soil Mechanics Bureau, New York State Department of Transportation, Albany, NY (tentative publication), 1988.

New York State Department of Transportation, "Soil Description Procedure", STP 2, Soil Mechanics Bureau, Albany, NY, 1975.

Suits, L.D., Gemme, R.L. and Masi, J.M., "The Effectiveness of Prefabricated Drains on the Laboratory Consolidation of Remolded Soils", Proc. ASTM Committee D18 Symposium on Consolidation of Soils: Testing and Evaluation, Ft. Lauderdale, FL, 1985, pp. 663-683.

GEOGRID SUBGRADE REINFORCEMENT AND DEEP FOUNDATION IMPROVEMENT YONO CITY, JAPAN

Y. Tsukada
Public Works Research Institute
Tsukuba, Japan

T. Isoda
Fudo Construction Co., Ltd.
Osaka, Japan

T. Yamanouchi
Kyushu Sangyo University
Fukuoka, Japan

In 1985, a street was built in Yono City, in the northern suburbs of Tokyo. The very soft ground of the construction site was improved using soil-cement columns (the Deep Mixing Method). A polymer geogrid was used for reinforcement in the street subgrade.

DESCRIPTION

Street and Subsoil

The street is about 10 m wide with sidewalks of 2 m width on each side. It accommodates two lanes of traffic. The subsoil is very soft, consisting of a 4 m thick layer of peat (water content: w = 500%) and a 4 m thick layer of clay. Because the area was already developed, methods such as preloading and sand drains were not applicable. Thus the Deep Mixing Method was used to prevent settlement.

The Deep Mixing Method

The Deep Mixing Method forcefully mixes cement into the subsoil to form soil-cement columns measuring 800 mm in diameter with an unconfined compressive strength of 1 MPa. The space between column centres for this project was of exceptional width (2.1 m).

Polymer Geogrid

Since the space between columns was wide, there was concern that the subgrade would settle causing deformations at the street surface. A single layer of polymer geogrid (Tensar SS2) was therefore placed in the subgrade for reinforcement. Total reinforced length was 1.4 km.

TECHNICAL CONSIDERATIONS

Construction

After the columns were formed, a surface layer of soil was excavated and replaced with subgrade material (mean grain size d_{50} = 14 mm; uniformity coefficient C_u = 46). The polymer geogrid was sandwiched between this and another layer of subgrade materials. Then the pavement was laid (Figure 1).

To estimate geogrid effectiveness, the geogrids in several sections were installed in different ways. Various measuring instruments (settlement plate, earth pressure cell, and strain gauge) were also installed for field observation during construction and for a year after completion. In addition, plate loading tests were carried out on top of the 800 mm thick subgrade layer.

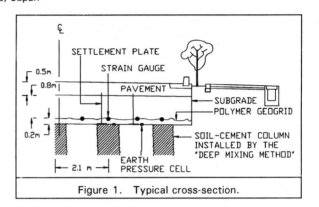

Figure 1. Typical cross-section.

Plate Loading Test

Figure 2 shows the K_s value (coefficient of soil reaction) obtained from the plate loading tests. The rigidity of the reinforced subgrade depends on the type of installation. Measurements obtained from an earth pressure cell show that, when two layers of polymer geogrid were installed, the vertical pressure on the soil between soil-cement columns, at the level of the top of the columns, was reduced to 2/3 of the value obtained with a single layer.

Field Observation

As shown in Figure 3, the differential settlement (ΔS) at the level of the top of the columns between a point at midway between the columns and a point on top of the columns stabilized at 15 mm over time. Almost all

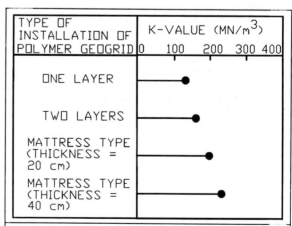

Figure 2. K_s values at mid-way between columns (from plate loading tests).

Photo 1. Condition after excavation (the top of the soil-cement columns are high-lighted in white).

Photo 2. Placement of polymer geogrid.

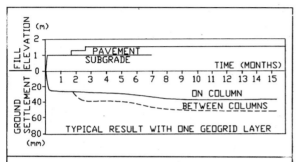

Figure 3. Subgrade settlement (with one layer of polymer geogrid).

differential settlement occurred during construction. As can be seen in Figure 4, strain in the polymer geogrid increased in response to the occurrence of differential settlement.

The pavement surface remains in good condition two years after the street was completed.

CONCLUSIONS

The following conclusions can be drawn from this case history:

- Polymer geogrid was effective in preventing differential settlement between the soil-cement

columns and the soil located between the columns.

- Subgrade rigidity has increased with the placement of the polymer geogrid. As a result, vertical pressure transmitted to the subsoil between the columns was reduced.

- The use of more layers of polymer geogrid or the use of mattress-type geogrid improves the subgrade rigidity compared to the use of one layer of geogrid.

ACKNOWLEDGEMENTS

The authors wish to thank the staff engineers of Yono City and Mr. A. Shimazu of the Public Works Research Institute, Ministry of Construction, who gave them valuable assistance.

REFERENCES

Chida, S., Murao, Y. and Iwase, S., "Development of Dry Jet Column Method and An Experiment for Peat Layer", Civil Engineering Journal, Vol. 24, No. 2, 1982, pp. 9-14 (in Japanese).

Tsukada, Y., Isoda, T., Okuda, T. and Kinoshita, E., "An Application of Deep Mixing Method with Geotextile on Peat Ground", Proc. of 22nd. Japan National Conf. on SMFE, Niigata, June 1987, pp. 1851-1852. (in Japanese).

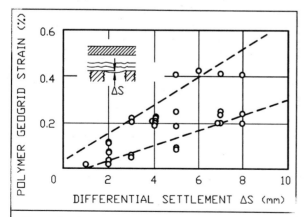

Figure 4. Relationship between subgrade differential settlement and polymer geogrid strain.

GEOTEXTILE AND VERTICAL DRAINS FOR DEEP FOUNDATION IMPROVEMENT
LOK MA CHAO, HONG KONG

P. Risseeuw and W. Voskamp
Akzo Industrial Systems bv.
Arnhem, The Netherlands

With the increase in border traffic and the envisaged further increases over the next few years, a new highway is under construction to connect the Peoples Republic of China with Hong Kong New-Territories.

DESCRIPTION

The Highway Embankment

Called the "Vehicular Border Link", this road meets the Chinese border at Lok Ma Chao. It is being built for the Hong Kong Government, Highways Department. This area consists of fish-ponds and swamps and has extremely weak soil conditions.

Soil Conditions

The subsoil consists of a layer of approximately 10 m of very soft clays. The undrained shear strength varies from 3 kPa in the top layer to 10-15 kPa at a level of minus 10 m. Underneath this weak soil, a stratum with higher bearing capacity was found. On top of this soil the design calls for construction of embankments up to 8.5 m high in some sections. Anticipated problems in these situations include the squeezing outwards of the clay and/or the loss of overall stability of the embankment, as well as a large settlement. The traditional method of overcoming such problems involve removal of the soft soil followed by backfilling with a more suitable fill material, and/or implementing slow preloading techniques.

The costs of the replacement method are very high, whilst the preloading method is very costly in terms of time, i.e. it requires a very long construction period. The construction of very shallow slopes or berms would partly solve the stability problem but still would not resolve the continuous settlements which would necessitate regular maintenance.

Design

The consultant, Binnie & Partners - Hong Kong, had collected positive experience with the application of reinforcing geotextiles to increase the stability of an embankment in Deep Bay, Hong Kong that was designed and constructed under their supervision between 1982 and 1983. The application of vertical drainage systems for soil improvement is also a well known technique in Hong Kong.

Subsequently the consultant decided to combine the use of both reinforcing geotextiles and vertical drains. The designs were based on the application of vertical drains to accelerate the consolidation and at the same time to increase the shear strength of the subsoil by this drainage system. Reinforcing geotextiles were used to assure the stability of the embankment built on top of the vertical drains during the consolidation process. It also allowed for fast construction of the embankment.

PERFORMANCE

Construction and Results

The actual works involved among other items, the construction of 2 kms of highway in the border zone, on soft soil. The maximum width at subsoil level is 280 m, maximum height 8.5 m and slope is 2H:1V. At five locations, test sections are being installed to monitor the forces in the reinforcing geotextile and the changes in the soil condition which occur during the construction of the embankment.

Figure 1 shows the cross section of such a test area. In total, 250 strain gauges were attached to the geotextile using a system developed by Akzo Industrial Systems who manufacture the Stabilenka 400 SP reinforcing geotextile being used here. Altogether, more than 500,000 m² of this

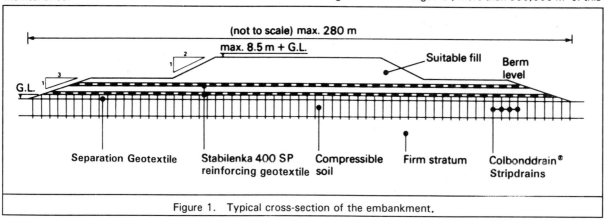

Figure 1. Typical cross-section of the embankment.

Photo 1. Enka's Stabilenka 400 SP reinforcing geotextile being installed in one of the test sections. Altogether more than 500,000 m² of such geotextile were used on the project.

Photo 2. In excess of 2 million metres of Colbonddrain vertical draining systems was installed in a 2 km long highway stretch.

high modulus polyester geotextile were used. The reinforcing geotextile was required to have an ultimate strength of 400 kN/m at a maximum elongation of 12% while creep was limited to 2% in 2 years at 133 kN/m force level. Next to the geotextile, some 2,000,000 m of Colbonddrain CX 1000 vertical drains were installed and approximately 200,000 m² of separation geotextile were used between the subsoil and the first layer of fill before the drains were installed. Work started in January 1986.

The combined system of vertical drainage together with reinforcing geotextile is proving to be a very effective method of coping with such soil conditions and is resulting in very short construction periods.

REFERENCE

Vehicular Border Link - Hong Kong

Client: Hong Kong Government, Highways Department
Consultant: Binnie & Partners, Hong Kong

Main Contractor: Korea Shipbuilding and Engineering Corporation Ltd.

Sub Contractor responsible for drain - and geotextile installation: International Foundations and Realty Associates & Co., Hong Kong

Construction period: 1986, 1987

GEOSYNTHETICS INCLUDING VERTICAL DRAINS FOR DEEP FOUNDATION IMPROVEMENT TIANJIN PORT, CHINA

X.T. Zeng
The Research Institute of the 1st Bureau of Navigation Engineering
The Ministry of Communications, Tianjin, China

The foundation of the container berths in basin No. 4 and of the container berths in the east pier of Tianjin Port were built in the 1970's. This was on reclamation land that was filled by the hydraulic dredge method. A total area 920,000 m² is being improved. Of this area 320,000 m² has been improved and 600,000 m² are in the process of being improved. Seventeen deep water berths will be completed by about 1992. Involved are metal berths, ore-construction material berths, coke berths, cargo berths and several specialized container berths. This is one of major extension projects in Northern China of the Seventh Five-year Plan.

SOIL PROPERTIES

The soil deposit in this area consists of recently deposited layers, 25 m thick, of the Quaternary period. Silty clay and silty sandy clay occur from the ground surface to a depth of about 17 m. The soil properties entail high water contents, high compressions, and low strengths. Their natural water contents are more than their liquid-limits. Natural void ratios are between 1.0 to 1.6. Figure 1 shows the physical and mechanical properties.

DESIGN

Considering the problem of minimising soil settlement and the increase of soil strength, the method of preloading was chosen to improve the soil foundation. Drain channels, made of geosynthetic material and other drainage materials, can be divided into two types. One is the geocomposite strip drain made of an internal polyethylene core board and an outside covering of polyester nonwoven geotextile. The other is a polypropylene knitted geotextile sock shaped drain made of a knitted geotextile filled with sand.

The preloading may be applied by vacuum-pumping as illustrated in Figure 2. A geomembrane is placed on the foundation soil after installation of the drain channel. It is then sealed at its edges into the soil. Then vacuum-pumping is started. Vacuum-preloading loads, of approximately 80 kPa, induced by the difference in atmospheric pressure inside and outside the geomembrane, could be obtained.

GEOSYNTHETICS

The cross section size of the plastic board drain is 100 x 3.5 mm. Installation depth is 15-20 m in accordance with the site specific requirements. Installed spacing is 1.3 m on a square form. The diameter of the packed drain is 70 mm. Installed depth, spacing and arrangement form are the same as for the plastic drain. The total quantity of plastic board drain used in this pier is nearly 6,200,000 linear m. The whole construction area will be improved by the vacuum-preloading method.

RESULTS

The test results are shown in Tables 1, 2, 3, 4 and 5. It may be seen that the consolidation effects on the foundation soil are the same for both kinds of drains. After 65 days by air-pumping 80% of the foundation soil settlement has occurred while the strength of soil mass has also increased. This will allow completion of the task of port construction on this very soft foundation soil quickly and safely.

A cohesive soil (e.g. clay core wall) could have been used as a sealing material in this project. A geomembrane was used as the sealing layer instead of traditional cohesive soil. In this way the construction is simple, the quantity of work is reduced, and a good sealing effect is obtained. Comparing the ordinary sand drains with the plastic board drains method the latter possess more advantages. These advantages are light installation machine, high efficiency, less transportation, simple installation and reliability of the drainage effect. Thus plastic board drain is easily found to be more suitable for this large area of very soft soil foundation. The foundation soil improvement engineering of the east pier of Tianjin Harbour is now under construction.

CONCLUSION

With a vast territory, China is just starting port construction on a large scale. A large quantity of soft foundation soil along the coast will be improved. Therefore, the application of geosynthetic materials will emerge as wonderful materials and result in great economic savings.

Table 1. Settlement at different stages (mm).					
Stage Zone	Installation of bearing stratum (1)	Installation of vertical drainage channel (2)	Vacuum preloading (3)		Total Settlement (2) + (3)
			Centre point	Average value	
Packed drain zone	56	242	1004	872.1	1246
Plastic board zone	56	232	1010	880.7	1246

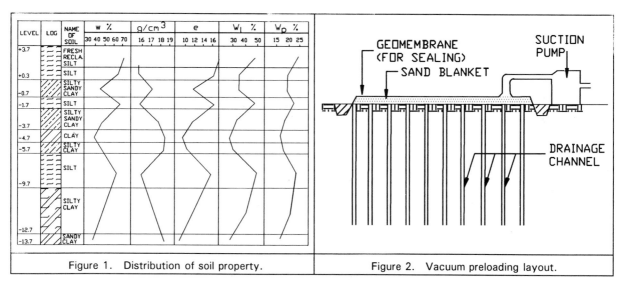

LEVEL	LOG	NAME OF SOIL	w % 30 40 50 60 70	g/cm³ 16 17 18 19	e 10 12 14 16	W₁ % 30 40 50	W_D % 15 20 25

+3.7		FRESH RECLA. SILT					
+0.3		SILT					
-0.7		SILTY SANDY CLAY					
-1.7		SILT					
-3.7		SILTY SANDY CLAY					
-4.7		CLAY					
-5.7		SILTY CLAY					
-9.7		SILT					
-12.7		SILTY CLAY					
-13.7		SANDY CLAY					

Figure 1. Distribution of soil property.

Figure 2. Vacuum preloading layout.

Table 2. Compression of each layer.			
Level (m)	Thickness of Soil Layer (m)	Soil Properties	Settlement Measured (mm)
+ 3.5	2.0	new soil by dredging fill	295
+ 1.5	-	soil with silty sandy	-
- 2.0	3.5	clay	225
- 6.0	4.0	silty sandy clay	165
- 9.0	3.0	silty	83
-13.0	4.0	silty clay	115
Sand stratum	> 10.0	sandy clay	130

Table 3. Soil property before and after consolidation.			
Item / Time	Water Content %	Density kg/m³	Void Ratio
Before consolidation	90	1600	2.2
After consolidation	55	1700	1.47

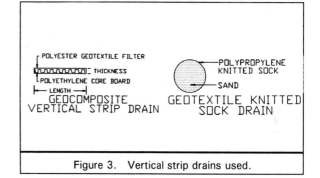

Figure 3. Vertical strip drains used.

Table 4. Consolidation degree at different times after air-pumping (%).										
Time (days)	40		60		65		99		Remarks	
Position	Centre point	Average	Centre point	Average	Centre point	Average	Centre point	Average	Final Settlement (mm)	
Zone									Centre Pt.	Average
Packed drain zone	72.10	70.46	79.86	78.88	80.10	80.45	37.10	88.70	1430	1270
Plastic board zone	71.44	70.37	78.95	78.09	81.08	80.05	88.02	88.37	1411	1270

Table 5. Deformation of vane strength with depth (kPa).												
Zone	Packed Drain Zone				Plastic Board Zone				Area Between Two Zones			
Time / Depth (m)	B.C.	A.C.	I.V.	I.R.	B.C.	A.C.	I.V.	I.R.	B.C.	A.C.	I.V.	I.R.
0-2.0	0.2	18.4	18.2	9100%	0.2	18.3	18.1	9050%	0.2	11.2	11.0	5500%
2.0-10.0	14.2	32.0	17.8	125%	14.2	30.4	16.2	114%	14.2	29.3	15.1	126%
10.0-13.0	17.6	25.5	7.9	44.9%	17.6	26.1	8.5	48.3%	17.6	24.7	7.1	40.3%

GEOSYNTHETIC FLOATING MAT METHOD AND DEEP FOUNDATION IMPROVEMENT OSAKA LAND RECLAMATION, JAPAN

K. Yonezu and I. Kitamori
Saeki Kensetsu Kogyo Co., Ltd.
Osaka, Japan

T. Yamanouchi
Kyushu Sangyo University
Fukuoka, Japan

This paper describes the "Floating Mat Method", used to construct a sand mat on extremely soft grounds, using plastic nets. This method provides trafficability on the sand mat, before building any embankment. The method takes advantage of sand buoyancy either by pumping sand and water together, or by flooding the entire area.

DESCRIPTION

Initial Conditions of the Soft Ground

In the Osaka South-Port land (930 ha total), the South-Wharf land was built on 80 ha of dredged silty clay deposit reclaimed by pumping the material from the sea bottom by means of a dredger boat and pipes. Depth of the reclamation land was 9.5 to 13.0 m and the material was extremely soft: water content of 90% to 180%, liquid limit of 70% to 100%, silt content of 36% to 50%, clay content of 34% to 55%, and cone bearing equal to $q_c = 0 + 10z$ (kPa) with z = depth (m), measured with a single pipe-type cone penetrometer.

Outline of the Work

Construction had to be done rapidly. Therefore, the "Pack-Drain Method" was used to improve the ground (Figure 1). This method consists of constructing vertical drains using long synthetic fabric bags into which sand is packed automatically during the installation. A sand mat was placed at the top. In order to provide trafficability, the sand mat was placed over plastic nets. The sandmat thickness of 1.2 m was placed as uniform as possible. This was achieved by taking advantage of the buoyancy of sand particles. The work was carried out from August 1978 to March 1980.

GEOSYNTHETIC SELECTION

The plastic net had the following properties: an opening size of 6 mm x 6 mm, a tensile strength of 5 kN/m. This kind of plastic net was appropriate because of

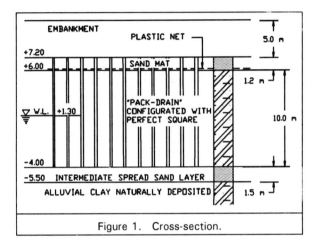

Figure 1.   Cross-section.

its properties such as structure, tensile strength, durability, and large strain of failure, 300% to 500%.

Roll dimensions were 2 m x 30 m or 3 m x 30 m. Adjacent rolls were thermally connected to form 6 m x 30 m panels. The in-situ connection between these panels was performed using polyethylene belts and steel staples with a 300 mm overlap between two adjacent rolls. This technique has proved to prevent stress concentration at the connections during the earth work.

CONSTRUCTION TECHNIQUES

Depending on the silty clay deposit surface conditions, the sand mat construction was carried out with either the first or the second method outlined below.

First Method

First, the plastic nets were laid by hand on the silty clay deposit by the installing crew (Photo 1); then, the sand mat was placed on the nets using pumps in which sand was mixed with sea water to make a suspension. As a

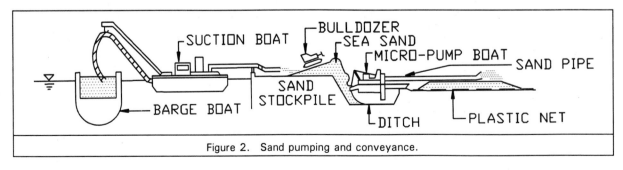

Figure 2.   Sand pumping and conveyance.

Photo 1. Placement of plastic net.

Photo 2. Sand placement.

result, the underlying silty clay deposit was subjected to a low pressure. The layout of the pipe network was such that the sand thickness was very uniform, with a very gentle surface gradient of 10H:1V to 30H:1V.

Second Method

The "Floating Mat Method", in its more rigorous meaning, was also conducted in another manner using pipe lines connected to floaters. Initially the deposit area is inundated (Photo 2). Then, after completion of the sand mat placement, the water table was lowered gradually so as not to impose excessive transient loads to the underlying silty clay deposit where pore water pressure had built up.

Sand Mat Construction

Using sea sand, the sand-mat spreading work was carried out after laying the plastic nets. The work was divided into three stages: the first was 300 mm high, the second, 400 mm, and the third, 500 mm. The total sand mat thickness was therefore 1.2 m. As shown in Figure 2, the sand was conveyed through a stock yard, a pond ("pocket"), micro pumps, and pipes. The pipes are 200 mm diameter, made of polyvinyl chloride (PVC) and work under pressure. The micro pump was capable of working at the rate of 40 m^3 per hour.

PERFORMANCE

After laying the plastic nets, vertical and horizontal displacement meters and surface-type settlement plates

were installed. Results are presented in Figure 3 for vertical displacement (settlement) and Figure 4 for horizontal displacement. It was found that the lateral displacement increased with increasing sand mat height and that the plastic nets were tensioned up to 2 to 5 kN/m.

REFERENCES

Mikasa, M. and Ohnishi, H., "Soil Improvement by Dewatering in Osaka South Port", Proc. of the 9th. Int. Conf. on SMFE, Tokyo, 1977, Case History Volume, 1981, pp. 639-664.

Yamauchi, H. and Kitamori, I., "Improvement of Soft Ground Bearing Capacity Using Synthetic Meshes", Geotextiles and Geomembranes, Vol. 2, No. 1, 1984, pp. 3-22.

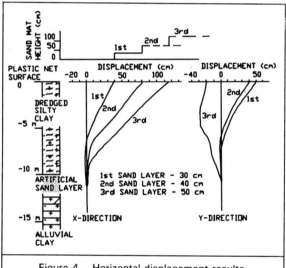

Figure 4. Horizontal displacement results.

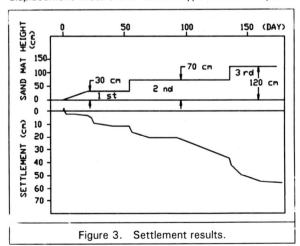

Figure 3. Settlement results.

GEOTEXTILE-AGGREGATE MAT AND VERTICAL DRAINS FOR DEEP FOUNDATION IMPROVEMENT GAS-HOLDER AT HANGZHOU, CHINA

T.R. Wang
Zhejiang University
Hangzhou, China

Z.X. Ye and S.M. Qi
Zhejiang Design Institute of Petrolic and Chemical Industry
Hangzhou, China

A circular gas-holder made of steel was built for the Hangzhou Printing and Dyeing Factory. The gas-holder has a bulk volume of 1,000 m³, a diameter of 15.4 m, and a height of 7.85 m. The thickness of the gas-holder's reinforced concrete base slab is 500 mm and its diameter is 16 m. The surface pressure on the foundation, after the gas-holder was filled with water, is 112.8 kPa. The soil where the gas-holder is located is a muck clay of about 14 m thickness. The physical and mechanical properties of the two layers of the muck clay are given in Table 1.

TECHNICAL CONSIDERATIONS

A gas-holder foundation does not allow large and unequal settlement. The engineering requirements could not have been met if the natural soil had been used as the foundation. After comparing various soil improvements, the scheme of using a mat foundation of aggregate in geotextile bags together with sand drains was selected. The foundation has four strata and each of them consists of closely arranged aggregate in geotextile bags. The thickness of each stratum is about 250 mm (the total is 1 m), and the diameter of the mat is about 23 m. The arrangement of strata of the aggregate in geotextile bags is shown in Figure 1. The geotextile is a knitted fabric of polystyrene made in the Hangzhou Xifang Plastic Factory, and its tensile strength is 16 kN/m. The sand drains as shown in Figure 1 have a diameter of 400 mm, intervals of 2.5 m and a depth of 16 m. The top of the sand drains is connected to a sand mat of 200 mm thickness. Above the sand drain, there is the mat of aggregate in geotextile bags.

In order to investigate the effect of reinforcement and stress state, some pore water pressure cells were located under the ground. The pressure cells were embedded beneath the bottom of the mat of aggregate in geotextile bags. Observation points were arranged around the ring footing as shown in Figure 2. The results measured are given in the next sections.

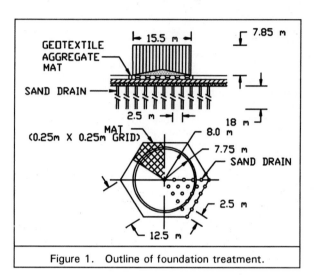

Figure 1. Outline of foundation treatment.

Settlement.

According to the results, the settlement of the foundation, as the load was increased, is shown in Figure 3. The maximum and minimum settlements and maximum settlement disparity are 277 mm, 259 mm, and 18 mm, respectively. They are smaller than the settlement of the buildings near the gas-holder. The settlement of the natural foundation caused by the filled water load is about 513 mm, according to the calculation of summation method. Therefore, the settlement of the mat foundation is only about 54% of the total settlement of the natural foundation. It shows that the mat of aggregate in geotextile bags can reduce settlement and control disparity of settlement effectively.

Pore-Water Pressure.

The relationship between pore-water pressure, load, and time is shown in Figure 4. In light of the measured information, pore-water pressure increases as the load increases. During the intermission of load, it decreases rapidly and then keeps constant until the compression in this load conditions ends.

Pressure at the Bottom of the Mats.

The results measured by pressure cells indicate that the pressure at the bottom of the mat of aggregate in geotextile bags increases when the filled water load increases. Figure 5 shows the relationship between the load of filled water and the pressure of the foundation base. Its pressure distribution is shown in Figure 6. The stresses are larger at the edge of the footing, but smaller beneath the line of the footing's centre. The diffusion

Table 1: Properties of the two layers of the much clay.

Item	Muck	Muck Loam
Thickness (m)	5.9	8.0
Density (t/m³)	1.7	1.8
Water content (%)	61.5	41.0
Void ratio (-)	1.7	1.8
Liquidity index (%)	25.3	18.3
Compressibility coeft. (GPa⁻¹)	18.3	8.3
Effective friction angle (°)	26.1	26.1
Modulus of deformation (MPa)	2.2	2.8
Effective cohesion (MPa)	0.0	0.0

Photo 1.   Gas-holder tank.

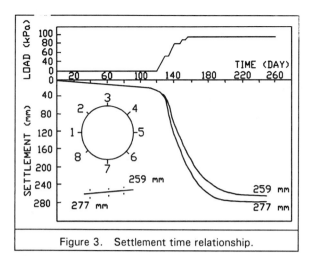

Figure 3.   Settlement time relationship.

angle θ and the ratio of diffusion area back calculated according to the concept of stress diffusion are $\theta = 61°$, b = 1.5 when loads are smaller, and $\theta = 43°$, b = 1.25 when loads are larger. It follows that the mat of aggregate in geotextile bags can diffuse the stress more effectively than the sand mat and thus decrease the average stresses in the foundation base.

CONCLUSIONS

- The mat of aggregate in geotextile bags can diffuse loads and prevent shallow soil failures more effectively than sand mats.
- The mat of aggregate in geotextile bags can reduce the settlement, control unequal settlement, and improve the stability of the foundation.
- The mat of aggregate in geotextile bags has the advantages of convenient construction and low cost.

REFERENCES

Kim, Y.S., Shen, C.K., and Bang, S., "Oil Storage Tank Foundation on Soft Clay", Proc. 8th. ECSMFE, Helsinki, Finland, 1982, pp. 371-374.

Wang, T.R., Ye, Z.X., and Qi, S.M., "Application of Geotextile on Soft Clay of a Gas-Holder", Proc. 1st. Chinese Conf. on Geotextiles, Tiangjing, China, 1986, pp. 175-184. (in Chinese).

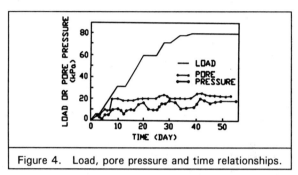

Figure 4.   Load, pore pressure and time relationships.

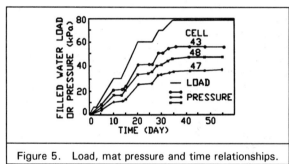

Figure 5.   Load, mat pressure and time relationships.

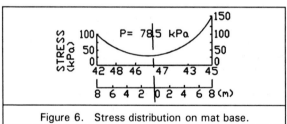

Figure 6.   Stress distribution on mat base.

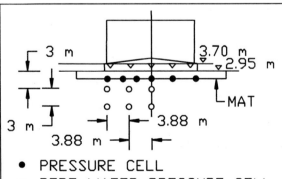

- ● PRESSURE CELL
- ○ PORE WATER PRESSURE CELL
- ▽ OBSERVED POINTS OF SETTLEMENT

Figure 2.   Arrangement of instrumentation.

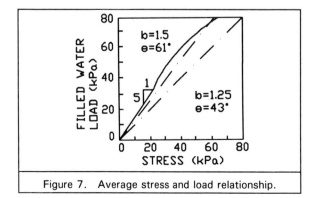

Figure 7.   Average stress and load relationship.

GEOTEXTILE AND RELIEF PILES FOR DEEP FOUNDATION IMPROVEMENT EMBANKMENT NEAR GÖTEBORG, SWEDEN

R.D. Holtz
University of Washington
Seattle, Washington, USA

K.R. Massarsch
Geo Engineering AB
Bromma, Sweden

In 1972, a multifilament woven polyester geotextile was used for the first time to carry the horizontal forces in a bridge approach embankment supported on vertically driven relief piles. The site of the bridge is in southwestern Sweden in the Göta river valley about 30 km north of Göteborg. Serious displacement and stability problems existed because the clays at the site were soft and sensitive.

DESCRIPTION

The Problem

In Sweden, relief piles are commonly used to support highway embankments on very soft clays [Bjerrum, 1972]. Typically the first few rows of piles around the edge of the embankment are driven inclined (batter between 1H:4V and 1H:10V) to take care of the horizontal forces imposed by the embankment. Serious problems can arise during driving of relief piles in clay slopes. These problems result from the remoulding of the clay during piling and may lead to large settlements, downslope movements, or even a slide. At the site, crooked and leaning trees indicated generally unstable conditions. The bedrock was highly irregular and dipped steeply towards the bridge abutment and adjacent creek. It was doubtful that batter piles would seat properly.

Conventional Solution

Lengthening of the rigid frame concrete bridge about 25 m was estimated to cost an additional 1,000,000 Swedish Crowns. If the piles were driven vertically, then the horizontal forces imposed by the embankment would have to be taken care of somehow.

Alternate Solution with Geotextiles

The solution was to use a geotextile at the base of the embankment (Figure 1). As this was the first such use in a piled embankment, instrumentation required for monitoring the pile driving was also used for observing the performance of the reinforcement.

Soil Conditions and Instrumentation

Below a 2 m dry crust, there was about 8 m of a uniform grey clay ($w_n \approx$ 80-90% at the top, decreasing to $w_n \approx$ 60% near the bottom; with $w_n \geq w_l$). Below 10 m the clay became increasingly silty. The average undrained shear strength below the dry crust was 35 kPa. Average $S_t \approx$ 30-40; range 14-60.

To monitor the pile installation, the site was

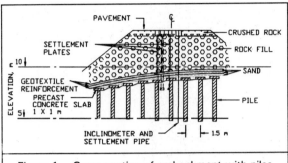

Figure 1. Cross section of embankment with piles and reinforcement.

instrumented with inclinometers, settlement plates and total stress cells. Three additional settlement plates were installed in the vicinity of the geotextile reinforcement (Figure 1). After completion of the embankment and surfacing of the roadway, settlement measurements were performed on the road surface by precise levelling. Additional information about the geotechnical conditions and instrumentation are given by Holtz and Massarsch [1976].

GEOTEXTILE SELECTION

The reinforcement was an industrial grade multifilament woven polyester manufactured by AB Fodervävnader of Borås, Sweden (No. 600). Its mass per unit area is 100 g/m^2, and its ultimate tensile strength is about 43 kN/m at a failure strain of about 15%. See Holtz [1977] and Holtz and Broms [1977] for additional property information.

CONSTRUCTION

Installation of Piles

Spliced timber piles were driven vertically at 1.5 m spacing (Figure 1). In order to reduce lateral movements during piling, clay plugs 200 mm in diameter and up to 10 m long were removed prior to pile installation. After the piles were driven and cut off at the foundation level, a 1 m square precast concrete pile cap was placed at the top of each pile. Additional details on pile installation are given by Holtz and Massarsch [1976].

Geotextile Placement

Three layers of geotextile were placed with about 150 mm of compacted sand between each layer (Figure 1). The geotextile was very easily handled in the field; it was simply rolled out over the compacted subgrade fill (Photo 1)

| Photo 1. Placing geotextile. | Photo 2. Completed project. |

and cut to the desired length with a propane torch, a procedure which very effectively prevented any tendency of the weave to unravel. About 300 mm of overlap was used between each 1.7 m wide strip. The machine direction of the bottom layer was perpendicular to the centreline of the roadway while the upper layers were laid at 45° and 135° to the centreline, respectively.

PERFORMANCE OF THE GEOTEXTILE REINFORCEMENT

Inclinometer measurements made after completion of the embankment indicated that both total and differential movements downslope towards the creek (Figure 2) and along the centreline towards the bridge abutment (Figure 3) were small. It appears that, in both directions, the reinforcement tended to restrain the movements. Total stress cells indicated that the stress transfer was indeed occurring. Pore pressures did not change during construction of the embankment, suggesting that both the lateral and vertical stresses were effectively carried by the reinforcement and piles. During the three years after construction, the measured vertical settlements were very small and no additional resurfacing, as is often the case with conventional construction of pile supported approach embankments, has been necessary in the pavement supported by piles. Re-surfacing has been needed only at one location, the junction between the embankment and the bridge due to localized differential settlement supposedly resulting from insufficient compaction of the rockfill next to the concrete abutment. This problem is not related to the geotextile-pile system which has performed satisfactorily ever since construction.

CONCLUSIONS

The woven multifilament polyester geotextile used to reinforce a bridge approach embankment on soft sensitive clays effectively reduced the horizontal movements and thereby probably prevented serious settlements and instability. The installation was significantly cheaper than a longer bridge structure.

REFERENCES

Bjerrum, L., "Embankments on Soft Ground", General Report, Session I, Proceedings of the ASCE Specialty Conf. on Performance of Earth and Earth-Supported Structures, Purdue University, West Lafayette, Indiana, 1972, Vol. 2, pp. 43-45.

Holtz, R.D. and Massarsch, K.R., "Improvement of the Stability of an Embankment by Piling and Reinforced Earth", Proc. of the 6th. ECSMFE., Vienna, 1976, Vol. 1.2, pp. 473-478.

Holtz, R.D. and Broms, B.B., "Walls Reinforced by Fabrics - Results of Model Tests", Proc. of the Int. Conf. on the Use of Fabrics in Geotechnics, Paris, 1977, Vol. 1, pp. 113-117.

Holtz, R.D., "Laboratory Studies of Reinforced Earth Using a Woven Polyester Fabric", Proc. of the Int. Conf. on the Use of Fabrics in Geotechnics, Paris, 1977, Vol. 3, pp. 149-154.

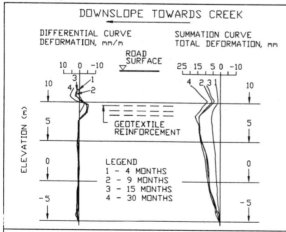

Figure 2. Inclinometer measurements at centreline of embankment downslope towards creek.

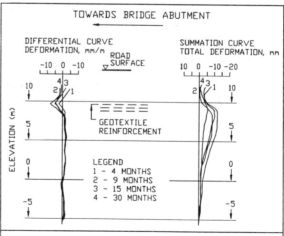

Figure 3. Inclinometer measurements at centreline of embankment towards bridge abutment.

GEOTEXTILE FILTER AND ANCHOR FOR SHEET PILING REHABILITATION OUDENAARDE, BELGIUM

F. De Meerleer
UCO Technical Fabrics N.V.
Lokeren, Belgium

Sheet piling was placed in 1970 at Oudenaarde on the river Schelde (Belgium). Later, due to piping of the backfill, a vertical geotextile filter was placed behind the existing piling to prevent particles being washed out through the joint openings. A horizontal geotextile anchorage was also added to improve the safety margin of the overall stability.

DESCRIPTION

The joints between two adjoining sheet piles (tongued and grooved) varied from a couple of mm to several cm. Small movements of the wall caused openings to appear. These allow sand particles from the land side to be washed out by the action of tides and waves. Settlements and damage of bank revetments occurred. In addition, as a result of non-uniform soil backfill, large sections of the retaining structure had a safety margin that was too low.

TECHNICAL CONSIDERATIONS

Vertical Screen and Horizontal Anchoring

A geotextile with an adequate opening size, placed vertically behind the sheet piles, prevents particles from being washed out through the openings. The normal method of installation would be to excavate the soil behind the sheet piles, place the geotextile and refill. To follow that procedure would require an existing road near the slope to be destroyed and replaced. The operation would be extremely expensive. It was a challenge for UCO to work out a solution where the geotextile could be placed vertically into the ground, avoiding any excavation. Also, the stability of the sheet piling wall was to be improved by horizontally anchoring a high modulus polyester woven geotextile near the top of the sheeting.

Geotextile Selection

For the site in Oudenaarde the polypropylene woven (tape yarn) geotextile SG 52/41 produced by UCO was selected for the vertical filter because of its opening size and mechanical resistance. Its properties are:

Mass per unit area	:270 g/m²
Tensile strength (roll direction)	: 52 kN/m
Tensile strength (cross-roll direction)	: 41 kN/m
Strain at failure (roll direction)	: 15 %
Strain at failure (cross-roll direction)	: 15 %
Coefficient of normal permeability	: 5 mm/s
Opening size	:150 μm

The anchoring geotextile, selected because of its

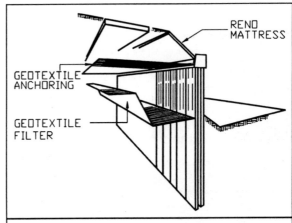

Figure 1. Conceptual view of cross-section of the sheet piling rehabilitation.

adequate strength, rigidity and very high creep resistance, was the high modulus polyester woven (multifilament yarns), named HS 200/45 and produced by UCO. Its characteristics are:

Tensile strength (roll direction)	:200 kN/m
Tensile strength (cross-roll direction)	: 45 kN/m
Strain at failure (roll direction)	: 10 %
Strain at failure (cross-roll direction)	: 20 %
Coefficient of normal permeability	: 6 mm/s
Opening size	:130 μm

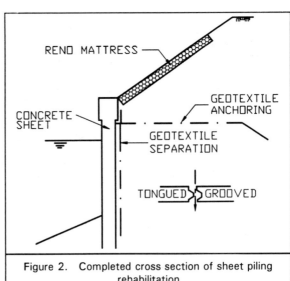

Figure 2. Completed cross section of sheet piling rehabilitation

Photo 1. Geotextile panel of 3 m x 5 m fixed on a steel frame with special soil proof locking system.	Photo 2. Vibrating geotextile and steel frame into the soil.

Photo 3. The geotextile attached to the capping beam by means of threaded rods, nuts and a "U" section.	Photo 4. Replacing the fill on the geotextile.

Geotextile Screen Placement

Geotextile strips 3 m wide and 5 to 8 m high were vibrated into the ground with a locking system between the different strips so as to prevent any open joints: the geotextile filter has to be continuous.

The manufacturer supplied the geotextiles made up into panels with a special profile opening on both sides. This makes it possible to fix them into a special soil proof locking system. The panels are fixed on a steel frame and vibrated into the ground. In order to protect the geotextile during the vibrating operation, a "U" section knife structure is installed at the base of the geotextile. After settlement into the soil, the steel frame is lifted and the geotextile remains in the ground. Numerous tests have proven that the geotextile strips remained at their maximum length in the ground and that the locking system is efficient.

Geotextile Anchor Placement

The geotextile for anchoring is attached to the capping beam of the sheet piling by means of threaded rods, nuts and a "U" section so that the forces are evenly distributed. After prestressing the geotextile, new fill is placed behind the sheet piling. The necessary anchor force occurs due to the friction between the soil of the backfill and the geotextile.

CONCLUSIONS

This new technique of introducing continuous geotextile screens vertically into the ground is certainly an original and relatively inexpensive solution for a typical erosion problem that occurs often in canals and harbours. The performance is quite satisfactory and installation rates are very competitive. A possible lack of stability can be eliminated by using a high modulus geotextile as anchoring.

REFERENCE

Van den Eede, E., Silence, P. and Himpe, J., "Renovation of Bank Defenses Consisting of Reinforced Concrete Sheet Piling Used on Waterways", PIANC Bulletin, No. 61, 1988.

CHAPTER 8

PAVEMENT SUBGRADE AND BASE REINFORCEMENT

GEOTEXTILE REINFORCED FORESTRY ROADS OVER SOFT SOIL
QUINAULT TEST ROAD PROJECT, WASHINGTON STATE, USA

J.E. Steward
United States Forest Service
Washington, D.C., USA

J. Mohney
United States Forest Service
Portland, Oregon, USA

J.R. Bell
Oregon State University
Corvalis, Oregon, USA

The Quinault Test Road Project was an early effort to evaluate the performance of commercially available geotextiles in aggregate-surfaced roads and develop design procedures and specifications. The project, located on the Olympic Peninsula in Washington State, USA, was constructed in October 1976. Log hauling was done in 1977. During this period, instrumentation readings were made to check design assumptions and gather data to evaluate the project objectives. In 1978, the test sections were excavated to obtain test samples of geotextiles and subgrade soils for accessing changes in properties.

DESCRIPTION

General

The road was initially designed to be constructed according to established procedures for the Quinault area. These procedures called for 300 mm of shot rock with 150 mm of glacial gravel topping in stronger areas and excavating the top 600 mm of subgrade and backfilling with 1.5 m of pit run or "shot" rock in weaker (swampy) areas. By using geotextiles directly on the subgrade it was possible to eliminate the excavation of unsuitable material, thereby reducing disturbance, and eliminate the need for waste areas while saving an average of 300 mm of rock thickness (20 to 30%). This amounted to a savings of $3,500 (1976 dollars) per km of single lane road.

The subgrade soils were highly organic clays and silts (Unified Classification OH) with low bearing strength (CBR < 1). Subgrade densities as low as 200 to 500 kg/m^3 with natural moisture contents as much as three times the liquid limit were observed. Before construction, CBR values from 0.07 to 0.45% were also measured.

The geotextiles used were nonwoven polyester needlepunched fabrics of 150, 325, and 420 g/m^2; nonwoven polypropylene needlepunched fabrics of 140, 320, and 420 g/m^2; and two heat-bonded polypropylene fabrics of 140 g/m^2.

Construction

The construction process started with falling, limbing, and bucking timber and cutting small trees and brush at ground level. A hydraulic shovel was used to move logs and brush to the side of the road where it would be picked up after construction was completed. The shovel worked off of timber mats to spread the load and minimize disturbance to the subgrade. After clearing, the geotextile was rolled out on the subgrade by hand as shown in Photo 1. For the test road, a different geotextile was used under each wheel track with the joint sewn along the centre line.

Rock fill was then dumped on the geotextile from trucks and spread using a D-6 dozer. Trucks were always travelling over rock fill. The rock fill material was shale quarried from a local pit. Plans called for 300 mm minus rock so that a thickness of 600 mm could be maintained. However, some of the shot rock contained pieces as large as 600 mm to 1 m in diameter. For this reason and because of the previous habits of the contractor's personnel, sections were generally thicker than planned. Compaction was accomplished by construction equipment (dozer and trucks), although no real attempt was made at compaction. Photo 2 shows the completed road.

Instrumentation

Each of the geotextile sections and the control sections contained strain gauges to measure geotextile or soil strain and settlement plates to measure vertical displacements.

In addition to monitoring these instruments, sections of the roadway were excavated in 1978 after 2 years of service and completion of log hauling to check changes in soil strength under the fill, durability of the geotextile, and rutting in the subgrade.

FINDINGS

Traffic during the first 2 to 3 days was rock hauling to the road. The area was logged and timber hauling completed 3 to 8 months after construction. Readings on the settlement plates took place within the first 2 to 3 days. There was 25 to 50 mm additional settlement in the next 7 months. No further settlement could be detected between June 1977 and August 1978.

The rut depths were estimated as the average difference between the low and high readings on the profiles. These readings indicated rut depths for both subgrade and surface to be approximately the same. Values ranged from 0 to 115 mm and averaged 43 mm. Much of this was due to initial compaction of the surfacing and subgrade under traffic since a low level of compaction was provided during construction.

The strain gauges, which were designed for very large strains, did not elongate enough to break continuity. This indicated that strain of the geotextile was less than 10% rather than the higher values anticipated. Experience since indicates anticipated strains were an order of magnitude too high.

| Photo 1.   Site conditions and construction. | Photo 2.   Completed project. |

Significant subgrade property changes were measured after 2 years service for the Quinault test roads. Subgrade strengths increased approximately 250%. Moisture content decreased, on average, from 218% to 55%, and dry densities increased from an average of 1,250 to 1,620 kg/m³. Geotextiles were tested before construction and after excavation by 24 mm cut strip and standard grab tests. These tests indicated geotextile strengths after 2 years of service to be approximately 60 to 100%, with an average of 80%, of their original values. More detailed results are presented by Steward and Mohney [1982]. Essentially no differences could be seen between performances of the various geotextiles.

SIGNIFICANCE

The Quinault test road demonstrated that roads with geotextiles will out-perform roads without geotextiles and was very important to the development of the widely publicized USDA-Forest Service design method [Steward et al., 1977].

Nonwoven (needlepunched and heat-bonded) and woven (slit film) geotextiles have been used successfully for many unpaved roads in the Pacific Northwest Region of the USDA-Forest Service. Most of the geotextiles had masses per unit area of 140 to 210 g/m² and grab strengths of 500 to 800 N. The majority of these projects were constructed by full-depth placement of the aggregate as described previously. Generally, the geotextiles survived the construction process and performed adequately.

FURTHER CONCLUSIONS

The large increases in subgrade strength after construction suggest the possibility of removing excess aggregate from unpaved roads after some period of service for use in new construction. Aggregate thickness calculated for conditions during construction and after two years of service are shown in Table 1 for a Quinault road segment.

The 52% potential savings without geotextile is not likely due to aggregate contamination. However, the potential 50% savings with geotextile may be possible by reusing the excess aggregate on another road after the subgrade is strengthened. This recycling of aggregate could boost savings to 70% over the conventional design.

Table 1.	Aggregate thickness requirements		
	Aggregate Thickness Required		% Aggregate Savings With Geotextile
	No Geotextile	Geotextile	
Construction Condition	840 mm	510 mm	39 %
After 2 yrs Service	406 mm	254 mm	37 %
% Aggregate Thickness Savings Potential	52 %	50 %	

Aggregate reduction: Construction with no geotextile to 2 years after construction with geotextile = 70 %

REFERENCES

Steward, J.E., Williamson, R., and Mohney, J., Guide-lines for Use of Fabrics in Construction and Maintenance of Low-Volume Roads, Report No. FHWA-T5-78-205 National Technical Information Service, Washington, D.C., USA, 1977 (Revised 1983).

Steward, J.E., and Mohney, J., "Trial Use Results and Experience for Low-Volume Forest Roads", Proc. 2nd. Int. Conf. on Geotextiles, Vol. II, Las Vegas, USA, 1982, pp. 335-340.

GEOTEXTILE REINFORCED EMBANKMENT OVER A DEEP PEAT DEPOSIT
U.S. HIGHWAY 45, WEST BEND, WISCONSIN, USA

B.R. Christopher
Polyfelt Inc.
Atlanta, Georgia, USA

A.B. Wagner
Graef, Anhalp, Schloemer and Associates Inc.
Milwaukee, Wisconsin, USA

The relocation of U.S. Highway 45 around West Bend, Wisconsin, was planned by the Wisconsin Department of Transportation. STS Consultants, Ltd. was retained by the design engineer, J.C. Zimmerman Engineering Corporation, to determine if the roadway could be constructed over a deep peat deposit located across the new highway alignment. Preliminary calculations indicated that placement of the embankment fill would result in a rotational shear failure of the peat soil. Several alternatives were evaluated, and the conclusion was made that reinforcing the embankment with high strength geotextiles was the most cost-effective solution.

DESCRIPTION

The new highway alignment was intended to cross a post-glacial peat deposit some 670 m long, extending to depths as great as 7 m at the edge of a partially filled lake. The design grades required that an embankment having a height of up to 2 m with 1 m of surcharge be placed above the peat. Conventional construction practices in the past would have involved removing the peat and replacing it with an engineered fill. However, there were several disadvantages with this procedure. They included:

- No peat disposal site was readily available.

- Peat disposal would result in environmental concerns.

- Dewatering would be required to permit direct inspection of the peat removal. This would be difficult and could affect adjacent wetlands.

- The peat removal and replacement would be extremely costly, since large volumes of material were involved.

As a result of these disadvantages, the geotextile-reinforced embankment alternative was chosen. In order to analyze its stability, it was necessary to obtain more refined measurements of the shear strengths of the peat soils. An innovative field testing program was undertaken that led to the actual calculation of the shear strength of the peat. Field tests were used to develop continuous profiles of the shear strength of the peat at several locations across the highway alignment.

The data were used to perform a computer analysis of the dike section stability. This analysis confirmed the preliminary calculations that yielded a factor of safety significantly less than 1. The results of the computer analysis were used to calculate the reinforcement necessary to increase the factor of safety to 1.5.

GEOTEXTILE SELECTION

Considering variations in the thickness and shear strength of the peat, as well as the embankment height, three typical fabric reinforcement details were selected for construction. At the least critical sections, a reinforcement with a tensile strength of 87 kN/m was required perpendicular to the roadway alignment. The intermediate sections required a reinforcement strength of 175 kN/m, and the most critical sections required a strength of 260 kN/m. Parallel to the alignment, a geotextile strength of 60 to 120 kN/m was required for constructibility and control of bending.

CONSTRUCTION CONSIDERATIONS

A "sacrificial" weak geotextile layer was placed directly above the subgrade to facilitate construction operations. For reinforcement, the selected design included placing a layer of geotextile having a strength of 87 kN/m across the entire peat deposits. For intermediate reinforcement, a second layer of 87 kN/m geotextile was placed 300 mm above the initial reinforcement layer. In the critical section which required the greatest reinforcement, a second geotextile layer, of 175 kN/m strength, was placed above the initial reinforcement geotextile layer. Field "J" seams were required to meet the cross direction (longitudinal) strength requirements.

As part of the project, specifications and detailed procedures for geotextile placement, geotextile sewing, and placement of fill were also developed. The project was constructed in the summer of 1984.

PERFORMANCE

Based upon the laboratory consolidation tests, a settlement of 1 m within 1 year of construction was predicted where the peat was 6 m thick. Where thinner organic soils were present, proportionately less settlement was predicted. Monitoring performed during construction indicated that the settlement was on the order of 600 mm to 1.3 m at the time of pavement construction. The post-paving performance of the embankment has been as good as or slightly better than predicted with 0 to 100 mm measured in the first year.

CONCLUSIONS

In summary, several key project results are noteworthy:

- The design uses geotextiles not only to facilitate construction, but more importantly to provide

| Photo 1. Geotextile placement over existing ground conditions and spreading of new embankment fill. | Photo 2. Equipment for field sewing. |

needed soil reinforcement against rotational shear failure.

- This project is one of the first in the USA to use geotextiles as a major structural element for a permanent structure.

- The use of the geotextiles resulted in significant cost savings, conservatively estimated to be approximately $400,000.

- The use of geotextiles allowed construction of the highway embankment over peat soils, rather than requiring displacement or excavation of the peat. This significantly reduced the environmental disruption and the concerns associated with the peat disposal.

STS Consultants, Ltd. received an achievement award from the Wisconsin Section of the American Society of Civil Engineers for the innovative and cost-effective project approach.

REFERENCES

Christopher, B.R. and Wagner, A.B., "A Geotextile Reinforced Embankment for a Four Lane Divided Highway -- U.S. Hwy 45, West Bend, Wisconsin", Proc. 2nd. Int. Conf. on Case Histories in Geotechnical Engineering, St. Louis, MO, 1988.

GEOTEXTILE USAGE FOR A MAJOR MOTORWAY
M11, BISHOPS STORTFORD, UNITED KINGDOM

J. King
Don and Low Ltd.
Forfar, Angus, United Kingdom

In 1978 the use of geotextiles in the U.K. was largely still considered to be a contractors aid for haul roads where use was of a temporary nature and the consequences of failure were negligible. Confidence by a number of contractors led to more imaginative use. This did much to demonstrate to the supervising Engineers that these "tools" had a great deal to offer in permanent works.

DESCRIPTION: Phase 1

The M11 Motorway runs virtually North/South between the outskirts of London and Cambridge. It was constructed by the Department of Transport in a number of separate contracts in the late 1970's.

On contract A4 between Bishops Stortford and Quendon the contractor found that the CBR of the formation after excavating some of the cuttings was below the 3% required by the designers W.S. Atkins and Partners. Consequently they were required to excavate a further 600 mm then backfill to formation level with rockfill or stonefill. Backfill of the required quality was not available locally. It had to be imported over considerable distances, with consequent high unit costs. Eventually clean brick rubble was found to be acceptable and used. The method of measurement and consequently payment was such that the contractor would be paid only for placing a 600 mm depth of backfill. From the contractors viewpoint there was a risk that some of the backfill would be lost by punching into the subgrade below the overexcavation. Having had previous experience of using geotextiles below access roads with satisfactory results the contractor examined the feasibility of using one placed over the overexcavation before placing the backfill.

Geotextile Selection: Phase 1

The geotextile was to be used as a separator between a clay/silt subgrade with a CBR of less than 3% and clean brick rubble backfill with a nominal size of 225 x 110 x 75 in a 600 mm layer. Robustness (now known as survivability) and price were the two selection criteria which led to the contractor purchasing Lotrak 16/15 120 g/m^2, a woven polypropylene geotextile with a minimum tensile strength of 18 kN/m at an extension of 22%, a 5% secant modulus of 120 kN/m and a minimum CBR puncture resistance of 2,100 N. The relative cost of geotextile and backfill meant that an average of only 20 mm of backfill had to be saved to cover the geotextile cost.

During construction with the geotextile the contractor used 54,000 m^2 of Lotrak 16/15 over 4 km of motorway for this purpose.

DESCRIPTION: Phase 2

The standard construction was a rigid pavement of concrete over subbase. To lay the concrete the contractor used a concrete train which paved the full width of the 12 m carriageway in one pass. Concrete supply from the batching plant was by truck travelling over the subbase of the second carriageway. In reality this second carriageway was performing as a haul road but the designed subbase thickness was for the final condition with the pavement slab in place. In the interim the subbase thickness was insufficient for the axle loading of the concrete supply trucks. Previously in similar situations the contractor had temporarily placed on additional thickness of subbase which subsequently required removal, this time he considered the use of a geotextile.

Geotextile Selection: Phase 2

At this time in geotextile history few design methods were available. Recommendations were empirical based largely on experience. Having used Lotrak 16/15 on phase 1 the contractor was willing to use it on phase 2 with the thickness of additional subbase reduced to 50% of normal practice. Some 88,000 m^2 of Lotrak 16/15 were placed between subgrade and subbase over 6.5 km of motorway with significant cost savings, resulting from only having to double handle half the expected volume of additional subbase.

CONCLUSION

This was one of the first motorways in the U.K. to use significant quantities of geotextile between subgrade and subbase. In addition to cost savings it demonstrated the engineering benefits to be gained from their use. Almost ten years later the Department of Transport included in its standard specification for Highway Works, Clause 609, Geotextiles used as separators in Earthworks.

REFERENCES

Department of Transport - "Specification for Highway Works" Her Majesty's Stationery Office, London.

| Photo 1.   Phase 1 construction. | Photo 2.   Phase 2 construction. |

GEOTEXTILE REINFORCED FILL FOR DRILL PAD AND ACCESS ROAD OVER MUSKEG ALBERTA, CANADA

D.A. Heaton
Bolter Parish Trimble Ltd., Consulting Engineers
Edmonton, Alberta, Canada

G. Bulman
Parkvalley Consulting Ltd.,
Calgary, Alberta, Canada

The work carried out consisted of the construction of an access road approximately 400 m long, running in a north-south direction. A drill pad 122 m square was constructed at the south end of the access road. Both road and pad were intended to handle loads associated with rig move-in and out, typically involving axle loads in excess of 250 kN, and those associated with servicing the rig. As drilling operations cannot cope with settlement, it was planned to support the important drill rig components on piles, in accordance with established practice.

DESCRIPTION

Generally, site conditions could be characterized as a muskeg bog, with a water table virtually at the surface, and with a ground cover of mosses and low bushes with the occasional small spruce tree attaining heights of 5 to 6 m. The area was almost impossible to walk on; typically persons traversing the area would sink up to midcalf or knee.

Access was possible to the start of the access road at its north end. Boreholes drilled at that location indicated the following:

0.0 -	4.3 m	Peat
4.3 -	5.5 m	Soft clay marl (c_u approx. 10 kPa)
5.5 -	10.7 m	Firm clay becoming stiff at 5.8 m
10.7 -	13.8 m	Stiff to hard clay till
13.8 m		Sandstone bedrock

It was planned to install a second borehole at the drill pad to confirm conditions and also to enable the piling design to be fine tuned.

Ordinarily, such drilling leases are constructed in winter when the muskeg is frozen. Due to various business reasons, such a procedure was not possible in this case. Business reasons also dictated that the start of construction be delayed and then executed as quickly as possible so as to be complete on or about the end of the summer months.

DESIGN CONSIDERATIONS

Various optional methods of constructing the road and pad were considered, as follows:

1. Use of native timber to form a "corduroy" road and pad.
2. Use of a piled foundation.
3. Use of a geotextile.

Option 1 did not appear to offer any advantages over Option 3 and was considered to be more expensive. Preliminary investigations into Option 2 indicated that a very large number of piles and cross members would be required with a corresponding delay in installation and a high cost. Option 3 appeared feasible, cost-effective, and also compatible with the time constraints. It was accordingly adopted.

Using the procedures developed by Rowe [1987], a woven geotextile with a minimum wide strip tensile strength of 35 kN/m and a minimum secant modulus, based on the lesser of 5% and 10% strain, of 175 kN/m was specified. The intent was to have the supplier factory sew the geotextile so as to provide one piece for the road and one for the drill pad. The normal practice of providing continuity by overlapping had proven useless in practice.

Various suppliers were contacted with a view to identifying suitable geotextiles. This caused some difficulties as some suppliers only had grab tensile test results. Also, some quoted mean or average test results while others quoted values based on various other statistical interpretations of test results. Very little information was available on seam strengths except that the factory sewn seams, by general consensus, were thought to have seam strengths approaching those of the virgin geotextile. Eventually a geotextile was chosen.

OBSERVATIONS DURING CONSTRUCTION

Access Road

Trees and bushes were felled and left in place. A minimum of disturbance was attempted so as to leave the root mat in place. The geotextile, supplied in one large piece, was laid down and pulled into position. Attempts were made to keep the geotextile taut so as to avoid folds.

Imported clay fill was placed using an "outside-to-in" technique, and the edges of the geotextile were turned back so as to anchor it. The nearest source of granular fill was located some 60 km away over gravel roads. Its use in significant amounts was prohibitively expensive.

Very light tracked machines were used to spread the fill. Attempts were made to bring the fill up in small lifts that were extensive in area rather than trying speedily to bring one area to finished grade. It was hoped in this way to minimize pore pressure build up by permitting the pore water to dissipate laterally. It was noted that after 300 to 400 mm of fill was in place, loaded tandem axle dump trucks could traverse the road with no observable heaving. After about 2.5 weeks, the road was complete and behaving perfectly. Approximately 1 m of fill was placed

Photo 1. Looking north along access road at division between areas with factory seams and areas with field seams.

and the top of the road stabilized some 100 mm above existing ground. Except for isolated locations, where a night shift loaded an area too quickly, no sloughing or heaving was noted and no water penetrated the surface.

Drill Pad

As soon as the road reached the drill pad, a second borehole was drilled at the edge of the pad. The results were as follows:

0.0 -	2.2 m	Peat
2.2 -	5.4 m	Soft clay marl (c_u approx. 10 kPa)
5.4 -	9.0 m	Soft clay becoming firmer with depth
9.0 -	14.6 m	Stiff to hard clay
14.6 m		Sandstone bedrock

Although these conditions differed slightly from those at the north end of the road, it was decided to continue using the same geotextile for the pad as that for the road.

In order to accelerate construction, a decision was made to sew the pieces together in the field. Accordingly, the vegetation was cleared as for the road and the geotextile laid out and sewn together. Again attempts were made to keep the geotextile taut, and fill and placement methods as used on the road were used for the pad. The work went well until about 1.5 m of fill had been placed and the top of the fill was some 250 mm above the existing ground. At that point, numerous failures occurred. Large parts of the pad sank out of site overnight, and large mud waves, reaching as high as 1.7 m above existing ground, developed around the edge of the pad. Water also burst through to the surface of the pad in large amounts, promoting softening and rutting of the fill. Ultimately, some 4 to 4.5 m of fill was placed until the pad stabilized approximately 300 mm above existing ground.

Photo 1 was taken looking north along the road from the pad. The dividing line between the factory and field

sewn seams is obvious and in fact was dramatic when viewed in the field.

CONCLUSIONS

1. Application of the design procedures adopted provided satisfactory results as evidenced by the good results achieved when constructing the access road.

2. The failures associated with the pad could be due in part to development of large pore pressures. In the future, the means to monitor these and, if necessary, to modify the rate and method of fill placement will be advocated.

3. The primary cause of the failures associated with the pad was believed to be the inadequate strength of the seam used to splice the geotextile together. Tests carried out on similar seams after the pad was constructed indicated that strengths less than 20% of virgin geotextile strength were probably achieved in the field. Even the factory sewn seams developed average strengths of only 65% of virgin geotextile strengths. Subsequently, it was found that use of heavier threads and use of different seams could increase the 65% figure to 90% plus.

In the future, suppliers should be required to provide statistical data on seam strengths and, if necessary, stronger geotextiles used to ensure that the weakest link "has sufficient strength".

REFERENCES

Rowe, R.K. Geotextile Reinforcement in the Design of Low Embankments on Very Soft/Weak Soil, Research and Development Branch, Ontario Ministry of Transportation and Communications, June 1987.

GEOGRID REINFORCED CAPPING LAYER FOR MAJOR HIGHWAY A51 TARVIN BY PASS, UNITED KINGDOM

C.D. Hall
Netlon Limited,
Blackburn, United Kingdom

In 1983 Cheshire County Council let a contract for the construction of a highway by-pass to the South West of Tarvin. A length in shallow cutting was required to pass through a weak and variable sub-grade. Traditionally, such problems are overcome by placing a capping layer of imported material to serve as an initial construction platform. A decision was made to reinforce the capping layer with a 'Tensar' geogrid and to test the achieved bearing capacity.

DESCRIPTION

Tarvin By Pass is a dual carriageway trunk road of standard construction [DTp, 1976] and provides two traffic lanes in each direction and a central reservation. For the areas where the subgrade was expected to be weak, the design called for 600 mm of capping layer material and 150 mm of high quality well graded granular aggregates for the sub-base. The sub-base then supports the bitumen macadam road base and flexible surfacing.

TECHNICAL CONSIDERATIONS

Capping layers are included in designs whenever the CBR of the sub-grade is less than 5% [DTp. 1978]. The main function of capping layer is to provide a firm platform on which to lay and compact sub-base. A wide range of locally available materials may be used (such as sands, gravels, shales and crushed concrete) and substantial economies can be achieved in road construction costs by the use of such 'lesser quality' materials. Having identified the source of capping layer material it was determined that 600 mm would be required. When the standard 150 mm of sub-base aggregate is then placed, experience indicated to the Engineer that the target CBR of 30% would be achieved at top of sub-base level.

In order to evaluate the reinforcing effect of a lightweight geogrid reinforcement, the Engineer specified two layers of 'Tensar' SS1 within the 600 mm capping layer of 75 mm down crusher run limestone. Such an aggregate grading ensures optimum mechanical interlock of the aggregate into the apertures of the geogrid. This is the principal reinforcing mechanism by which horizontal strains are imparted from the aggregate to the geogrid.

For a length of 120 m, in a wet and weak area of sub-grade, a geotextile filter was used to prevent the ingress of wet fines into the voids of the capping layer rock.

Plate bearing tests were conducted on both capping layer and sub-base and the equivalent CBR values are given in Table 1.

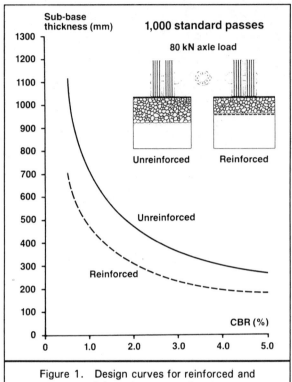

Figure 1. Design curves for reinforced and unreinforced aggregate layers.

CONCLUSION

This simple demonstration indicates the reinforcing effect obtainable from geogrids and highlights the potential for savings in aggregate thicknesses in highway construction. This line of enquiry has been pursued by the County, in conjunction with the Transport and Road Research Laboratory, on two further contracts where trafficking trials have examined surface deformations. Along with other such trials in the U.K. and U.S.A., design curves such as shown in Figure 1 have been compiled for 'Tensar' geogrids, [Netlon, 1987].

REFERENCES

Department of Transport. "Specification for Road and Bridge Works", 5th. Edition, H.M.S.O., London, 1976.

Department of Transport, Technical Memorandum No. H6/78, London, 1978.

Photo 1. Installing 'Tensar' geogrids at Tarvin.

Netlon Limited, "Tensar Grid Reinforced Sub-bases", Netlon Limited, Blackburn, 1987.

Robinson, B.J. "Polymer Grid Reinforcement" Proc. of Conf., written contribution, Thomas Telford, London, 1985.

Table 1. Equivalent CBR values (Robinson, 1985)

Chainage	Capping Layer%	Sub-base layer % (target 30%)
770 EB	40	70
850 WB	44	>75
910 WB *	30	50
923 EB *	12	33
938 CL *	16	48
* geotextile filter incorporated		

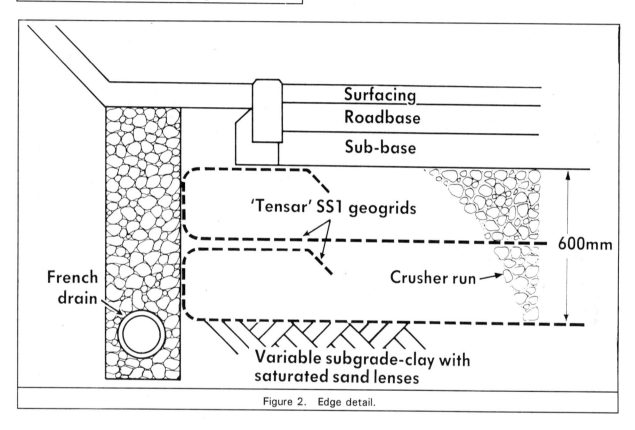
Figure 2. Edge detail.

GEOGRID STABILIZED LOG STORAGE YARD ON UNCONSOLIDATED SAWMILL DEBRIS QUESNEL, BRITISH COLUMBIA, CANADA

R.E. Graham and D.J. McDougall
R.E. Graham Engineering Ltd.
Prince George, British Columbia, Canada

Weldwood of Canada Limited has a plywood plant on the east bank of the Fraser River immediately downstream of Quesnel, British Columbia. The plant was constructed in 1950. In 1987, the log storage yard was upgraded using geogrids.

PROJECT BACKGROUND

The flow-through of lumber was designed for most of the logs to be delivered to the plant by floating them down the Quesnel and Fraser Rivers. The logs moved from the Fraser River into the plant by a system of canals and jack ladders. This system elevated the logs from the Fraser River elevation to the higher plant elevation. A storage yard compensated for the seasonal nature of log hauling and river driving, allowing continuous plant operation. Limited room was available at the site so an ancient backwater channel of the Fraser River was filled in with gravel and sawmill debris.

In recent years, the river drive has been supplemented by an increasingly large percentage of truck-hauled logs. The plant has improved and expanded, so a larger and more efficient log handling facility was required.

The owner studied the feasibility of various alternatives including a rail-mounted portal crane and high-capacity, rubber-tired log stackers. As a result of the study, the owner decided to phase out the canals in stages and to use large, rubber-tired log stacking machines rather than the rail-mounted portal crane. R.E. Graham Engineering Ltd. was hired for input to geotechnical aspects of the study. The new log storage facility covers approximately 6 ha.

SITE INVESTIGATION

A subsurface investigation consisted of eight backhoe test pits and five drill holes. The test pits encountered layers of gravel and log-yard debris deeper than could be investigated with the equipment. It was expedient to attempt drilling with a mud rotary drilling rig. The equipment could not maintain circulation in the open-graded debris so a continuous-flight auger drilling rig was brought in. The drill found layers of gravel and debris varying in depth from 300 mm to a maximum of 6.0 m. The debris included wood chips, bark, branches, stumps and log ends intermixed with sand and gravel. The authors recognized that the drill may have missed deeper pockets but estimated from the topography that the debris was not likely to be deeper than 7.5 m.

The fill was underlaid by river-deposited sand and gravel over hard, immediate-to-high plastic clay with layers of wet, dense, non-plastic silt and fine sand. The water table was approximately 4 m below the surface.

LOG-YARD SURFACE DESIGN

Two factors were important in the design of the log-yard surface: one was the need to support heavy logging trucks and rubber-tired stackers with high wheel loads; the other was that the subgrade material consisted of unconsolidated random fill with a high organic content.

Logs are typically brought into the storage yard during the period from mid-June to mid-March with an interruption during spring breakup. Other interruptions occur during extremely wet weather if the logging haul roads become impassable or during extremely dry weather if the forests are closed for fire hazard. Logs are removed from the yard during all seasons and weather conditions.

Log-yards typically have main, heavy-traffic areas used by loaded trucks to deposit logs and by stackers to move the logs to a bucking station in preparation for entry to the plant. The part of the yard which has less dense traffic is still critical because it is used by the heavy stacker during spring and other periods of adverse weather.

The loaded logging trucks are restricted to legal highway loads. The log stacker is a Wagner Model 130 (130,000 lb total weight) supported on six wheels. The front wheels are dual, and the full load often concentrates momentarily on one set of dual wheels with contact pressures in excess of 610 kPa.

The problem was considered from several points of view. The design logic which was chosen was a procedure developed by Giroud [1981]. He developed a semi-empirical design procedure using the number of passes, the design axle load, design rut depth and either unconfined shearing strength of the subgrade or California bearing ratio (CBR) values.

Giroud [1981] warns that the method applies to purely cohesive subgrade soils and is applicable to roads subject to light to medium traffic. The subgrades in this case are not cohesive materials, but it was considered that deflections of material with a high organic content will be similar to cohesive material with a low CBR value. The traffic density might be more than assumed by Giroud [1981], but the owner is prepared for annual maintenance because of surface deterioration typically caused by bark, mud and other debris being ground into, and reducing the shearing strength of the surface.

The procedure developed by Giroud [1981] was

Photo 1.   Log yard before upgrading -- note canal on right.

Photo 2.   Gravel, geogrid, sand and original ground from left to right.

supplemented in consultation with The Tensar Corporation, particularly using Tensar's technical documents, "Granular Base Reinforcement of Flexible Pavement Using Tensar Geogrids" and "Design Guideline for Flexible Pavements with Tensar Geogrid Reinforced Base Layers".

The log yard surface was prepared using a 150 mm thick layer of river sand, a layer of Tensar geogrid SS-1, and 750 mm of gravel with a sand content in the order of 50% and stones to a maximum size of 75 mm.

PERFORMANCE

The construction took place during the summer of 1987. The owner reports, in 1992, that the log-yard surface has given good surface to date. No noticeable deflection is noted under the fully loaded stacker where backfill was placed with adequate compaction.

In some areas, the owner elected to place material without compaction. These areas experienced surface rutting and a few base failures had to be patched. The owner has recently applied clinkers from hog fuel burners to the surface in lieu of the recommended crushed gravel and reports that this has increased serviceability.

ACKNOWLEDGMENTS

The authors would like to thank Weldwood of Canada Limited, and Mr. M.W. Brines in particular, for permission to submit this case history. The authors would also like to thank Mr. J.R. Kerr of The Tensar Corporation and Mr. Ian Wilson of Geo Products Inc. for their assistance and for some of the photographs accompanying the text.

REFERENCES
Giroud, J.P.,   Journal of the Geotechnical Engineering Division. Proc. A.S.C.E., Sept. 1981.

"Granular Base Reinforcement of Flexible Pavement Using Tensar Geogrids", The Tensar Corporation.

"Design Guideline for Flexible Pavements with Tensar Geogrid Reinforced Base Layers", The Tensar Corporation,

GEOGRID REINFORCEMENT FOR HAUL AND ACCESS ROAD
TORNESS-SMEATON, UNITED KINGDOM

A.J.T. Gilchrist
Netlon Limited
Blackburn, United Kingdom

Torness Nuclear Power Station is sited on the east coast of Scotland some 30 miles to the east of the City of Edinburgh. It is being constructed for the South of Scotland Electricity Board and will produce power to be fed into the national grid. The main interception point with the grid is at Smeaton, some 5 miles to the south east of Edinburgh.

The main communication link by road and rail follows the coast between the power station and the city. Permission to run the overhead cables by this route was blocked on grounds of visual damage to the environment. The high cost of an underground alternative forced the line route inland and to the south west through the Lammermuir Hills and then northwards to Smeaton lengthening the distance by some 50%.

OBJECTIVES

Access roads were required to follow the overhead cable lines for both construction purposes and for future maintenance work. The inland route was also subject to planning permission. Three major conditions had to be met by the 'Board'.

(a) Where possible, the road was to be built on top of natural vegetation with no major excavation. This was for environmental reasons and ensured continuity of biological life after road construction.

(b) All road making materials had to be won locally with imported materials kept to a minimum. This minimised disturbance to local communities.

(c) The road was to adopt as natural an appearance as possible with all cut and exposed surfaces of slopes being clad in natural vegetation.

TECHNICAL CONSIDERATIONS

Local Conditions

From the early design stages it was clear the inland land route, some 35 km long, would cross very variable terrain, from fairly stable glacial till to peat. Where possible the route followed natural avenues along valleys and existing farm tracks but considerable lengths were required to transverse long open peat bogs where peat depths varied from 500 mm to 6 m.

Two conditions had to be borne in mind: condition (a) a geosynthetic material had to be selected that would allow the road to be floated over the peat and condition (b) that road aggregate thicknesses would have to be kept to a minimum as quality road building rock was not available locally.

Due to problems with planning permission very few quarries and borrow pits were available along the route and this in turn meant that the road would be subjected to high numbers of vehicles during the construction period.

Locally available material was also very variable, from loose sands and gravels to highly weathered mudstone and sandstones. None of the materials available would have generally been suitable for highway construction.

Geosynthetic Selection

The geosynthetic materials selected were Tensar geogrids and selection was based as follows-

(a) Mechanical interlock between geogrid and base of the aggregate layer. This enabled the high transient stresses developed under loading to be carried by the geogrid with minimum rutting. Anchorage lengths outside of the wheel paths were therefore kept to a minimum.

(b) The thickness of aggregate layer could be reduced considerably without any appreciable increase in subgrade pressures.

(c) Aggregate was prevented from punching into the soft peat layers. The interlock principle prevents pumping of soft material into the aggregate.

Two types of geogrids were used: Tensar SS1 and Tensar SS2. Properties of these geogrids are given in Table 1.

CONSTRUCTION OF ROAD

The contract for the power lines was won by B.I.C.C. whose civil's arm, Balfour Beatty, carried out the civils work. The road construction was sub-contracted to Alec McLarty of Crieff, who have extensive experience in the construction of forestry roads.

The road sub-contract was valued at some £1.3 m and was to be completed in 15 months, the construction period being from September 1984 to late 1985 and involved constructing the road from several start points with access to existing roads and tracks.

Some 75,000 m² of Tensar SS1 geogrid and some 20,000 m² of Tensar SS2 geogrid were installed. The SS2,

Photo 1. Rolling geogrid out without any formal ground preparation.

Photo 2. Dumping aggregate onto already placed road aggregate rather than onto the geogrid.

Photo 3. Finished access road.

Table 1. Typical properties of Tensar geogrids

Property	SS1	SS2
Mass per unit area (g/m^2)	200	200
Aperture size (mm)	35x25	35x25
Tensile stength (kN/m)		
Roll direction	12	17
Cross roll direction	20	31
Strain at break (%)		
Roll direction	14	12
Cross roll direction	13	11

being a stronger geogrid, was used in areas where deeper peat was encountered and under exceptionally high traffic loads. Material was excavated from borrow pits and quarries and transferred to the point of deposition by off-highway Moxi dump trucks each with a payload of between 20 and 30 tonnes over 2 and 3 axles. Some 3 axle on-highway trucks were also used. The road was nominally 4 m wide and regular passing places were constructed to allow for two way working of construction vehicles.

At the point of construction the geogrid was rolled out across the existing surface with no formal preparation and vegetation was not removed (Photo 1). The aggregate was tipped from the delivery vehicles onto the constructed road and not onto the geogrid (Photo 2).

Aggregate was then spread in a cascading fashion to prevent damage to the geogrid and subsequent grading profiled the road to a depth of between 450 mm and 700 mm depending on the strength of the subgrade (Photo 3). Compaction was by vibrating drum roller towed by the dozer spreading the aggregate.

At the quarry there was no formal selection of material but face excavated directly onto the delivery vehicles. However, at one borrow pit some screening was carried out due to particularly high silt contents within the sand and gravel. This silt made compaction very difficult and a geotextile was used for separation to prevent intermixing.

CONCLUSIONS

The use of 'Tensar' geogrid sub-base reinforcement allowed the contractor to build a serviceable road of minimum thickness very rapidly using poor quality materials. At the peak of construction some parts of the road were carrying in excess of 3,000 tonnes per day over a period of several months with minimum maintenance. The road successfully carried the civil contractors plant and equipment to allow the towers to be constructed and rigged and has now been surfaced with quarry scalpings and is used as a service road. The road has carried regular traffic including snow clearing equipment since 1985 and a site inspection in 1992 showed that it was still performing well and was in good condition.

REFERENCES

Giroud, J.P., Ah-Line, C. and Bonaparte, R. "Design of unpaved roads and trafficked areas with geogrids". Symposium on Polymer Grid Reinforcement in Civil Engineering, I.C.E., London, 1984, No. 4.1

Jarrett, P.M. "Evaluation of geogrids for construction of roadways over Muskeg". Symposium on Polymer Grid Reinforcement in Civil Engineering, I.C.E., London, 1984, No. 4.5.

Kennedy, L.J. "Stanley Airfield, Falkland Islands 1982". Symposium on Polymer Grid Reinforcement in Civil Engineering, I.C.E., London, 1984, No. 4.3.

Kroshus, J.B. and Varcoe, B.E. "Geogrid applications in the construction of oilfield drilling pads and access areas in Muskeg regions of Northern Alberta. Symposium on Polymer Grid Reinforcement in Civil Engineering, I.C.E., London, 1984, No. 4.4.

GEOGRID REINFORCED ROADWAY STRUCTURE
NORTH EAST BRITISH COLUMBIA, CANADA

N.C. Polysou and G.A. Lachmuth
Ministry of Transportation and Highways
Victoria, British Columbia, Canada

Previous studies [Giroud et al., 1984, and Haas, 1986] indicate that inclusion of geogrid reinforcement into roadway base gravels allows a reduction in gravel thickness of 30 to 50% with no loss in load carrying capacity. The theoretical thickness reduction resulting from geogrid reinforcement is accomplished partly by subgrade confinement and partly from improved load distribution characteristics produced by geogrid-base layer material interlocking [Giroud et al., 1984]. In view of the potential for aggregate cost savings and preservation of the resource, the Ministry of Transportation & Highways decided to undertake a test installation in northeastern British Columbia. In September of 1987, 7,500 m² of Tensar SS-1 geogrid were included in the reconstruction of an unpaved industrial frontage road, No. 702, along the Alaska Highway near Fort St. John. This case history describes the design concept, installation procedure, field performance to date, and plans for future evaluation.

DESIGN CONCEPT

Field investigation of the Road 702 project site indicated that the subgrade would consist primarily of high plastic clay ($W_L = 57$, $W_p = 25$) with moisture contents ranging between 22 and 34%. Traditional design methods [CGRA, 1965], tempered with local experience, dictated a new road structure of 300 mm of 0/25 mm crushed base gravel overlying 400 mm of select granular sub-base (pit run gravel), for a total new structure thickness of 700 mm (see Figure 1). It was planned to surface this structure with a thin, graded aggregate seal until such time as a paved surface was warranted.

Design procedures for a geogrid reinforced base for unpaved roadways generally followed those outlined in technical notes produced by The Tensar Corporation [Tensar, 1986a; Tensar, 1986b; and Haas, 1986]. Calculations suggested that inclusion of a Tensar SS-1 geogrid could reduce the required aggregate thickness from 700 to 450 mm, a reduction of 35%. Although experimental studies suggested this reduction could approach 50%, these studies assume a single crushed aggregate base layer placed directly on the subgrade. Since it is common in British Columbia to construct part of the roadway structure of cheaper, uncrushed (weaker), pit run sub-base, we were reluctant to take advantage of the full theoretical thickness reduction. The calculated thickness reduction was proportioned such as to create a new reinforced section consisting of 225 mm of crushed base overlying 225 mm of select granular sub-base.

Research [Haas, 1986] also suggests the optimal location for the geogrid is at the midpoint of the aggregate layer for a total aggregate thickness in excess of 254 mm. Again this assumes a single unit of crushed base gravel

placed directly on the subgrade. This would put the geogrid in the reinforced gravel structure directly at the interface of the crushed base layer, and the underlying sub-base, with its inherently lower interlocking characteristics. Other, apparently conflicting research [Giroud et al., 1984], suggested that the optimal geogrid placement depth is related to surface load width. For dual truck tires, this is about 100 to 200 mm below the running surface [Giroud et al., 1984]. In order to resolve the geogrid placement dilemma, two different reinforced test designs were selected. Test Design A has 225 mm of crushed base overlying 225 mm of sub-base with the geogrid at the midpoint (Figure 2). Test Design B has the geogrid shifted upward by 75 mm into the crushed base layer (Figure 3).

TEST SECTION CONSTRUCTION

Three separate test sections of geogrid reinforced base were incorporated into the reconstruction of 1.8 km

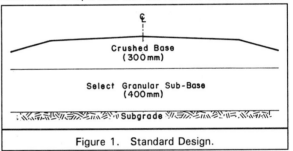

Figure 1. Standard Design.

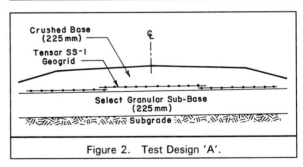

Figure 2. Test Design 'A'.

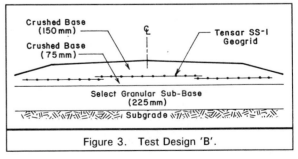

Figure 3. Test Design 'B'.

Photo 1. Unrolling geogrid.

Photo 2. Placement of aggregate on geogrid.

of Road 702. A single 230 m long section of Test Design A was installed, while two sections of 300 m and 200 m respectively of Test Design B were used. The remainder of the road was reconstructed with the standard 700 mm thick design. Once the sub-base (Design A) or the lower 75 mm of base material (Design B) was placed and compacted, geogrid placement proceeded in a fairly simple and rapid manner. Initially, in 50 m increments ahead of the base gravel placement operation, a single 4 m wide roll of geogrid was unrolled along the centreline (Photo 1). This was followed by the two flanking 3 m wide rolls with a sidelap of 300 mm. Early problems with the overlying base gravel getting under the overlap during placement necessitated reversing this procedure such that the central 4 m roll overlapped on top of the two flanking rolls.

The technique for placing base aggregate on top of the geogrid also required refinement as the project proceeded. Initially, large-belly dump units slowly dumped material along the centreline of the geogrid. Unfortunately, the size and manoeuvring characteristics of these units caused considerable distortion of the geogrid layout. Tandem axle dump trucks were more successful, but gravel placement rates were too slow. The finally adopted technique had the tandem axle trucks backing onto and dumping backwards down the centreline of the geogrid (Photo 2). A small JD450 Cat bulldozer was used to spread the material sufficiently to maintain a central running surface and to 'seal' the longitudinal seams between geogrid rolls. Once this central lift extended the full length of the section, large-belly dump units could then proceed rapidly down the centre, dumping additional material as they went. A grader was then used to wing the material out to the sides and to grade the base layer to specified thickness. Once spread, the base material was compacted in excess of 95% standard Proctor density using a vibratory steel drum roller. Placement of the geogrid, base gravel, and compaction of a 300 m test section was easily accomplished in a 4 hr. period. Final surfacing with a graded aggregate seal was delayed until the spring of 1988.

PERFORMANCE AND COST EVALUATION

A performance evaluation program has been carried out to ascertain the long term load carrying capacity of the road sections and to help resolve the question of optimal geogrid location. The Benkelman beam method has been used to evaluate the condition of the road in the spring (which is the most critical period of time for the subgrade) every year since the completion of the road. To date, all test sections have performed satisfactorily (regardless of the geogrid location), and at least as well as the standard design sections.

For this particular case, the placement cost of the standard 700 mm thick design was about \$4.22/m² of roadway. With the inclusion of the SS-1 geogrid (at \$1.78/m²), the construction cost for the reinforced test designs was on the order of \$4.55/m² of roadway. Since the aggregate source was unusually close (7 km), the geogrid costs were not fully offset by the reduction in aggregate thickness. It is estimated that the break-even point between the standard and this type of reinforced design occurs when gravel haul distances approach 15 km.

CONCLUSIONS

From the performance to date, it appears that the geogrid reinforced sections are performing at least as well as the thicker standard roadway design. For similar projects in excess of 15 km from an aggregate source, the geogrid reinforced base section becomes cost effective through decreased aggregate haul costs. Since most projects in north eastern British Columbia are in excess of 50 km from aggregate deposits, there is a significant economic benefit to be derived from this design. In addition, this approach will help conserve the rapidly diminishing aggregate resources of the region.

REFERENCES

Canadian Good Roads Association, "Guide to the Structural Design of Flexible and Rigid Pavements in Canada", CGRA, Ottawa, Canada, Sept. 1965.

Giroud, J.P., Ah-Line, C. and Bonaparte, R., "Design of Unpaved Roads and Trafficked Areas with Geogrids", Proc., Symposium on Polymer Grid Reinforcement in Civil Engineering, London, England, Mar 1984.

Haas, R., "Granular Base Reinforcement of Flexible Pavements Using Tensar Geogrids", Tensar Technical Note: BR1, Jan 1986.

The Tensar Corporation, "Design Guidelines for Flexible Pavements with Tensar Geogrid Reinforced Base Layers", Tensar Technical Note: BR2, Mar 1986a.

The Tensar Corporation, "Design Guidelines for Haul and Access Roads Reinforced with Tensar Geogrids", Tensar Technical Note: BR4, Jun 1986b.

GEOTEXTILE REINFORCED EMBANKMENT FOR HEAVY TRAILER TRANSPORT UPPLANDS VAESBY, SWEDEN

L. Bjerin and L. Eriksson
Swedish Geotechnical Institute
Linköping, Sweden

In 1974 a new road was constructed at Upplands Vaesby, some 20 km north of Stockholm, through a 1 km long area of soft clay. The road was designed to carry vehicles transporting transformers with a total mass of 700 tonnes. To increase the stability of the road, a woven polyester geotextile was put into the embankment in two layers and anchored in adjacent loading berms on both sides of the road.

By order of the Swedish National Road Authorities, measurements of the deformation of the geotextile were carried out, which included long-term deformations as well as deformations due to vehicles transporting transformers.

DESCRIPTION

The heavy transport vehicle, with a total mass of 700 tonnes, is equivalent to two load areas, 3.65 m wide and 17.6 m long, with a pressure of 60 kPa.

The soil consists of soft clay down to a maximum depth of 12 m. The undrained shear resistance of the clay varies between 7 and 15 kPa.

The road embankment was 1.2 m high and 7 m wide with two 8 m wide adjacent loading berms of the same height as the road embankment (i.e., the embankment crown was 23 m wide, with the 7 m wide pavement in the centre).

The geotextile reinforcement consisted of hardened woven polyester, quality 600, produced by AB Fodervävnader, Boraas, Sweden. The geotextile was put into the embankment in two layers with a total length of 17 m. The geotextile was prestressed by 1% when put into place to reduce the initial strain in the geotextile. Each layer of geotextile has a tensile strength of 65 kN/m at a strain of about 15%. The reinforcement was anchored in the loading berms on both sides of the road and calculations indicated a maximum geotextile tension of 70 kN/m.

DESIGN

The design was made in the early 1970's. In Figures 1 and 2, the calculated most dangerous slip-circles are shown without and with consideration of the reinforcement. By introducing a horizontal force simulating the reinforcement, the centre of the most dangerous slip-circles are displaced downwards and the factor of safety increases from 1.0 to the desired 1.3. For ordinary traffic load (i.e., 10 kPa instead of 60 kPa) the factor of safety is 2.3.

By using soil reinforcement with geotextiles, it was possible to make an inexpensive construction which could withstand high traffic loads. The total height of the construction could also be kept low, which reduces potential settlements. The chosen geotextile was one of the few geotextiles that were available in Sweden at that time.

PERFORMANCE

Long-term Deformations

The horizontal deformation of the geotextile was measured with the help of small magnets fixed to the geotextile. Measurements were carried out during construction and for about half a year thereafter [Bjerin, 1977].

The largest geotextile strain, 0.3 to 0.4%, was measured under the pavement while the strain under the loading berms was 0.1%. The strain rate was largest in the beginning and continued to decrease.

The vertical displacement of the geotextile, during the period indicated above, was 300 mm under the centre of the road and 220 mm under the loading berms.

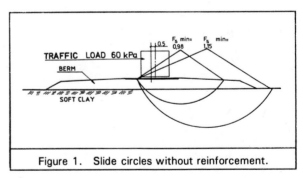

Figure 1. Slide circles without reinforcement.

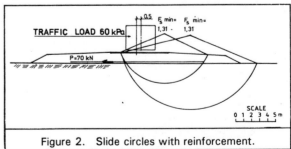

Figure 2. Slide circles with reinforcement.

| Photo 1.   Construction of the road with two layers of geotextile reinforcement. | Photo 2.   Heavy trailer transport. |

Deformations Due to Heavy Transport Load

Figure 3 shows the measured maximum displacement of the geotextile at the passing by of the 700 t vehicle. Under the centre of the road, the vertical displacement was 17 mm downward (i.e., settlement), while a small heave (1.5 mm) took place under the loading berms. The geotextile strain was 0.06% under the centre of the road and 0.1% under the edge of the traffic load. The vertical displacement was almost reversible while the horizontal displacement seemed to be permanent.

CONCLUSIONS

The long-term strain in the geotextile is not due to the differential settlements under the road embankment as these could only contribute to a strain in the order of 0.002%. The strain is probably an effect of creep movement in the soil despite the overall high factor of safety. Evidently, the geotextile exhibits creep under permanent load as continuing strain was measured. This was despite the fact that the load in the geotextile was very small compared with its total strength.

The small measured geotextile strains during the passing by of the vehicle show that the reinforcement does not significantly affect the stability of the road.

This depends probably partly on the short loading period (about 1 min) and partly on the fact that the factor of safety without considering the geotextile is about 1.0. Since the time of the design of the road, new design techniques have been developed. Using a design method proposed by Jewell [1982], the soil reinforcement shear strength is limited to a fraction of the soil shear strength. This method increases the required reinforcement and decreases the available anchor force. The calculated overall factor of safety for the embankment loaded with the trailer transport is however kept above 1.2.

REFERENCES

Bjerin, L., "Results of Deformation Measurements on Woven Polyester Fabric used as Reinforcement in a Road Embankment", Coll. Int. Sols et Textiles, Volume 3, Paris, April 1977, pp. 28-29.

Jewell, R.A., "A Limit Equilibrium Design Method for Reinforced Embankments on Soft Foundations", Proc. 2nd. Int. Conf. on Geotextiles, Las Vegas, Aug. 1982, pp. 671-676.

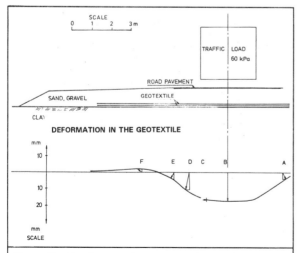

Figure 3.   Settlements in correspondence of geotextile due to the heavy trailer transport.

GEOTEXTILES FOR THE CONSTRUCTION OF A MOTORWAY MOTORWAY A-45 BETWEEN GIESSEN AND HANAU, GERMANY

B. Vosteen and W. Wilmers
Baustoff- und Bodenprüfstelle des
Hessischen Landesamtes für Straßenbau, Wetzlar, Germany

The construction of the Motorway A-45 in the Hanau area in 1976 and 1977 required long embankments to be built in the flood plain of the River Kinzig. Improvement of the subgrade soil was possible only to a limited extent. Geotextiles were therefore used as separators between the subgrade and the embankment fill to enable the first lift to be trafficked and prevent mixing of the subsoil and the fill. Large movements of the water table in the flood plain had to be incorporated in the design.

SITE TRIALS

Four full-scale site trials were carried out between 1974 and 1977 to determine how geotextiles work and whether they were suitable. The first trial involved the installation of several different nonwovens on the same trial area to compare their ease of handling and their behaviour during aggregate placement and under subsequent traffic loads. In the course of further tests their influence on the bearing capacity of a granular layer was studied.

Construction Site Bypass in Bisses (1974/76)

Nonwovens were utilized in the construction of an embankment of up to 1.2 m height which formed part of the site bypass. The subgrade consisted of a 2.0 m thick layer of organic silts of soft to medium consistency, which would otherwise have had to be excavated and replaced.

The embankment was constructed in the summer of 1974 and subsequently removed in the spring of 1976. Care was taken to minimize damage to the geotextiles during recovery and it was observed that all the nonwovens had successfully separated the two layers; in-situ organic soil and placed coarse granular fill. All the geotextiles had deformed round deeper-seated stones, and all had been punctured by the odd angular or pointed stone without the tear propagating further. Under the mainly static load exerted on the geotextile, the stones had remained in the holes they had created, so that the separation function was in no way impaired.

Trial Embankment at Bisses (1975)

A trial embankment was constructed in the Horloff valley near the Giessen-Hanau motorway in order to test the behaviour of the organic soils of the valley under the embankment fill. The following were to be investigated:

1. The speed of settlement.
2. The effect of compaction equipment and construction traffic on the subgrade soil.
3. The influence of different embankment heights on the subgrade.

4. The influence of geotextiles on the subgrade/embankment system.

Lutradur LDH 7225 nonwoven geotextile was used. A sketch of the embankment and the layout of the instrumentation are shown in Figures 1 and 2. The settlement behaviour shows a very quick reaction to the individual loading stages. This reaction is particularly evident in the pore water pressure curve, which rises rapidly after each loading, and falls just as quickly as a result of consolidation. The rise and fall of the water table - in parallel with the pore water pressure - shows that the excess water was mainly displaced laterally.

In order to examine the load behaviour of embankment and subgrade, the embankment was loaded by a truck next to the settlement gauges and the deflection under load, and the recovery on load removal, were measured by levelling. Figures 1 and 2 show the results. It can be seen that at embankment heights of 2 m and 3 m, no significant deflections are achieved. At heights of 1.5 m, however, deflections are measurable, and these become very significant at heights of 1.0 m and 0.5 m. A distinct difference in deflection was registered between bays 2 and 9, the bays with and without nonwoven geotextile. This was increased by the considerable difference in the depth of the water table in the two bays.

The water table was much higher under the area with geotextile. A high water table goes hand in hand with greater sensitivity to load. A high pore water pressure under the additional load results in large deflections and "rebound" of the soil.

Bay 10 with nonwoven geotextile shows on average similar or slightly higher figures than bay 1 without geotextile. It should be noted here that the difference in the water table is even more pronounced than in bays 2/9. With certain reservations it is thus possible to conclude that the bearing behaviour of the embankment was improved by the geotextile.

A study of the settlement readings at different times (Figure 2) shows that

- the readings vary widely with the axle load
- the values of settlement at constant axle load reduce with time.

This second phenomenon is due to the consolidation of the subgrade and the subsequent strength improvement of the soil. This means that the importance of the geotextile for the load behaviour of the embankment decreases with time. The long-term strength of the

Photo 1. Motorway under construction.

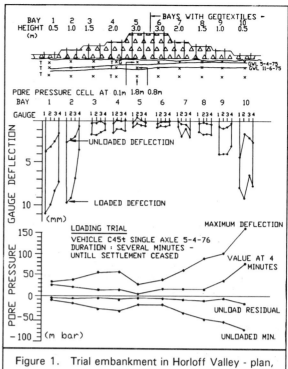

Figure 1. Trial embankment in Horloff Valley - plan, loading trial.

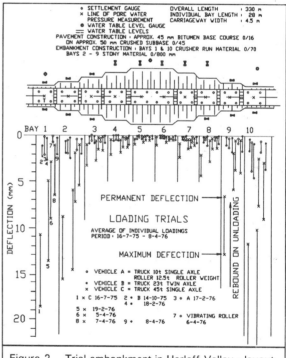

Figure 2. Trial embankment in Horloff Valley - layout, loading trials.

geotextile is thus not particularly important if the subgrade can consolidate.

After 4.5 years, the embankment was removed in the autumn of 1979 and samples of the geotextile were recovered. The residual grab strength was about 90% of the original value.

FINAL CONSTRUCTION (1976/77)

The A-45 and A-66 motorways are closely connected over a length of about 2 km. The B-40 and B-43 main roads both join the motorways in this junction area, which is entirely on embankments. The subgrade consists of claystone and siltstone underlying either sands and gravels from the Main and Kinzig rivers or alluvial deposits, loams and muck.

More or less well-grade basalt and gravelly sands were used as fill up to the high water mark of the River Kinzig. The remainder of the embankment was constructed of claystone and siltstone of varying strength - strong when freshly excavated, but crumbling readily when weathered.

Approximately 120,000 m² of nonwoven geotextile were used as a separator between the soft subgrade and the embankment base layer, which was not always optimally graded. The geotextile strips were laid across the axis of the embankment and overlapped by about 500 mm.

PERFORMANCE

Since the embankment fill was compacted to a low void content (Void content < 20%, air content < 12%), the use of geotextile prevented ingress of subsoil into the fill, and because settlement of the subgrade had been induced by intensive dynamic compaction before the pavement was constructed, the motorway is still in excellent level condition today without repair work having had to be effected.

REFERENCES

Non supplied.

GEOTEXTILE REINFORCEMENT OF A TEMPORARY ROAD
SMOLENSKAYA REGION, USSR

V.D. Kazarnovsky and B.P. Brantman
All-Union Highway Research Institute (Soyuzdornii)
Moscow, USSR

One of the first roads in the USSR where a domestic geotextile was first used was a temporary road in Smolenskaya region. Construction of the road had to be accelerated to evacuate populated localities from areas to be flooded when the reservoir of Vazuzskaya hydrosystem was being filled with water, and to allow for the movement of construction vehicles.

DESCRIPTION

The Temporary Road

The temporary road, about 20 km long, was to be constructed within the shortest period of time and with a minimum thickness of fill.

Construction Conditions

The site was characterized by soft plastic loam soils with a moisture coefficient up to 1.5 (i.e., the ratio of natural moisture content to optimum moisture content determined according to Soyuzdornii method), by a high ground water level, and by a prolonged stagnation of water above ground.

To accelerate construction of the temporary road, which at the same time provided a passage for construction vehicles delivering sand for the fill, the geotextile "Dornit" ϕ-1 was used on several sections of the road where the soil consisted of a light silty loam and had a moisture content, at the time of construction, equal to 27-30%.

TECHNICAL CONSIDERATIONS

Geotextile Properties

"Dornit" ϕ-1 is manufactured from waste synthetic fibres by needle-punching and has the following characteristics: mass per unit area = 600 g/m^2; roll width = 1.7 m; nominal thickness = 4.5 mm; tensile strength roll direction = 12 kN/m and cross-roll direction = 6 kN/m; strain at failure 70% roll direction and 130% cross-roll direction.

Construction Procedures

A medium grained sand containing gravel and 2% of silty and clayey particles was delivered from the pit in dump trucks and used for the fill. Grading of the fill was performed with a bulldozer. Taking into account the properties of the fill soil and the soft subgrade, the vehicle load, and the fact that a geotextile was used, a required fill thickness equal to 400 mm was determined by means of calculations.

Construction procedures of temporary road sections on which the geotextile was used included: a rough grading of the soft subgrade by a bulldozer going back and forth with a lowered blade; unrolling the geotextile across the fill axis with 300 mm overlaps between adjacent rolls; filling and grading of 450 to 500 mm thick sand layer followed by compaction with a light weight roller.

Observations at Construction

The difference in driving conditions on sections with the geotextile and without it could be observed immediately after installation of the geotextile. It was actually impossible to perform work after 8 to 10 passes of dump trucks along the same ruts in the section where the geotextile was not used and the sand fill thickness was limited to 400 mm for comparison. On the road section where the geotextile was placed under the sand fill, the rut depth did not exceed 100 to 120 mm and intermixing of the fill sand with the subgrade soil did not occur.

Observations During Road Usage

Each working day, 300 vehicles, mostly dump trucks, travelled in both directions. After the temporary road was used for several months the ruts on the road section without a geotextile had to be graded continually. Every morning, before the main traffic drove on the road, both the sections with and without the geotextile were graded with a bulldozer.

Measurement of the ruts showed that, on the section without a geotextile, ruts from 200 to 250 mm deep were formed, and the traffic speed slowed to 5 km/h. On the road section with a geotextile, the rut depths were only 100 to 120 mm in spite of the fact that dump trucks travelled along the same rut. The traffic speed was able to maintain 25 to 30 km/h and the vehicles could pass each other using the whole width of the fill.

The results of the measurements of the rut depths are shown in Figure 1. The geotextile was in a good state: there was no significant difference between its characteristics before and after traffic.

Extent of Experience

Experience gained in constructing temporary roads on soft soils with geotextiles in various regions of the USSR made it possible to use geotextiles for the construction of several temporary roads in the Moscow region.

Photo 1.   Haul road under construction.

Figure 1.   Change in the rut depths depending on the number of vehicles passing (sand fill thickness = 400 mm); (1) Section with Geotextile, (2) Section without Geotextile and, (3) The design rut depth for a 2,500 mm thickness without geotextile.

In 1982 a slide occurred in an embankment of the main railway track of one of Moscow's regional railways. It was necessary to carry out repair work in the shortest possible period of time, so that the railway traffic was not interrupted. For that purpose 200,000 m³ of sand were delivered, but, first, it was necessary to construct (also in a very short time) a temporary access road about 300 m long on the swamped land of a river flood basin.

The area where the temporary access road to the railway was to be built was a sphagnous swamp. The peat depth was 2 m, and the vane shear resistance was from 14 to 16 kPa.

Two alternatives were considered: the first alternative consisted in making a sand fill 1.5 m thick and 9 m wide and the second one included the use of a geotextile "Dornit" ϕ-2 in 2.5 m wide rolls. On the basis of Soyuzdornii calculations, it was found that, to provide stability of the temporary access road with the use of geotextile, a 700 mm high sand fill was sufficient, i.e. half that required without a geotextile. To speed up the construction of the temporary access road, the geotextile alternative was adopted.

Construction procedures involved unrolling the geotextile over the subgrade with a 300 to 400 mm overlap of adjacent rolls, stapling the fabric at the overlaps, placing the 800 to 850 mm thick coarse-grained sand layer on the geotextile, grading the surface with a bulldozer, and rolling the surface with dump trucks. The use of a geotextile made it possible to accelerate construction of the access road, to provide a passage for construction vehicles, and to begin the repair of the railway embankment.

CONCLUSIONS

The use of geotextiles in temporary roads on soft soils made it possible to increase the bearing capacity of the soft soil and sand fill. This allowed the passage of dump trucks over the fills of reduced thicknesses. This, in its turn, allowed decreased consumption of materials, transport expenses, and duration of construction.

REFERENCES

Brantman, B.P. and Polunovsky, A.G., "The use of non-woven synthetic fabrics in road construction on soft soils", Review information, M. VPTITransstroy, 1979, p.40.

Brantman, B.P., "Experience in using "Dornit" in difficult situations", in the book: Use of geotextiles in transport construction, M. VPTITransstroy, 1988, pp. 42-44.

GEOTEXTILE REINFORCED EMBANKMENT FOR AIRPORT TAXIWAY ON PEAT
DULUTH INTERNATIONAL AIRPORT, MINNESOTA, USA

S.M. Gale
STS Consultants, Ltd.
Minneapolis, Minnesota, USA

B. R. Christopher
Polyfelt Inc.
Atlanta, Georgia, USA

The dilemma faced by the City of Duluth, the Minnesota Air National Guard, and the Federal Aviation Administration was to find the most economical and efficient construction approach for supporting an airport taxiway to be built over swamp deposited peat soils at the Duluth International Airport. After a review of several alternatives, STS Consultants, Ltd. recommended and designed a geotextile-reinforced embankment for the taxiway. This was constructed in 1983/84. To date, measurements indicate settlement within predicted ranges.

DESCRIPTION

Design constraints made it necessary to raise the existing grade 2 to 3 m in order to tie in the new taxiway pavement with the existing taxiway system and the existing turnaround. The taxiway pavement was to be 23 m wide with 3 m shoulders on each side of the pavement. The embankment section thus required approximately 191,000 m³ of granular fill.

The most obvious and costly approach to the problem would have been to excavate the peat and replace it with compacted fill. In previous construction at the site, all peat had been removed from beneath the existing runway. Upon a review of the specifics of the project, three construction schemes were proposed to deal with the unstable peat:

- Complete excavation and replacement of the peat with compacted fill.
- Displacement of the peat with final surcharging.
- Placement of a geotextile and stage loading of the peat with the final surcharge.

The cost and applicability of each alternative was analyzed on the basis of the following criteria:

- the amount and quality of necessary fill,
- the distance to borrow and disposal sites, and
- environmental concerns over preserving water quality and altering the existing drainage patterns in the area.

The placement of a geotextile and the stage loading of the peat with final surcharging was chosen as the most cost-effective and environmentally acceptable construction method. Because of the fibrous nature of the peat, shear strength gain was expected to occur during consolidation and compression of the peat. The use of a geotextile over the natural soil/fill interface was designed to meet the following criteria:

- Prevention of puncturing of the fill into the peat

during the initial loading phases.
- Prevention of the failure of the embankment side slopes.
- Provision for relatively uniform settlement.

DESIGN CRITERIA

It was especially critical that settlement of the peat be kept to a minimum after placement of the pavement. Thus, a surcharge load was required to accelerate the compression of the peat. This material was placed 2 m above the proposed pavement surface. To predict the amount and rate of settlement, long-term compression tests were performed. An extrapolation of the time/settlement curve to 50 years indicated that the 3 m peat deposit would settle approximately 1 m based upon a void ratio decrease from 4.6 to 2.7.

GEOTEXTILE SELECTION

The geotextile was selected based on a design strength requirement of 17.5 kN/m across the alignment, as well as construction survivability strength requirements.

A geotextile with slit film filaments in the roll direction and fibulated tape filaments in the cross-roll direction was selected. Wide width tensile testing with 200 mm wide strips indicated the geotextile had a peak strength of 36 kN/m in the machine direction and 42 kN/m in the cross-roll direction. The geotextile was rolled out parallel to the taxiway alignment so that the highest tensile strength direction of the geotextile was in the primary loading direction. This placement required field seams perpendicular to the principal strength direction.

Since the seam strength was especially critical, a high strength Kevlar™ thread was used with a double stitched "J" seam to achieve seam strengths exceeding the design strength requirements.

PERFORMANCE

Observation wells, pore pressure cells sealed within the peat, and settlement plates situated approximately 20 mm above the geotextile were monitored during fill placement.

After an approximate 2 month period with 2.6 to 3 m of fill in place over the geotextile, 500 mm of settlement had occurred. It was concluded that the slow rate of settlement during the first month of filling was due to the rather large excess pore pressures within the peat. This implied a slow rate of water drainage. During a period of 2 weeks, 1 m of fill was placed over the geotextile, and

Photo 1. Geotextile placement and review of field seams.	Photo 2. Field sewing with high strength Kevlar™ thread.

this resulted in an excess pore pressure within the peat ranging from 300 mm to 1.5 m of water head. After the 2 month period, an excess pore pressure within the peat of 1.5 to 3.0 m of water head was measured.

Long-term settlement measurements indicate values of 1.0 to 1.2 m, which is within the predicted ranges.

CONCLUSIONS

The selection of the geotextile alternative proved to be the most cost-effective and environmentally acceptable construction method. When consideration was given to the amount and quality of necessary fill, the distance to borrow and disposal sites, and environmental concerns over preserving water quality and altering the existing drainage patterns of the area, the geotextile solution proved to be superior to that of the conventional alternative of removing the existing peat and replacing it with compacted fill. Furthermore, a total cost savings of $800,000 was realized using the geotextile alternative.

REFERENCES

Gale, S.M., "Design and Construction of a Geotextile Reinforced Taxiway Embankment over Peat", Geotechnical Fabrics Report, Vol. 2, No. 1, Summer 1984.

GEOGRID REINFORCEMENT FOR AIRCRAFT PARKING AND TAXIING FACILITY AREAS
SPOT LOCATIONS, EUROPE

A. Arman
Woodward-Clyde Consultants
Baton Rouge, Louisiana, USA

P.M. Griffin, Jr.
Louisiana Transportation Research Center
University of Louisiana, Baton Rouge, USA

In the summer of 1986 the need arose for the development of a means of quickly constructing an inexpensive, easily hidden aircraft parking, taxiway system in Europe for the U.S. Air Force. It is a valid assumption that established co-located operating bases (COBs) are well mapped and targeted for aerial bombardment or missile attack. Most of these installations in Europe have been in place since World War II and cannot be totally hidden from aerial or satellite surveillance.

Initial phases of aerial attack will be directed at preventing defensive aircraft from ever leaving the ground. Aircraft locations on parking ramps and in hardened shelters are unpredictable and numerous. It is likely, then, that initial attacks will be principally aimed at runways and taxiways leading to runways.

A United States Air Force Reserve Fighter Group was deployed to a COB in Europe in August of 1986 for what is called "Checkered Flag Training". As a portion of that military training exercise, a few members of the Group PRIME BEEF (Primary Base Emergency Engineering Force) were tasked to provide expedient parking for the Group aircraft.

DESCRIPTION

A parking space on native soil that was not visible to aerial or satellite surveillance was to be constructed suitable for enabling the A-10 ground attack aircraft to be taxied onto and serviced for further flights. It was necessary to construct this facility with minimum manpower and virtually no equipment.

The A-10 aircraft when fully loaded, has a mass of 15,000 kg. Nose wheel tire pressure is 950 kPa and each main wheel pressure is 1,260 kPa.

The native soil at this site was a light grey, gap graded, medium coarse to very fine sand, with fine roots and some organics mixed with it. The sand contained a very fine black residue and had an unusual musty odour. (This installation was constructed during World War II as a Luftwaffe Base and the residue may be from petroleum spills in the vicinity of the runways.) The specific gravity of the sand was 2.60. The sand possesses an angle of internal friction of 27.5° as measured from direct shear tests.

It was determined that with the constraints of limited manpower and equipment and a very short time to prepare the site for use, ordinary construction methods would not suffice. The soil seemed ideal for application of a geosynthetic. A geogrid was chosen for this application and geotextiles were ruled out because of the problem posed by their weight and transporting them by air to the site.

The parking area was to be a rectangle approximately 30 m long by 9 m wide to accommodate the A-10 aircraft. The geogrid chosen was a biaxial type Tensar SS-1. Other geogrids might have served the same purpose, however, this brand was readily available for purchase and delivery on short notice. The geogrid was flown to the site with the troops.

CONSTRUCTION

The site was cleared of grass using a rented 0.56 m³ capacity front loader/backhoe. The sand was removed to a depth of 150 mm and stockpiled close to the site. The geogrid was placed in two layers, the first layer of geogrid was installed 150 mm below grade and the second layer was placed 75 mm below grade. The sand was then replaced over each layer of grid and smoothed manually by using ordinary garden rakes.

The grid was lapped 600 mm longitudinally and tied using plastic wire ties to hold it in place while the soil was being placed over it. The edges of geogrids were held in place by tent stakes.

At the conclusion of the installation, the sand was thoroughly wet down by the base fire department to "densify" it.

An untrained crew of six men, using hand tools, with the assistance of a backhoe/loader, completed the installation in less than twelve working hours.

TESTING

Only rudimentary testing of the strength of the geogrid-soil parking area could be made. A four thousand pound block of concrete was placed on wooden supports that would impose 1,260 kPa on the surface. It was recognized that errors of scale would be present but that this would demonstrate, within reason, whether or not it was safe to risk an aircraft on it.

Ordinary motor vehicles also were driven over the parking area to determine how subject the surface was to rutting and shifting. Prior to insertion of the geogrids, these same vehicles could not traverse the natural area without bogging down.

The loaded blocks of wood penetrated approximately 12 mm and the tires of the motor vehicles barely left a

| Photo 1.   Joining grid with wire ties. | Photo 2.   A-10 parked on geogrid supported parking area. |

The loaded blocks of wood penetrated approximately 12 mm and the tires of the motor vehicles barely left a mark.

The ultimate test was performed by pushing the A-10 aircraft onto the parking area. The main wheel tires penetrated the sand layer to a depth of up to 40 mm. The pushing vehicle had no difficulty manoeuvring the aircraft onto the parking pad. The aircraft was later serviced and inspected and started. The aircraft taxied off of the parking area onto the main runway and departed. The pilot stated that he had no difficulty moving the aircraft or steering it on the sand.

CONCLUSIONS

1. Where soil conditions permit a geogrid is a viable means of providing taxiways and parking stands which can be constructed very quickly and inexpensively by unskilled help.

2. Geogrids can be used to provide redundant aircraft facilities or to replace combat damaged facilities much more quickly than ordinary construction methods.

3. Since native soil is used as the final cover, the taxiways and parking areas can be made virtually undetectable except perhaps to infrared detection devices.

REFERENCES

Non supplied.

GEOSYNTHETIC MESHES FOR RACE COURSE STABILIZATION
SHA TIN RACE COURSE, HONG KONG

D.B. Sweetland
Netlon Limited
Blackburn, United Kingdom

In 1884, the Hong Kong Jockey Club was formed to improve and control horse racing in Hong Kong. Sha Tin Racecourse was completed in 1978, and annually holds 26 grass track meetings. Grass racing is more popular in Hong Kong as it is regarded as the optimum racing surface for the horses.

In 1985, discrete pieces of oriented polypropylene mesh were incorporated into sand to form the basis of a 400 m trial length of turf track at Sha Tin Racecourse.

DESCRIPTION

The purpose of the mesh in the trial was to improve the "going" (racing condition) by providing a more durable turf track which could be used more frequently.

The original track construction used incinerator ash as a substitute for sand to form a firm base for the final layer of soil and grass. Unfortunately, severe compaction in the topsoil/ash layers, with a chemical reaction within the ash layer itself, created an impermeable base which prevented drainage. This resulted in the turf track becoming shallow rooted. The turf remained saturated after heavy rain resulting in severe divotting of the grass during racing with the transfer of meetings from grass to sand.

To overcome this problem the Chief Civil Engineer of The Royal Hong Kong Jockey Club conducted research into new track materials which would be permeable, support a deep-rooted grass system, yet remain stable under the weight of horses. In 1977, the performance of grass cultivated in pure sand was evaluated. This medium was satisfactory for growing and maintaining grass, but the surface was not strong enough to withstand the impact of hooves. To increase cohesion within the sand, without affecting drainage or root growth, Netlon Mesh Elements, discrete pieces of oriented polypropylene mesh, typically measuring 100 mm x 50 mm and with 10 mm x 10 mm apertures, were chosen as the reinforcing medium.

TECHNICAL CONSIDERATIONS

Extensive research over three years in the Department of Civil Engineering at the University of Strathclyde [Mercer et al., 1984; McGown et al., 1985; Andrawes et al., 1986] concluded that sands can be strengthened substantially using discrete geosynthetic meshes without affecting their permeability. Repeated loading experiments at the University of Nottingham [Thom and Brown, 1985] indicated that the composite formed by sand and mesh elements was more resistant to permanent settlement. Research programs in the UK and the USA indicated that the composite did not impair the growth of grass; and the presence of elements within the sand provided additional anchorage points for the root system.

A 400 m long by 35 m wide section at the beginning of the 1,000 m chute was selected for full evaluation in January 1986 (Figure 1).

A quartz sand with the required particle grading was obtained from two sources in China. Research conducted at the University of California [Davis et al., 1974] has shown that it is desirable to have between 12% and 18% air-filled voids within the sand for optimum root growth.

A theoretical depth of 325 mm was required for this sand grading after considering the addition of a sand amendment. However, physical and economic constraints limited the total sand depth to 250 mm. Concentrations of mesh elements (Photo 1) of 0.2%, 0.3% and 0.4% by weight were selected for composite sand depths of 100 mm, 125 mm and 150 mm (Figure 2). The moisture retention of the sand, moisture movement through the sand plus the relationship between heavy rainfall and fertilization loss due to leaching through the base was studied.

Construction of the Trial Length at the Sha Tin

The original grass and topsoil/ash mixture was removed down to the aggregate drainage layer. The sand and mesh elements were mixed on an asphalt hardstanding using front loading traxcavators. The base layer of sand was spread to a depth of 100 mm, 125 mm and 150 mm using light construction equipment. The overhead sprinkler irrigation system was used to achieve the specified level of compaction.

The experience gained suggests that the design parameters for future work will comprise a composite layer 150 mm thick with a mesh element concentration of 0.4% by weight.

The grass selected was Tifton 419, an improved sterile Hybrid Bermuda, a warm season grass over-seeded with rye during the cool winter months. A new fertilization program, with a greater emphasis on potassium for hardness of growth, was compiled.

The trial area on the 1,000 m chute was completed in June 1986, opened for barrier trials in November 1986 and used for racing in March 1987.

OBSERVATIONS

The Royal Hong Kong Jockey Club has monitored

Photo 1. Mesh element.

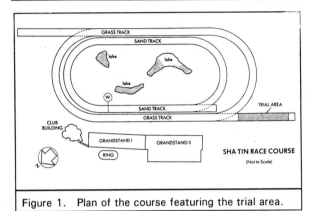

Figure 1. Plan of the course featuring the trial area.

same mesh element concept. This would allow the effect of horses' hooves to be monitored. This second trial was opened for racing in November 1987. After several race meetings the new mesh element concept was declared a success.

CONCLUSIONS

The Royal Hong Kong Jockey Club is convinced after the trials that they had found an adequate natural grass racing surface. Complete reconstruction of both Happy Valley Racecourse and Sha Tin Racecourse using Tensar meshes followed over a three year period ending in 1990. This is an excellent example of thorough geotechnical engineering research spreading into other fields. The Royal Hong Kong Jockey Club have subsequently reported [Halliday, 1991] that they have a track surface which allows racing in all weather conditions.

Following this work the oval and hillside tracks at Santa Anita, Los Angeles, USA have adopted the mesh element concept and several other tracks around the world have incorporated sections for evaluation.

REFERENCES

Andrawes, K.Z., McGown, A., Hytiris, N., Mercer, F.B. and Sweetland, D.B., "The use of mesh elements to alter the stress-strain behaviour of granular soils", Proc. 3rd. Int. Conf. on Geotextiles, Vienna, April, 1986.

Davis, W.B., Farnham, D.S. and Gowans, K.D., "The Sand Football Field", California Turfgrass Culture, Vol. 24, No. 3, Summer 1974.

Halliday, J., "Natural turf tracks, their construction and care", Proc. Sym. on Racing, Tucson, Arizonia, Dec. 1991.

McGown, A., Andrawes, K.Z., Hytiris, N. and Mercer, F.B., "Soil strengthening using randomly distributed mesh elements", Proc. 11th. Int. Conf. SMFE, San Francisco, August, 1985.

Mercer, F.B., Andrawes, K.Z., McGown, A. and Hytiris, N., "A new method of soil stabilization", Proc. Symposium on Polymer Grid Reinforcement in Civil Engineering, ICE, London, March, 1984.

Thom, N.H. and Brown, S.F., "Mesh element stabilization of a granular pavement layer", Department of Civil Engineering Report, University of Nottingham, April, 1985.

the physical condition of the turf, the damage from racing and recovery rate of the turf, and the racing condition or 'going'. Rainfall, irrigation requirements and the moisture content of the sand rootzone were also recorded.

The amount of racing damage, i.e. divoting, was found to be significantly reduced by the inclusion of the mesh elements. The track condition or going was substantially unaffected by weather conditions. Video recordings of races confirmed that the surface remained adequate for racing even after heavy tropical rainfall

Following the sucess of the 1,000 m chute, a new home bend was constructed at Sha Tin racetrack using the

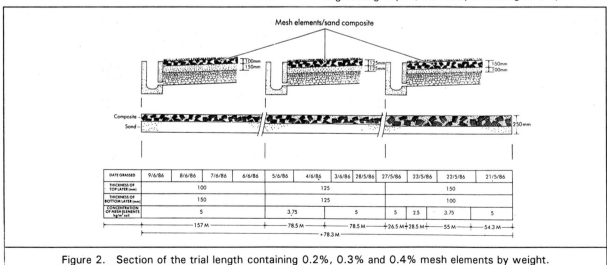

DATE GRASSED	9/6/86	8/6/86	7/6/86	6/6/86	5/6/86	4/6/86	3/6/86	28/5/86	27/5/86	23/5/86	22/5/86	21/5/86
THICKNESS OF TOP LAYER (mm)	100				125				150			
THICKNESS OF BOTTOM LAYER (mm)	150				125				100			
CONCENTRATION OF MESH ELEMENTS kg/m³ soil	5				3.75		5	5	2.5	3.75		5

Figure 2. Section of the trial length containing 0.2%, 0.3% and 0.4% mesh elements by weight.

GEOTEXTILES FOR STABILIZATION AND DRAINAGE IN LUMBER-YARDS SAINTE-MARIE DE BEAUCE, QUEBEC, CANADA

P. Anderson
Texel Inc.
St-Elzear, Beauce Nord, Quebec, Canada

The problems most frequently encountered in lumber yards or storage yards can be divided into three categories, (1) irregular topography, (2) soils made up of fine particles such as clay or silt, and most damaging of all (3) a poor drainage capacity. When one or all three of these factors are present in any worksite there exists an immediate correlation to the extra costs of repairs for machinery and/or heavy vehicles that circulate throughout.

DESCRIPTION

To better understand these facts, let us present a specific case where the site presented the majority of the problems already cited. This site is owned by Chassé Inc., a lumberyard located in the city of Sainte-Marie de Beauce, Québec, Canada. Because of the problems mentioned above the entire surface of their yard used to become bumpy, muddy and unsatisfactory for heavy truck loads during spring time. These problems reduced the traffic volume through the lumberyard, resulting in a measurable loss of time and money. The cost of adding new gravel on the surface of the soil in any one year was small, but large when considered on a long term basis. Since production was dropping, the owners had to find a fast solution. They were ready to spend a limited amount of money provided that it would solve the problem for several years. Mainly because of the economical aspect, the use of nonwoven needlepunched geotextiles were chosen.

Geotextiles help to distribute the loads in areas used for the storage and/or movement of heavy vehicles. In the case under consideration this was throughout the entire surface of the worksite. Secondly, nonwoven fabrics work constantly to drain the terrain in order to keep the surface dry, resulting in more efficient movement of vehicles throughout.

The project began in June 1986, the surface of the land to be restored with geotextiles was approximately 2,600 m². The soil was composed of silt, more or less clay like, with a water table close to 1.2 m below the surface.

TECHNICAL CONSIDERATIONS

Stage 1: Excavation

To obtain a level surface at the end of the construction, the first step is to excavate the entire surface to be restored. The depth of the excavation and the mass per unit area of the geotextile will both vary depending upon every lumberyard's needs. At Chassé Inc., the geotextile Texel 7611 (290 g/m²) was recommended combind with an excavation of 460 mm depth. Vehicles such as loaded truck (54,000 kg), lifts (22,600 kg) and grappling trucks (13,600 kg) were used on the site at a frequency that varied from 12 times per day to 5 times an hour depending upon the type of vehicle.

Stage 2: Drainage

For the Chassé Inc. lumberyard, in order to install a drainage system that would be both effective and durable, a series of trenches were dug to permit the installation of french drains. The depth of the trenches varied from 1.2 m to 2 m to allow good gravitational drainage. The french drains were formed with a layer of geotextile Texel 7607 (210 g/m²) and a large quantity of rounded stones.

Stage 3: Stabilization

The next step consists of covering the french drains so as to completely fill in the trenches and then, the entire surface of the worksite before installing the geotextile. A fine sand with good drainage properties is generally recommended for this purpose. This permits an even better planar flow towards the french drains. The geotextile Texel 7611 is now laid on the top of the sand and covered with a gravel possessing a good drainage capacity (0/19 mm).

Stage 4: Compaction

The last step is to compact the soil to obtain a flat and smooth surface that will last for years.

COST OVERVIEW

Undertaking a project comparable to the Chassé Inc. lumberyard was appraised at a geotextile cost of approximately $22,000. The smooth surface constructed for the geotextile contributed to construction speed of the first granular lift. It also resulted in a decision to eliminate a second lift at a cost savings of $150,000. It turned out to be a relatively economical solution. Moreover, since the completion of the work at Chassé Inc., it is estimated that vehicle efficiency has doubled.

Figure 1 provides a general overview of the drainage system installed at the Chassé Inc, lumberyard.

REFERENCES

Non supplied.

Photo 1. Texel 7611 was installed directly over excavated area to give a better stability of the soil.

Photo 2. For the best surface and subsurface drainage trenches must be dug to allow for installation of french drains.

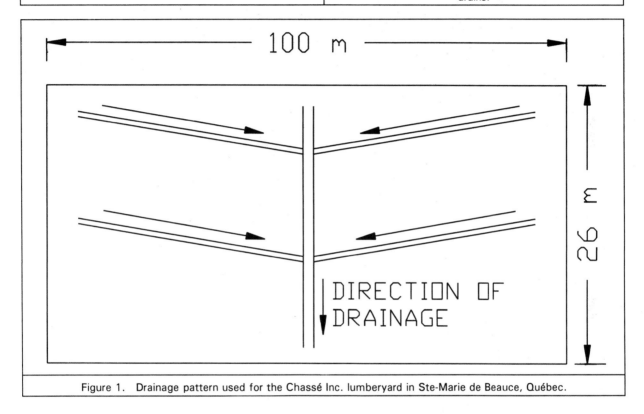

Figure 1. Drainage pattern used for the Chassé Inc. lumberyard in Ste-Marie de Beauce, Québec.

100 m

26 m

DIRECTION OF DRAINAGE

GEOTEXTILE INTERFACE BETWEEN PEAT AND ROAD EMBANKMENT
MOTORWAY A14, AUSTRIA

W. Schober
University of Innsbruck
Austria

P. Gmeiner
Government of Vorarlberg
Austria

S. Resl
Polyfelt Ges. m.b.H.
Linz, Austria

From 1975 to 1978, a 2.5 km long section of the Rheintal-Autobahn (Rhine Valley Motorway) A 14, located in the West of Austria (Vorarlberg), had to be constructed over extremely poor subsoil. A nonwoven geotextile was used as a separation layer between the subsoil and the up to 12.5 m high embankment.

DESCRIPTION

Subsoil Conditions

The subsoil in that area consists of up to 600 m deep normally consolidated sediments. At the surface, peat with a thickness of up to 8 m can be found, followed by changing layers of clay, silt, sand and gravel. The main properties of the peat layer are as follows:

Density:	1.10 - 1.30 t/m³
Water content:	136 - 672%
Stiffness modulus:	150 - 200 kPa
Undrained shear strength:	3 - 9 kPa

Embankment

The embankment height ranged from 1.5 to 12.5 m (see Figure 1). As good coarse-grained fill material was not available, excavation material from the nearby Pfaender Tunnel that was under construction had to be used. This material compacted well and had a friction angle of 34°.

PROPOSED CONSTRUCTION TECHNIQUES

The construction was planned in 3 stages (see Figure 2):

Stage I: Placement of the geotextile directly on the grass cover followed by slow filling of boundary strips with excavation material from the Pfaender-pilot-tunnel. This procedure was chosen in order to preconsolidate the toe areas of the final embankment.

Stage II: Over placement of the embankment fill to give an excess load, using excavation material from the Pfaender-tunnel full-face excavation. The excess load, as percentage of embankment height, ranged from 16% (at 12.5 m height) to 67% (at 1.5 m height).

Stage III: Removal of the excess load to the required level and grading of the slopes with an inclination of 1.5H:1V.

In order to optimize the balance of earthworks quantities, the settlements had to be calculated as accurately as possible. Besides field and laboratory tests,

the experience from a four year old embankment nearby was taken into account.

The purposes of the geotextile were:

* to separate the fill and subsoil,
* to stabilize the fill, and
* to avoid local shear failures during construction.

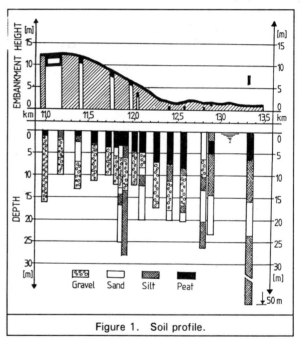

Figure 1. Soil profile.

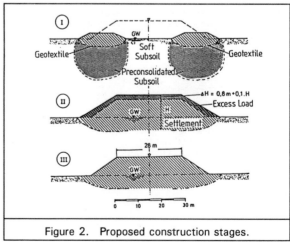

Figure 2. Proposed construction stages.

Photo 1. View of the construction site.

A polypropylene needlepunched nonwoven, produced by Polyfelt, with tensile strength of 21 kN/m and strain at failure of 50% was selected.

ACTUAL CONSTRUCTION AND PERFORMANCE

As a result of a lack of fill material, the planned construction procedure of Stage I had to be changed from two boundary strips to one construction road at the centre of the embankment alignment. The settlement behaviour at km 12.120 illustrated in Figures 3 and 4 can be stated as typical for the whole section.

The observed actual settlement illustrated in Figure 5 had a good correlation to the predicted ones. Therefore, the actual earthworks quantity was only 17% lower than calculated.

At km 12.500 a base failure occurred. This would have been prevented if the initially proposed construction with the preloaded boundary strips had been executed.

CONCLUSIONS

When using a nonwoven geotextile as separation layer, high embankments can be constructed economically even over extremely poor foundation.

Due to the permanent separation, settlements, and thus the balance of earthworks quantity, can be predicted more accurately.

The danger of local shear failures during construction can be reduced significantly by using a separating geotextile.

Due to its high extensibility, the needlepunched nonwoven geotextile was not damaged by the sharp-edged block-size tunnel excavation material despite a considerable drop during placement.

REFERENCE

Schober, W., Gmeiner, P. and Teindl, H.: "Grundung auf weichen Boden beim Bau der Rheintal-Autobahn A14 in Vorarlberg [Foundation on Soft Soils During Construction of Rhine-Valley-Motorway A14 in Vorarlberg, Austria]", Geotechnik, Journal of the Deutsche Gesellschaft fur Erdund Grundbau, 1981, No. 1, pp. 9-15.

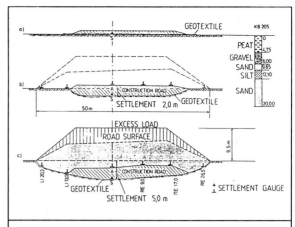

Figure 3. Actual construction stages and settlement measurement at km 12.120.

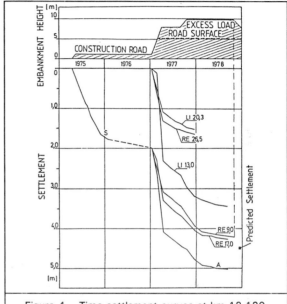

Figure 4. Time-settlement curves at km 12.120.

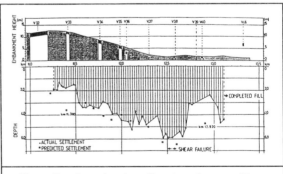

Figure 5. Actual and predicted settlements (Nov. 1978).

CHAPTER 9

FILL AND EMBANKMENT REINFORCEMENT

GEOTEXTILE-GRAVEL-GEOGRID SYSTEM FOR REINFORCEMENT OF AN EMBANKMENT ZBLEWO ROAD, POLAND

L. Hapka
Regional Headquarters of Public Roads
Gdansk, Poland

In 1987, a 7 m high road embankment near Zblewo in the northern part of Poland (70 km from Gdansk) was founded in very difficult subsoil conditions on a flexible slab made of gravel wrapped in a nonwoven geotextile and placed over a layer of geogrid.

DESCRIPTION

The Embankment

The embankment is 80 m long and 7 m high with 1.5H:1V slopes. The width of the crown is 12 m. The embankment allows the Warlubie-Leba main road No. 214 to cross the valley of the Piesienica River.

The Foundation Soil

A layer of peat and other saturated highly organic soils was found in the foundation soil. The maximum thickness of the layer was 6.30 m on the centreline of the old river bed and it diminished to zero near the slopes forming the valley.

The Slab

A flexible slab (width 30-45 m, length 80 m) made of gravel wrapped in one layer of a thick needlepunched nonwoven geotextile (mass per unit area: 400 g/m²) was placed under the base of the embankment. The tensile strength of the geotextile was not sufficient to allow light equipment used for building the gravel layer to enter the area. Because of that, a layer of geogrid had to be placed on the ground under the geotextile layer. Adjacent strips of grid and geotextile were joined and fixed to the ground by metal pins.

Although the tensile strength of the geotextile was rather low, it gave the cohesionless gravel layer some tensile strength, which allowed a better distribution of the load caused by the embankment on the weak subsoil.

Construction

Construction started in October 1986 and ended in May 1987, with a break during the frost period. The embankment was built with use of conventional methods and equipment. Until a height of 2 m was reached, the embankment layers were compacted with use of light equipment; then, heavy compactors were used. The time interval between placement of successive layers depended on the ability of the already placed gravel layer to drain the water expelled from the foundation soil to ditches situated on both sides of the slab. The pavement was built in September and October 1987, when it was sure that consolidation of the organic layer had finished.

Importance and Special Features of the Structure

Piesienica River ensures water balance of a large territory of nearby meadows and fields. It was essential that the selected construction method did not disturb the water balance during and after the construction period, and did not influence the course of the river.

Road No. 214 is an important main road. As a part of the modernization aimed at the improvement of traffic conditions on the road, by-passes of small towns and villages were designed. In the beginning of 1986 almost the whole length of the road, except in two places, had been modernized. Extremely difficult soil conditions in the area of the planned by-pass of Zblewo and Lubichowo caused heavy traffic to still go through narrow streets of those small towns.

Flexible slabs made of gravel wrapped in a geotextile had been previously used only for culvert foundations. After the successful application of this method in Zblewo, a decision was made to use it for building an embankment under similar conditions in Lubichowo.

TECHNICAL CONSIDERATIONS

Design

Design parameters of the foundation soil were determined on the basis of laboratory tests performed on samples taken from cased boreholes. The influence of the loads exerted by the embankment on the value of the oedometer modulus of the foundation soil was investigated.

Heaving of the soil was prevented by designing berms on both sides of the main embankment. The berms were also founded on the flexible slab. The safety factor of the structure assumed for the calculations was 1.3.

An alternative conventional solution was considered. It required driving sheet piles and complete replacement of the organic layer.

The Geotextile

The geotextile used was a Polish needlepunched polypropylene nonwoven produced by Zaklady Przemyslu Filcowego in Lódz.

Basic properties of the geotextile are as follows: nominal thickness 6.5 mm; mass per unit area 400 g/m²; tensile strength and strain of failure: 9 kN/m and 85% (in

| Photo 1. Placement of the geogrid, and placement of the geotextile in the background. | Photo 2. Placing of the first embankment layer on the flexible slab - a general view. |

the roll direction) and 7 kN/m and 75% (in the cross-roll direction); coefficient of permeability k_g 1.2 mm/s (under a normal pressure $\sigma = 1$ kPa), 0.46 mm/s ($\sigma = 100$ kPa), 0.2 mm/s ($\sigma = 250$ kPa). The tensile parameters were obtained from tests on 500 x 100 mm specimens.

Performance and Benefits

A system of surveying points on the slab and in the surrounding area allowed constant monitoring of deformations of the foundation soil. Consolidation of the foundation soil was completed in October 1987 (i.e., 6 months after the end of embankment construction). Settlement of the embankment was 750 mm, compared to the calculated value of 720 mm. No measurable heaving of the foundation soil on both sides of the embankment occurred.

The described solution gave remarkable economical and technical benefits. 24,000 m^3 of earthworks and the driving of sheet piles had been avoided. The construction method was very simple and easy to perform with use of conventional equipment. The method did not disturb the water balance of the area and there was no danger of influencing the course of the river.

REFERENCES

Dembicki, E., "Parcie, odpór i nósność gruntu", Arkady, Warszawa, 1979.

Kisiel, I., Dmitruk, S. and Lysik, B., "Zarys reologii gruntów. Nośność i stateczność gruntów", Arkady, Warszawa, 1969, 305 p.

Lambe, T.W., and Whitman, R.V., "Mechanika gruntów", Arkady, Warszawa, 1977, 668 p.

Molisz, R., Baran, L. and Werno, M., "Posadawianie nasypow na gruntach organicznych metoda wstepnej konsolidacji", Wydawnictwa Komunikacji i Laczności, Warszawa, 1981, 126 p.

Rowe, R.K., and Soderman, K.L., "Geotextile reinforcement of embankments on peat", Geotextiles and Geomembranes, Vol. 2, No. 4, 1985, pp. 277 - 298.

GEOTEXTILE REINFORCED BREAKWATER ON SOFT FOUNDATION SOIL
PORT SAID, EGYPT

P. Risseeuw and W. Voskamp
Akzo Industrial Systems bv.
Arnhem, The Netherlands

Port Said is the entrance to the Suez Canal from the Mediterranean Sea. As a part of a new canal bypass, two rock-filled breakwaters of length 1.5 km each were constructed, reaching into the Mediterranean Sea. Both were reinforced with a high strength woven geotextile.

DESCRIPTION

The subsoil on the site consisted of an upper layer of sand, 8 meters of silts and clays, and a lower layer of plastic clay. It was determined that the weak, thin layers of the stratum (see Table 1 and Figure 1) might fail under the loading imposed by the breakwaters and trigger a slide.

Table 1. Description and properties of soils in Figure 1.

A	: sand	$\phi = 30°$	$\gamma = 18$ kN/m³
B	: silt	$\phi = 28°$	$\gamma = 19$ kN/m³
C	: clay	$c = 11$ kPa	$\gamma = 19$ kN/m³
D	: sand	$\phi = 32°$	$\gamma = 19$ kN/m³
E	: clay	$c = 10$ kPa	$\gamma = 19$ kN/m³
F	: sand	$\phi = 32°$	$\gamma = 19$ kN/m³
G	: clay	$c = 15$ kPa	$\gamma = 17$ kN/m³
H	: sand	$\phi = 28°$	$\gamma = 19$ kN/m³
I	: clay	$c = 20$ kPa	$\gamma = 19$ kN/m³

A slide was most likely to occur during the construction stage, if heavy equipment (like an American Hoist 165 t crane) was used for the laying of armour stones. Stability calculations showed the safety factor was 1.28, if the crane was to stand in the middle of the breakwater under construction and rest on one of its two tracks. The factor of safety would be significantly less if the crane was at the edge of the breakwater crest. The value of 1.28 for the factor of safety was regarded as a minimum, thus limiting freedom of movement of the crane.

DESIGN

Geotextile Reinforcement

The problem was solved by using a heavy duty reinforcing geotextile which, at the interface of the fill and subsoil, reduces horizontal stresses in the subsoil, thereby improving the global stability. The geotextile used was Stabilenka 200, a woven polyester with the following characteristics:

- mass per unit area: 450 g/m²
- tensile strength (roll direction): 200 kN/m
- strain at failure (roll direction): 9%
- secant modulus (roll direction): 2,200 kN/m

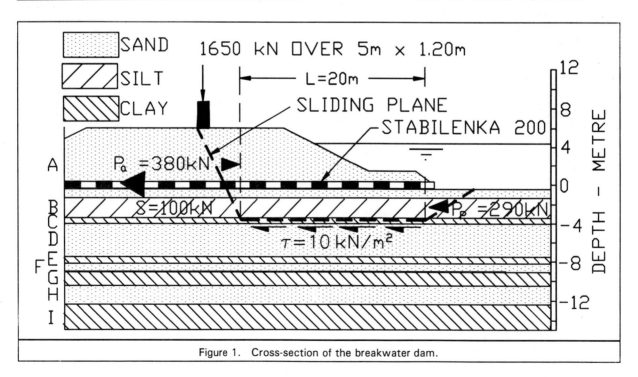

Figure 1. Cross-section of the breakwater dam.

Photo 1. Typical heavy crane required to work on breakwater during construction.

Photo 2. Installation of geotextile.

Photo 3. Construction of initial lift of breakwater.

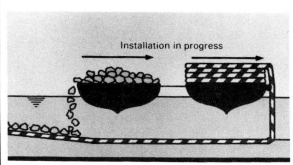

Figure 2. Installation of mat by winching between two barges.

Apart from the stress-strain behaviour of this material, which matched the Young's modulus of the clay, another property was very important: polyester does not float. In this case, this was a considerable advantage, as the mat had to be installed at a depth of 4.5 m below sea level.

Stability Calculations

Stability calculations were conducted assuming that a horizontal sliding surface would be located in the uppermost clay layer (C in Figure 1). By founding each breakwater on a 50 m wide mat of geotextile, the safety factor increased to 1.54. And if the crane had to move to the edge of the crest, the safety factor would still exceed the 1.28 minimum.

CONSTRUCTION

Construction took place in 1978 and 1979. In order to form large prefabricated panels required in this project, ten widths of the selected geotextile were sewn together, with an overlap of 300 mm. Sewing was done on shore, by hand, by a crew of 50 local women using sewing needles; it took them no more than a day to assemble a panel of 50 m x 50 m. Using a special sewing thread, a seam efficiency of 70% in the cross-roll direction was obtained. The 50 m wide zigzag-folded panel of geotextile was then hoisted on board a barge and slipped from the deck to the sea bed (Photo 2 and Figure 2). A carrier following the barge anchored the mat immediately after sinking by loading it with rocks (Photo 3). In such a way a total quantity of 58,000 m² was placed.

PERFORMANCE

Thanks to geotextile reinforcement, heavy equipment could be used from the start saving the contractor months of labour, and increasing the factor of safety. The building of the breakwater armour was successfully completed and no loss of stability occurred.

In the years after construction, the breakwaters improved the shear strength of the soft clay layers, due to the consolidation process. Consequently, the most critical phase was at the end of the construction period. In the decade since completion of the project, no failures, or exceptional settlement were reported.

REFERENCES

Anonymous, "Egypt: woven mats improve breakwater slope stability", Construction Industry Int., April 1980.

V. Van Zanten, R., "Geotextiles and Geomembranes in Civil Engineering". Balkema, Rotterdam, 1986.

GEOGRID AND OTHER GEOSYNTHETICS FOR DIVERSION DITCH OVER SOFT WASTE EASTERN USA, USA

M.F. Houlihan and N.D. Williams
GeoSyntec Consultants
Boca Raton, Florida, USA

In order to facilitate drainage of surface run-on around a waste facility, a 3 m high diversion ditch was constructed over a large waste pond. Among the several applications for geosynthetics used in the project, a specifically designed high strength woven geogrid was used as base reinforcement for the ditch.

DESCRIPTION

The site is a regulated hazardous waste unit which is located in a mountainous region of the eastern United States. The waste "pond" is 283,000 m² in surface area and is bounded by a river on one side and by a steep slope on the other side. In order to minimize leaching of hazardous constituents into the adjacent river from the unit, a 610 m long, 3 m high diversion ditch was constructed in 1987 adjacent to the hill side. The structure replaces an existing ditch built in 1983 which was no longer functional due to failure in several sections of the ditch. These failures were caused by mass instability resulting from the weak waste foundation, seepage infiltration, and poor construction techniques. The reconstruction scheme called for complete reconstruction of two severely distressed sections using a high strength, PVC-coated polyester woven geogrid base reinforcement, modifications to the remainder of the ditch, and inclusion of several features to prevent seepage into the reconstructed structure.

DESIGN

General Considerations

Several factors were considered in preparing the detailed design. The foundation for the ditch structure is a saturated, loose, silty material with an undrained shear strength of approximately 5 kPa. This weak foundation limited the final grade along the structure invert, and the practical height to which the structure could be built. The high pH (between 10.5 and 11.5) of the waste limited the choice of geosynthetics which could be in contact with this waste. Finally, subsurface seepage from the hill side had to be controlled to prevent saturation of the fill material.

Two alternatives were identified for treatment of the weak foundation. First, the waste material beneath the reconstructed sections could be excavated and replaced with soil. This option was rejected due to the high cost associated with excavation and fill placement. The second alternative, construction of the structure over the waste using base reinforcement, was chosen.

Technical Considerations for High Strength Reinforcement

The design cross-section for the completely rebuilt sections was analyzed for slope stability failure, bearing failure, and plastic failure to determine the critical mode of failure. Based on these analyses, a single layer of base reinforcement with a tensile strength of about 160 kN/m was required. The design tensile strength, which included reduction factors for creep, constructibility, and chemical compatibility, was 60 kN/m. However, no single-layer geosynthetic having this strength was available from geosynthetic manufacturers, and the use of multiple layers of geosynthetics was not desirable, particularly because of the short height of this structure. Therefore, Nicolon, Inc. was contracted to specially design a woven geogrid having the required strength.

The polymers chosen for the geogrid were selected based on stress-strain characteristics, creep potential, and chemical compatibility. Polyester was chosen over polypropylene and nylon as the base polymer due to its good creep characteristics and its stress-strain properties, which closely match the predicted strain levels of the weak waste foundation material in the range of stresses expected after construction. Since polyester is not generally compatible with high pH wastes, a covering of high-pH compatible PVC was placed on the polyester woven geogrid. The resulting geogrid had a wide width tensile strength of approximately 350 kN/m, and the PVC coating remained continuous over the polyester during testing, even at high strains.

Analyses indicated that the critical failure circle passed closer to the intersection between the waste foundation and the adjacent rock hill side than the expected bond length of the soil/geosynthetic system. Therefore, the geogrid was extended up the slope of the hill for 1.5 m to provide adequate embedment length. To minimize the effects of chemical degradation on the geogrid due to the waste, the geogrid was placed over a 300 mm layer of granular drainage material, as shown on Figure 1.

Other Geosynthetic Uses

Geosynthetics were used in several other capacities in the project, particularly in the drainage features: Nicolon's Geolon 300 woven geotextile was used as a separator for the subsurface seepage collection layer; the invert of the ditch surface was lined with a 1 mm Gundle HDPE geomembrane to prevent surface infiltration and was covered with a Nicolon Armorform grout blanket for protection; and subsurface seepage from a high flow area was collected using a specially fabricated Gundle 2.5 mm HDPE interception gallery. In areas where only partial

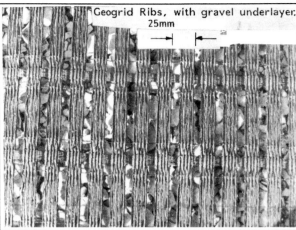

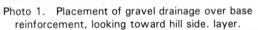
Geogrid Ribs, with gravel underlayer.
25mm

Photo 1. Placement of gravel drainage over base reinforcement, looking toward hill side. layer.

Photo 2. Close-up of high strength base reinforcement.

reconstruction of the structure was required, the embankment was stabilized using Nicolon's Geolon 1250X for base reinforcement.

CONSTRUCTION

Installation of the high strength geogrid woven reinforcement layer was simplified by Nicolon by sewing nearly all seams in the factory. This eliminated the need for experienced field labour for installation of the fabric, and Nicolon's representative directed all of the installations. Installation of the other geosynthetics was quick and straightforward. However, slippage of the grout blanket occurred on the side slopes of the HDPE-lined ditch. The problem was solved by anchoring the blanket at the top of the slope, but could also have been prevented by using a roughened-surface treated HDPE.

One section of the structure was instrumented with horizontal inclinometers and settlement monuments to monitor mass movement.

CONCLUSIONS

The significant lesson learned from this case history is the flexibility of designs which incorporate geosynthetics and the ease of producing a geosynthetic for very particular requirements. The use of geosynthetics in this project benefitted the client with respect to function, ease of implementation, and cost.

REFERENCES

Chen, W.F. and Baladi, G.Y., "Soil Plasticity: Theory and Implementation", Development in Geotechnical Engineering, Vol. 38, Elsevier Press, London, 1985.

Duncan, J.M. and Wong, K.S., "STABGM: A Computer Program for Slope Stability", Virginia Polytechnic Institute and State University, Blacksburg, Virginia, 1984.

Jewell, R.A., "A Limit Equilibrium Design Method for Reinforced Embankments on Soft Foundations", Proc., 2nd. Int. Conf. on Geotextiles, Vol. 3, pp. 671-676.

ACKNOWLEDGMENT

The project described in this case history was designed when the authors were at Law Environmental, Inc., Kennesaw, Georgia, USA.

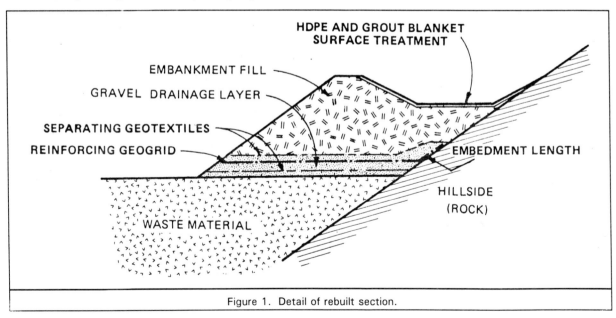

HDPE AND GROUT BLANKET
SURFACE TREATMENT

EMBANKMENT FILL

GRAVEL DRAINAGE LAYER

SEPARATING GEOTEXTILES

REINFORCING GEOGRID

EMBEDMENT LENGTH

HILLSIDE
(ROCK)

WASTE MATERIAL

Figure 1. Detail of rebuilt section.

GEOSYNTHETICS FOR A WHARF QUAY
HEWETTS QUAY, RIVER RODING, UNITED KINGDOM

P. Risseeuw and **W. Voskamp**
Akzo Industrial Systems bv.
Arnhem, The Nertherlands

As part of a redevelopment programme at Hewetts Quay on the tidal River Roding by Barking Oil Wharves Ltd., a small dock was backfilled. To that end, the entrance to the dock was closed by a reinforced soil wall founded on soft soil. Geosynthetics were used in this wall to provide reinforcement and drainage. The design was by Geostructures Consulting.

DESCRIPTION

The 5.4 m high, 15 m wide geotextile-reinforced soil wall was required to have a vertical concrete facing to allow mooring of ships against it. The vertical facing consists of concrete panels 4.8 m high and 3.0 m wide. On top of these panels is a 1.5 m high in-situ reinforced concrete parapet having a 1.5 m wide balancing slab.

The wall includes nine layers of geotextile reinforcement, several strips of geogrid to anchor the facing, and a geocomposite drain. The reinforced soil wall is founded on 1.0 to 1.5 m of soft alluvium resting on a layer of gravel overlying London Clay.

In a subsequent contract, industrial units were to be built over the reclaimed land behind the reinforced soil wall. Accordingly, the wall has been designed to carry a surcharge load of 25 kPa.

DESIGN

The water level in front of the wall can fluctuate significantly. Free drainage is therefore essential to prevent excess pore water pressure in the reinforced soil mass when the water level moves down quickly. To provide for free drainage, permeable soil was used to construct the reinforced soil mass, and a geocomposite drain was placed along the concrete face. Water collected by the geocomposite can drain through the 15 mm wide open joints between concrete facing panels.

The reinforcement length in the reinforced soil mass is 8 m (Figure 1). This design can be considered conservative. Stability could have been ensured with shorter reinforcement lengths.

For a number of reasons, excavation of the soft deposits was not permitted. To ensure a satisfactory foundation, a reinforced gravel mattress forms the first layer of the reinforced soil mass. To reinforce this mattress, the lower two layers of geotextile are longer than 8 m; they extend 20 m and 14 m, respectively, from the face of the wall. These layers of geotextile provide reinforcement against a potential slip surface passing behind the reinforced soil mass.

GEOSYNTHETICS

Stabilenka 150/45 woven geotextile was used to reinforce both the wall and the foundation mattress. The characteristics of this geotextile are: (1) Polymer: polyester in roll direction, polyamide in cross-roll direction; (2) Mass per unit area: 365 g/m^2; (3) Tensile strength: 150 kN/m in roll direction, 45 kN/m in cross-roll direction; (4) Elongation at break: 9% in roll direction, 18% in cross-roll direction.

Enkadrain geocomposite was used to provide drainage behind the concrete facing panel. This geocomposite consists of three layers: polyester nonwoven/polyamide mat/polyester nonwoven. The mat is a 20-mm thick three dimensional structure made with tortuous polyamide yarns. This structure is very permeable.

CONSTRUCTION

The wall was built by Star Groundwork Ltd. using the wrap around facing technique whereby a succession of geotextile-wrapped soil layers are constructed to form a steep faced soil mass. It was impossible to use formwork at the front of the wall due to the tidal movements of the water. Instead, the geotextile was wrapped around sandbags (Figure 2). The construction took place from March 1985 to January 1986 and is described below.

The first layer of geotextile was placed directly on the alluvium. This geotextile layer extends over the entire dock area, i.e., approximately 20 m from the wall face. Sand bags (total height 600 mm) were placed on this geotextile, at the location of the wall face (Figure 2). The geotextile was then covered with a 600 mm layer of gravel over the entire dock area and the geotextile flap was wrapped around the sand bags.

A second layer of geotextile extending 14 m from the wall face was placed on top of the gravel. This layer of geotextile was covered with 600 mm of granular fill and the flap was wrapped around the sand bags.

Six layers of geotextile extending 8 m from the wall face and wrapped around sand bags were then placed, alternating with 600 mm layers of compacted granular fill. Then, the parapet was cast and the last layer of geotextile, also 8 m long, was placed. This layer did not need to be wrapped around sand bags because the parapet acted as a form for the last fill layer.

The drainage geocomposite was then placed vertically against the front of the reinforced soil mass. The 1 m wide mat panels (which constitute the core of the geocomposite)

Photo 1.   Foundation preparation.

Photo 2.   Geotextile wrap around reinforcement.

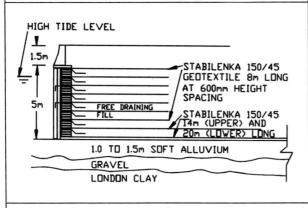

Photo 3.   Partially built wharf quay.

Photo 4.   Finished wharf quay with facing.

Figure 1.   Cross section of the reinforced soil wall.

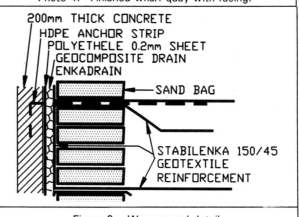

Figure 2.   Wrap around detail.

are butted, whereas the slightly wider nonwoven filters are overlapped. To prevent cement particles from entering into the geocomposite, a polyethylene foil was attached to the geocomposite before the concrete was cast.

Reinforced concrete facing panels, 200 mm thick, were cast against the geocomposite. The facing panels were tied back into the reinforced soil mass by 300 mm wide 2 m long strips of geogrids cast into the panels and sandwiched between envelopes of fill at three levels up the face.

To ensure free drainage, the polyethylene separating foil was removed in line with the 15 mm wide open joints between facing panels, after the panels were cast.

Backfilling of the dock behind the reinforced soil mass with granular fill proceeded at the same rate as the reinforced soil mass construction.

CONCLUSION

The reinforced soil technique was chosen by the client because previously adopted conventional sheet pile walls had experienced early corrosion. The client wanted to evaluate the potential of this recent technique with its advantages of speed and economy for use in future river wall rehabilitation. While the short length of this wall precludes realization of the full benefits of the technique, other features of the selected design listed below have contributed to its adoption:

• capacity to economically carry heavy loads,
• absence of need to fill around and between long sheet piles, tie rods and anchor piles,
• greater durability than sheet piles.

The performance of the wall has been good and expectations have been met.

GEOTEXTILE REINFORCEMENT FOR A HIGHWAY EMBANKMENT ACROSS SWAMP LAND IR SEDYATMO HIGHWAY, INDONESIA

P. Risseeuw and W. Voskamp
Akzo Industrial Systems bv.
Arnhem, The Netherlands

Twenty kilometres outside Jakarta, the capital of Indonesia, a new international airport was build at Cengkareng. To connect the Sukarno-Hatta airport to the city, a 14 km long highway was to be constructed.

PROJECT BACKGROUND

A major length of the road crossed an area of swamps and fish ponds. Subsequently the subsoil was very weak, with an undrained shear strength of only 5 kPa up to depths of 8 to 11 m. To complicate matters further, the road crossed some rivers that regularly flooded the area. Therefore the road slab had to be built well above this "banjir level", on top of an embankment rising 3.50 m above subsoil level.

DESIGN

Conceptual Design

Evidently, without special measures a road embankment of this size, width 24 m, slopes 2H:1V, would be unstable, and the weight of the embankment would squeeze out the soft subsoil. However, the constrained building schedule did not allow for traditional methods of soil improvement. Therefore, the Indonesian consulting engineers tried a different method which had proven successful in similar projects elsewhere. This method consists of using a heavy duty reinforcing mat sunk down to 1 m below GWL. This would, allow sand fill to be raised, up to 500 mm over GWL.

Stability Calculations and Geotextile Selection

To satisfy the requirements for foundation and slope stability it was established that a service load of 120 kN/m at 6% elongation would be permitted for the reinforcing mat during the consolidation period. This led to the choice of Stabilenka 200/45. This high modulus polyester geotextile has a breaking strength of 200 kPa at an elongation of 10%. By applying Stabilenka 200/45 the factor of safety against sliding and squeezing out was actually raised to the required levels of 1.25 during construction, and 1.40 after consolidation of the subsoil. These factors of safety were verified during the construction of a test embankment. Because of the improved bearing capacity, steeper slopes could be built, thus, requiring less fill. Also, trucks and bulldozers could immediately move into the construction area without the risk of causing slides.

All this resulted in a considerably reduced construction time and quantity of fill involved. The layer of Stabilenka geotextile also reduced differential settlements. After an initial settlement of 450 mm, no differential settlements occurred under permanent load conditions. Subsequently a concrete road slab could be constructed.

INSTALLATION

Construction started by stripping off the dense vegetation and installing the reinforcing geotextile 1 m below GWL. Since Stabilenka 200/45 is supplied on rolls

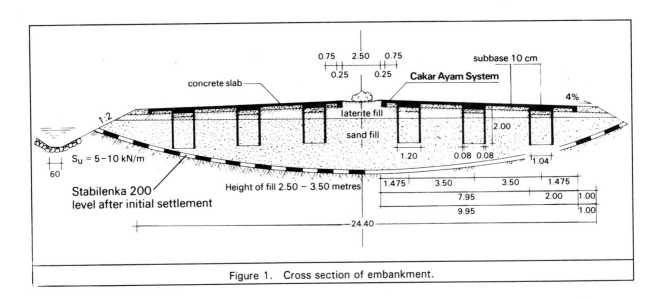

Figure 1. Cross section of embankment.

Photo 1. Sewing geotextile.

Photo 2. Placing fill.

construction yard to form large sheets of 100 x 30 m. The sewing was done by means of electric portable sewing machines, utilizing local labour. After installing the large panels, these were attached to each other to form rafts floating in the working corridor, by a final seam. About 2,000,000 m³ of coral sand were transported to the site by trucks and spread by means of bulldozers over the Stabilenka fabric. After reaching GWL each layer of 500 mm thickness was compacted.

CONCLUSION

The project was completed successfully, and is now classified as a major highway. The project not only proved the value of a reinforcing geotextile, it also proved the accuracy of the calculation models used in designing the embankments constucted on the Stabilenka geotextile.

REFERENCE

Report: Toll Road Cenkareng-Pluit
Client: Jasa Marga/Indonesian Highway Authority
Consultants: P.T. Cipta Strada, P.T. Secons, P.T. Sofoco
Contractor: Yala Perkasa International
Construction period: 1983/84

GEOTEXTILE REINFORCED LOW EMBANKMENT OVER SOFT SOIL BLOOMINGTON ROAD, ONTARIO, CANADA

K.L. Soderman
GeoSyntec Consultants
Boca Raton, Florida, USA

R.K. Rowe
University of Western Ontario
London, Ontario, Canada

M.D. MacLean
Ministry of Transportation of Ontario
Downsview, Ontario, Canada

The Bloomington Road embankment forms part of an extension to Bloomington Road, also known as Regional Road 40, in the Regional Municipality of York. The extension to Bloomington Road is located between Leslie Street and Highway 404 near Aurora, Ontario, Canada, and was constructed between July 1981 and July 1982. A section of the embankment, which incorporated geotextile reinforcement and was carefully instrumented, is the subject of this case history. The road had an average annual daily traffic (AEDT) of 6,410 vehicles in 1986.

DESCRIPTION

The general area is hummocky with numerous poorly drained organic deposits. The extension to Bloomington Road traverses one of these deposits which has a maximum thickness of 7.6 m and a length of almost 300 m. The geotextile reinforcement was installed on this section. A detailed report describing the design of the embankment and presenting the basic engineering properties of the peat together with the results of the field measurements has been published elsewhere [Rowe et al., 1984a].

The geotextile reinforced section had a length of almost 300 m, a height above the original ground level of 1.5 m, a crest width of 13.4 m and a base width of 20 m. A single layer of geotextile reinforcement was placed directly on a sand working platform prior to placement of the general embankment fill (Photo 1). The working platform was constructed directly on the surface of the cleared site.

The geotextile was expected to provide general reinforcement in an attempt to reduce tensile strains and lateral and vertical deformations and increase the embankment stability. By performing these functions, it was considered that the geotextile reinforcement would result in a more cost-effective embankment design.

The embankment was constructed in three stages and included a surcharge. Construction was stopped after each stage to allow time for the excess pore pressures measured in the organic deposit to dissipate to an acceptable level.

Field instruments were installed at two of the deepest sections of the swamp (referred to as Station A and Station B) to allow monitoring of the construction procedures and the embankment performance. The field instrumentation of the embankment included piezometers, profilometers and inclinometers. Auger borings were carried out at various stages of construction to confirm the settlement readings. In addition, two independent sets of

gauges were installed on the geotextile reinforcement to measure elongation in directions parallel and transverse to the roadway alignment.

TECHNICAL CONSIDERATIONS

The embankment was designed by the Ministry of Transportation and Communications using the technology available in the early 1980s.

The following construction methods were considered during the design stage: 1) complete excavation and backfilling; 2) partial excavation and displacement; 3) displacement by surcharging; 4) direct construction on top of the organic deposit using lightweight fill; 5) direct construction on top of the organic deposit using local granular fill; and 6) direct construction on top of the organic deposit using local granular fill and geotextile reinforcement.

Complete excavation and backfilling was considered to be impractical at this location because of the depth of the peat. Displacement methods were rejected due to the unfavourable geometry of the underlying firm deposits. Lightweight fill was not locally available and was therefore not an economic solution. Based on the results of design calculations, there were concerns regarding the short-term stability and long-term settlements associated with direct construction on top of the organic deposit. It was postulated that the short-term stability of the embankment could be increased by the use of geotextile reinforcement placed near the peat-fill interface.

A circular arc stability analysis assuming negligible geometry changes under "undrained" conditions and including the effects of geotextile reinforcement was carried out. The results indicated that a tensile force as large as 39 kN/m would be required in order to obtain a factor of safety of 1.3.

It was considered that this stabilizing tensile force provided by the geotextile should be developed at relatively small strains. For this reason, together with economy and availability, two "strong" (at that time) woven geotextiles were selected for embankment reinforcement. A 130 m long section of the embankment was constructed using a Geolon 1250 geotextile described as a plain weave, twisted, polypropylene, multifilament material, produced by Nicolon Corporation. The remainder of the embankment was constructed using a Permealiner 1195 geotextile distributed by Synflex Industries and described as a calendered polypropylene monofilament with a plain weave. The physical and mechanical properties of the two geotextiles are given in Table 1.

Photo 1. Geotextile being wrapped back to provide anchorage.

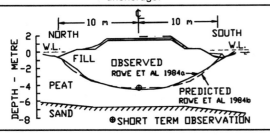

Figure 1. Observed settlements after Stage II construction, Station B.

Table 1. Geotextile properties (unaged fabrics)		
Properties	Permealiner 1195[4]	Geolon 1250[5]
Mass per unit area (g/m²)	225	730
Thickness (mm)	0.4	2.26
Mullen bursting pressure (MPa)	3.5	11
Equivalent opening size (μm)	212	425
Breaking force in grab test[1] (kN)	1.78	5.56
Estimated ultimate strength from grab test[2] (kN/m)	42	133
Ultimate tensile strength[3] (kN/m)	41	178
Elongation at rupture in grab test (%)	30	18
Ultimate tensile strain[3] (%)	37	24
Modulus[3] (kN/m)		
$\epsilon < 3\%$	150	230
$\epsilon > 3\%$	150	850

Notes:
1. In the warp direction.
2. Estimated ultimate strength = 24 x grab strength.
3. Determined from wide strip test on 500 mm wide x 100 mm gauge length samples - warp direction - strain rate 2%/minute.
4. Used at Station A - chainage 1 + 982.
5. Used at Station B - chainage 2 + 119 - see Photo 1.

PERFORMANCE

During Construction

Large settlements were observed at both instrumented sections, with a maximum fill thickness of 5.7 m and a maximum settlement of 4.7 m being recorded. The measured settlement profile at Station B at the end of Stage II construction is shown on Figure 1.

A significant component of the settlement appears to have been due to shear distortion, particularly during Stage II construction. Lateral movements from "mud waves" and adjacent to the embankment were evident.

The geotextile instrumentation indicated that large geotextile strains (in excess of 21% for Permealiner 1195) were developed in Stage II of the construction when large shear deformations were apparent.

Post Construction

Since completion of Bloomington Road, settlement of the roadway embankment has continued to occur. In general, differential settlements in the transverse direction are minor, while significant differential settlement has occurred in the longitudinal direction. The pavement was taken up after 1 year (1983) and brought back to grade. No additional paving has been necessary since then (1987).

CONCLUSIONS

Following construction of the Bloomington Road embankment, a detailed finite element analysis of the embankment has been carried out, and the results have been reported elsewhere [Rowe et al., 1984b].

Based on the results of the finite element analysis and the instrument measurements, it is apparent that in this case, the use of a relatively strong geotextile did not prevent large shear deformations nor large consolidation settlements from occurring.

The results of the finite element analysis indicated that at high load levels, the inclusion of the stiffer geotextile (Geolon 1250) at the deeper section of peat reduced the lateral spreading and increased the stability of the embankment compared to the case in which no geotextile was used. However, both the results of the finite element analysis and the observed performance of the embankment indicated the geotextile reinforcement had little effect on consolidation settlements.

Finally, although the procedures used in the design represented the state of the art at that time, they did not prove to be a good indication of how the embankment would perform in the field. It is recommended that simplified limit equilibrium design procedures should be viewed with considerable caution when designing geotextile reinforced embankments constructed on peat. Since then improved design methods for embankments on peat have been developed [Rowe and Soderman, 1985, 1986].

REFERENCES

Rowe, R.K., MacLean, M.D. and Barsvary, A.K., "The Observed Behaviour of a Geotextile-Reinforced Embankment Constructed on Peat", Canadian Geotechnical Journal, Vol. 21, 1984a, pp. 289-304.

Rowe, R.K., MacLean, M.D. and Soderman, K.L., "Analysis of a Geotextile-Reinforced Embankment Constructed on Peat", Canadian Geotechnical Journal, Vol. 21, 1984b, pp. 563-576.

Rowe, R.K. and Soderman, K.L., "Geotextile Reinforcement of Embankments on Peat", Geotextiles and Geomembranes, Vol. 2, No. 4, 1985, pp. 277-298.

Rowe, R.K. and Soderman, K.L., "Reinforced Embankments on Very Poor Foundations", Geotextiles and Geomembranes, Vol. 4, No. 1, 1986, pp. 65-81.

GEOTEXTILE REINFORCED MOTORWAY EMBANKMENT OVER INDUSTRIAL WASTE AULNOIS SITE, FRANCE

Ph. Delmas and B. Soyez
Laboratoire Central des Ponts et Chaussées
Paris, France

J. Lenglet
Laboratoire Régional des Ponts et Chaussées
St. Quentin, France

J.P. Puech and J.Y. Buffard
Scetauroute, France

Confronted with the difficult problem of constructing embankments over disposal areas of compressible and heterogenous industrial wastes, the design engineer proposed innovative solutions due to the inadequacy of traditional techniques. At the Aulnois site, the combination of geotextiles and of an ultra-light material turned out to be technically and economically wise.

DESCRIPTION

The A26 Motorway crosses north of Laon an alluvial area constituted of compressible soils, about 3 m thick. This geotechnical problem is locally complicated by the presence on the alignment of a settling pond for mud washed from sugar beets. Over an area 320 m long, the pavement was planned 700 mm above the existing level of the wastes, the average thickness of which is 6 m in the axis of the motorway (Figure 1).

Due to its method of placement (hydraulical filling), the waste is heterogeneous. Its main geotechnical characteristics are given in Table 1. Additional data can be found elsewhere [Delmas et al. 1986].

The chosen solution included four phases:

- partial punching of the compressible soil aimed at reducing considerably the height of compressible soil under the final embankment,
- preloading in order to provide partial consolidation of the remaining soft soil,
- unloading of the embankment to a certain level to interrupt the primary consolidation process and cause ageing of the compressible soil from the standpoint of secondary consolidation,
- construction of a light embankment to support the pavement at its final level.

The reinforcement of the 6.5 m high punched embankment was necessary, in order to ensure:

- the integrity of the embankment during punching,
- its stability during the next consolidation phases.

The reinforcement consists of two layers of polyester woven geotextile (Enka 200, a_f = 200 kN/m, working tensile force per unit width = 100 kN/m).

TECHNICAL CONSIDERATIONS

Design and Experimental Embankment

The theoretical design was based on the following assumptions:

- depth of punching: between 1.5 and 2 m,
- consolidation settlement: 1 m for a loading duration of 1 year.

The design of such a solution, already difficult, was further complicated in the present case by the absence of representative data regarding the creep characteristics of the wastes. Moreover, due to the heterogeneity of the site, it also appeared desirable to "reset" the parameters of primary consolidation.

For all these reasons and on the initiative of Scetautoroute, the project contractor, it was decided to build an experimental embankment in order to refine the final design. This experimental embankment has been described in a previous publication [Delmas et al., 1986]. Nevertheless, it is of interest to mention the following data:

- the experimental embankment was 15 m x 15 m and 5 m high,
- for practical reasons, the geotextile used was a polypropylene woven (Robusta, a_f = 200 kN/m),
- the design of the reinforcement to ensure the local stability was made on the basis of the so-called "displacement method" [Gourc et al., 1986] with factor of safety F = 1.3,
- four layers of Robusta geotextile were necessary due to its working tensile force of 50 kN/m, which is lower than that of Stabilenka 200.

Settlement and pore pressure data, confirmed the feasibility of the construction procedure.

The observed values of the local deformations in each layer of geotextile were rather uniformly distributed, ϵ_{av} = 2.5%. This particular distribution can be explained by the fact that there was no sliding failure that induces a non-uniform distribution of the strains, with a peak along the slip surface. The observed uniform distribution is corroborated by recent theoretical researches carried out in the French Laboratoire Central des Ponts et Chaussées (Kebibeche, 1987). Those researches demonstrate that the strains in the geotextiles are mainly induced by the lateral displacements occurring at the interface between the earth fill and the soft soil.

Constructional Behaviour of Actual Embankment

The actual embankment (320 m long) was constructed between June and December 1985. The punching phase under the 6.5 m high highway embankment, and the following consolidation settlement could not be clearly separated. The reason is due to (1) the greater width of this structure (compared to the

Photo 1. General view of the site

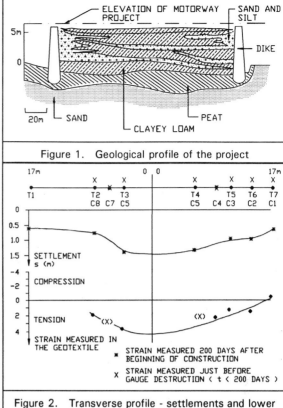

Figure 1. Geological profile of the project

Figure 2. Transverse profile - settlements and lower layer geotextile strains

Table 1.	Main geotechnical characteristics of waste		
13.	$< \gamma <$	19. kN/m³	(av.:16kN/m³)
22.	$< w <$	100. (%)	
0.75	$< e_o <$	2.3	(av.:1.7)
0.63	$< C_c <$	0.84	(av.:0.63)
7.	$< c_u <$	19. kPa	(av.:14 kPa)

experimental embankment), and (2) job-site considerations, as the contractor was obliged to build it in 3 phases (1.8, 4.8, 6.5 m respectively) in a period of 200 days.

The generated pore pressures were very high (up to 124 kPa) in the wastes and the settlement after 240 days was close to 1.5 m, and was estimated to reach a value of 1.8 m at time = 400 days. This time of 400 days corresponds to the unloading operations. The graphical analysis of the settlements before 400 days shows that the consolidation process (phases 1 and 2) was nearly completed. On Figure 2 are summarized the transverse settlements and corresponding geotextile strains on the lower layer of the reinforcement. Attention is directed to the following comments:

1) no theoretical conclusion should be drawn from the similarity of the shape of the two curves,

2) the maximum value of the strain (4.0%) agrees fairly well with the design value extrapolated from the experimental embankment data,

3) here also, the transverse strain distribution corresponds with the theoretical profile, as deduced form Kebibeche's work [1987].

Unloading took place in 1987. No swelling was observed during unloading. The embankment was then taken to its final level by placing lightweight parallelepipeds on the embankment top surface. (polypropylene honeycomb structures). The placed parralelepipeds (approximately 3 m high) were wrapped in a geotextile blanket prior to being covered with soil. The pavement was then constructed above the soil layer.

CONCLUSION

The geotextile reinforcement of the motorway embankment can be considered to have been the "right choice" for the crossing of the industrial waste disposal at Aulnois (France), both from the technical and economical points of view. The excellent performance of the motorway since 1987 justifies the technical choice. Economically, the geotextile reinforcement was cheaper

than more drastic technics such as a low-level bridge (40%) or a root-piled embankment (60%).

BIBLIOGRAPHY

Delmas, Ph., Soyez B., Lenglet J., and Puech, J.P., (1986) "Experimental puncturing of a reinforced embankment over an industrial waste site", Proc. 3rd. Int. Conf. on geotextiles, Vienne, Vol. 4, pp 1049-1054.

Gourc J.P., Ratel A., and Delmas Ph., (1986) Design of fabric retaining walls: the "displacement method", Proc. 3rd. Int. Conf. on geotextiles, Vienne, Vol.4, pp 1067-1072.

Kebibeche M., (1987) "Les géotextiles dans les remblais sur sols compressibles" Rapport de DEA, Ecole Nationale des Ponts et Chaussées, Paris, 150 pages.

GEOTEXTILE REINFORCED TEST EMBANKMENT SECTION
PINTO PASS, MOBILE, ALABAMA, USA

J. Fowler
USAE Waterways Experiment Station
Vicksburg, Mississippi, USA

A study was undertaken in 1978 concerning the use of Pinto Island, Mobile Harbour, Alabama, as a long-term confined disposal area to contain fine-grained maintenance dredging from the harbour. It was found that site feasibility was contingent on the ability to construct approximately 1,524 linear m of retaining embankment across both ends and along the south shore of Pinto Pass, a sedimented channel used in the Civil War period for access to the harbour. The unconsolidated, undrained shear strength of the cohesive materials ranged from 2.4 to 7.2 kPa, and standard penetration test N-values were 0.5 along much of the alignment to a depth of 12.2 m.

DESCRIPTION

A highly variable alluvial soil profile existed along the proposed dike alignment, and approximately 50% of the alignment was in the intertidal zone and had water depths of 200 to 500 mm under mean tidal (El. 0 m (mean sea level)) conditions. Initial calculations indicated that an embankment could be constructed to approximately El. 0.9 m without bearing failure of the foundation. Conventional alternatives for constructing the embankment to El. 2.4 m included preloading and staged construction, use of lightweight construction material, and end-dumping displacement. Non engineering considerations dictated that the embankment be constructed in less time than was estimated for the preloading and staged construction alternative, and use of the lightweight construction material was not suitable because this would reduce the effectiveness of the embankment as a preload fill for future raising. End-dumping or mud wave displacement is the procedure normally used by the U.S. Army Engineer District, Mobile, to construct embankments on soft soil. Sufficient quantities of relatively clean fine sand were available at nearby locations for construction of a displacement section. However, based on previous experience with Mobile Harbour soil conditions, it was estimated that the volumetric ratio of below-ground to above-ground material required would be approximately three to one for displacement construction. This quantity of fill material would be expensive, and the relatively large lateral displacements produced might have disturbed pipelines, utility lines, roadways, and a bridge located adjacent to the proposed embankment alignment. It was also doubtful that the quality control during the displacement operations would be sufficient for the construction of a satisfactory base section for future embankment raising.

Analysis of the proposed embankment-raising sequence by use of consolidated, undrained shear test data for the foundation indicated that, if the initial embankment to El. 2.4 m could be constructed without failure, the foundation strength would increase such that the next raise increment, to El. 3.7 m, could be placed without foundation failure, and once pore pressures from this raising dissipated, a second raising could be conducted, and so on. Geotextile reinforcement would be needed only for initial construction. In addition to the higher probability of successful initial construction, the use of geotextile reinforcement was postulated to result in a cost saving of 40 to 60% because of the reduced volume of fill needed.

DESIGN

The geometric configuration of the test section was controlled by the base section size needed to obtain stable side slopes for future raised sections and consisted of an embankment with a 3.7 m wide crest at El. 2.4 m and 10H:1V side slopes, resulting in a section 52.4 m wide at El. 0. Potential failure modes for the embankment that were investigated indicated that the geotextile must have a minimum uniaxial tensile strength of 17.5 kN/m at not more than 10% elongation and a minimum ultimate strength of 39 kN/m. The 10% elongation criterion was selected to limit the average lateral spreading to approximately 5%. Also, the coefficient of soil-geotextile friction should be at least equal to the friction angle ($\phi = 30°$) for the fill sand in a loose relative density condition.

In addition to the geotextile strength and frictional requirements, a sequential construction scheme was developed that placed balanced forces on the soft foundation and provided proper geotextile anchorage along the toes of the embankment before the placement of fill along the centre.

The key to successful completion of soft-ground engineering projects is the selection of appropriate construction equipment that will maintain mobility on soft soils. Based on previous U.S. Army Corps of Engineers research, small dozers with a maximum 17 kPa ground pressure were selected for fill placement. Previous work in geotextile-reinforced haul-road construction on soft soils had indicated that a double-geotextile-layer reinforced haul road along the outer edges of an embankment could carry loaded 7.6 m³ tandem-axle dump trucks. The most critical construction operations were those related to placement and sewing of geotextile, as they were hand-labour intensive.

CONCLUSIONS

Geotextile-reinforced construction techniques are based on the concept that low foundation strength and point-to-point foundation variability can be compensated for by use of geotextiles that have more easily predicted

Photo 1. Placing aggregate on geotextile.

Photo 2. Embankment under construction.

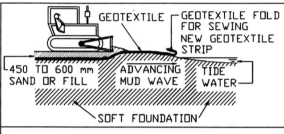

Figure 1. Preparing for seaming on mud wave.

engineering behaviour. The design concepts and construction procedures involved are relatively simple and based on application of logical engineering principles rather than on detailed mathematical analyses. Based on the results of the test program summarized in this paper, the following may be concluded:

1. Use of geotextiles to provide transverse tensile reinforcement is a technically feasible method of rapidly constructing embankments on foundations too soft to support the unreinforced embankments without failure.

2. If procedures are used that provide essentially balanced loading on the foundation and that cover the outside edges of the geotextile to provide suitable anchorage before placement of the interior embankment fill, construction of geotextile-reinforced embankments by using available low-ground-pressure dozer equipment and conventional dump-truck material hauling is operationally practical.

3. Compared with conventional end-dumping displacement methods, geotextile-reinforced embankment construction appears particularly cost effective. The additional construction costs of purchase and placement of the geotextile are more than recovered by the savings in fill required to construct the above-ground embankment cross section.

4. Although specific situations will dictate exact geotextile strength requirements, high-tensile-strength and high-deformation-modulus geotextiles should prove most suitable for embankment reinforcement.

5. There appears to be no particular advantage to constructing a working table before geotextile placement, as long as the ground surface is reasonably level. When

the mud-wave-displacement method of geotextile stretching is used, the longitudinal seam strength should be equal to or greater than the fill-direction tensile strength of the geotextile.

REFERENCES

Fowler, J., "Analysis of Fabric-Reinforced Embankment Test Section at Pinto Pass, Mobile, Alabama", Graduate College, Oklahoma State University, Stillwater, OK, PhD thesis, July 1979.

Haliburton, T.A., "Evaluation of Construction Procedure for Fabric-Reinforced Embankment Test Section, Pinto Pass, Mobile, Alabama", U.S. Army Engineer Waterways Experiment Station, Vicksburg, MS, March 1979.

Haliburton, T.A., Anglin, C.C. and Lawmaster, J.D., "Selection of Geotechnical Fabrics for Embankment Reinforcement", U.S. Army Engineer District, Mobile, AL, May 1978.

Haliburton, T.A., Douglas, P.A. and Fowler, J., "Feasibility of Pinto Island as a Long-Term Dredged-Material Disposal Site", U.S. Army Engineer Waterways Experiment Station, Vicksburg, MS, Miscellaneous Paper D-77-3, December 1977.

Haliburton, T.A., Fowler, J. and Langan, J.P., "Perimeter Dike Raising with Dewatered Fine-Grained Dredged Material at Upper Polecat Bay Disposal Area, Mobile, Alabama", U.S. Army Engineer Waterways Experiment Station, Vicksburg, MS, Miscellaneous Paper D-78-3, December 1978.

Haliburton, T.A. and Haliburton Associates, "Design of Test Section for Pinto Pass Dike, Mobile, Alabama", U.S. Army Engineer District, Mobile, AL, June 1978.

Willoughby, W.E., "Assessment of Low-Ground-Pressure Equipment for Use in Containment Area Operations and Maintenance", U.S. Army Engineer Waterways Experiment Station, Vicksburg, MS, Technical Report D-77-8, November 1977.

GEOTEXTILE REINFORCED DIKES ON SOFT DREDGE MATERIAL
CRANEY ISLAND, NORFOLK, VIRGINIA, USA

J. Fowler
USAE Waterways Experiment Station
Vicksburg, Mississippi, USA

In 1982, three geotextile-reinforced test sections 91, 122, and 229 m long were successfully constructed on very soft dredged material deposits within the Craney Island dredge material disposal area (Norfolk District, Norfolk, Virginia). Subsequently, two dikes, each about 1217 m long, were constructed using this innovative construction technique to divide the 1,092 ha area into three separate areas for improved dredged material management. Prior attempts to construct these dikes with conventional displacement construction techniques had failed. Successful construction of these geotextile-reinforced dikes was a key element in the rapid implementation of the dredged material management program.

DESCRIPTION

Extremely poor foundation conditions existed along the interior dike alignments for about 1,524 m for closure of the north dike and 1,067 m for the south dike. Soft dredged material, which extended to depths of 9 to 12 m, had undrained shear strengths that ranged from 1.2 to 4.8 kPa. The predominant underlying in-situ material was very soft marine clay (CH and OH). The land surface enclosed by the completion of the perimeter dike in 1957 was at El. -3 m with the very soft marine clay extending to El. -27 m.

Approximately 40% of the alignment area had a dried crust 80 to 100 mm thick. The other 60% was covered by recent deposits of dredged material, and there was surface water near the weirs.

DESIGN

Site conditions dictated a wide, shallow-sloped dike 10H:1V to be raised incrementally as filling of the containment area progressed. Previous experience indicated that the magnitude of dike displacements would be 8 to 10 volumes below the surface of the dredged material. To provide the necessary initial containment area capacity, the dikes were to be 3.4 m above present surface at the embankment centre line.

End-dumping of displacement sections is an accepted method of dike construction where marginal foundation conditions exist. Clean sand dredged material was available nearby, but the large quantities required for construction of an unreinforced displacement section were not economically feasible. Also, engineering judgment led to the conclusion that it would be difficult if not impossible to control displacement dike sections to achieve the desired width and stable base for future dike raising anticipated at the Craney Island facility.

Analysis of the use of conventional dike construction without any reinforcement indicated that the factor of safety against bearing capacity failure would be less than 1.0. Unreinforced dikes constructed on the soft foundation in the disposal area could exceed the foundation bearing capacity and result in one of three types of failure:

- Localized foundation failure with propagation of a rotational failure through the dike.
- Lateral splitting and outward spreading and sliding of the dike.
- Bearing failure caused by excessive subsidence caused by excessive consolidation and displacement.

A design concept developed by the author and the late Dr. T. Allan Haliburton supported by the Dredged Material Research Program (DMRP) and the Dredging Operations Technical Support (DOTS) Program, was considered, i.e., floating a dike on the soft foundation by using a geotextile for tensile reinforcement. The geotextile would be placed on the soft foundation, transverse to the dike alignment, followed by placement of a sand layer for a working table, with a wide-based, shallow-sloped dike to be raised as soon as pore water pressure dissipated and the dredged material foundation consolidated.

The design considerations and construction techniques are described by Fowler [1981]. Test Sections 1 and 2 were designed by the author and the late Dr. Haliburton. Test Section 3 was not designed but was built as a worst-case exercise.

Design analyses indicated that the geotextile would provide the reinforcement necessary to prevent rotational foundation failure or embankment spreading and splitting until the soft foundation consolidated sufficiently to support the embankment. A similar system was used successfully to construct a multi-purpose dike at Pinto Pass in the Mobile District [Information Exchange Bulletin, 1979].

Experience from prior end-dumped dike construction at Craney Island and from geotextile-reinforced dike construction at Pinto Pass indicated that the latter could be accomplished for about 40% of the cost of end-dumping and that better control of the desired section could be maintained with the geotextile-reinforced dike. Based on these two factors, geotextile-reinforced construction was elected for installation of three dike sections to determine the feasibility of using floating dikes at Craney Island. Construction began in mid-July 1982 and was completed in mid-November 1982.

The planned construction sequence was essentially

Figure 1. View of dike.

the same as that used for the dike at Pinto Pass. The geotextile was laid on the dredged material surface in 4.9 m wide panels placed transverse to the longitudinal axis of the dike, and the panels were sewn together with very strong polyester thread (breaking strength approximately 350 N).

As the geotextile placement progressed, sand was end-dumped and then spread with small wide-track dozers with 16 kPa contact pressure. The sand layer was 600 to 800 mm thick. Where the dredged material was very soft, the weight of the sand caused a small surface mud wave that launched the geotextile forward. Labourers used 5 m long poles to assist in launching and spreading the geotextile. The low ground pressure dozers pushed sand onto the in-place geotextile, creating a wave in the underlying mud that stretched the wrinkles from the newly placed geotextile panels.

Initially, all dump truck traffic was confined to the outside edges along the toe of the test section to provide lateral spreading that would pretension the geotextile. After the geotextile was placed and the sand was spread for the working table, the dikes were raised in increments to heights of 3.4 m for Test Sections 1 and 2 and 2.4 m for Test Section 3.

CONCLUSIONS

The reinforced embankments at Test Sections 1 and 2 were finished to design width and grade without excessive lateral spreading or rotational bearing failure in the foundation, despite excessive pore water pressure of about 6 m that developed above the dredged material surface. The embankment of Test Section 3 experienced a downward displacement of about two volumes for one volume raised above the surface during construction, but no embankment failure occurred.

The geotextile performed satisfactorily when the geotextile rolls were oriented perpendicular to the long axis of the dike. However, in Test Section 3 (where the geotextile rolls were oriented perpendicular to the long axis of the dike) failure occurred in the cross-roll yarns. This particular geotextile was weaker in the cross-roll direction than in the roll direction. Nonetheless, the geotextile provided sufficient reinforcement to support rapid dike construction to the desired height and to maintain the

structural integrity of the embankment. Geotextile creep was determined to be a critical factor in dike performance.

Foundation pore pressures are dissipating gradually. After the excess pore pressures have been reduced, the height of the dikes can be increased to provide additional storage area.

Long-term settlement and pore pressure data are being collected and evaluated to determine the performance of the dikes and to refine the design and construction procedures and criteria.

When time constraints will permit, construction of a floating dike will progress with a minimum of difficulty if construction is delayed until a crust is formed that will support the geotextile-laying activities. Crust formation can be accelerated by drainage/dewatering techniques such as progressive trenching. The crust along the alignment of Test Section 1 was 80 to 100 mm thick and supported geotextile laying and construction of the initial sand layer, eliminated the mud wave construction technique, and reduced the geotextile strength requirements in the cross-roll direction.

REFERENCES

Fowler, J., "Design Construction, Analysis of Fabric-Reinforced Embankment Test Section at Pinto Pass, Mobile, Alabama", Technical Report EL-81-7, Geotechnical Laboratory, U.S. Army Engineer Waterways Experiment Station, Vicksburg, MS, 1981.

GEOTEXTILE TO SUPPORT BUNDS IN A LAND RECLAMATION
PASIR RIS, SINGAPORE

P.J. de Geeter
Marecon Pty. Ltd.
Perth, Australia.

H.J. Dunnewind
Robusta Fabrics
Genemuiden, The Netherlands.

For the creation of a waste tipping area at the North Eastern shore of Singapore Island (at the eastern edge of Serangoon creek), a total length of approximately 1 km of partition bunds was constructed on a thick stratum of soft soil.

Sand was dumped onto a separation layer of woven geotextile, to a target height of approximately 5 m (after consolidation).

The work was carried out by a local Contractor and commissioned by the Housing and Development Board of Singapore.

DESCRIPTION

Tidal currents and wave action in the project area are slight.

The water depth ranges from zero to approximately 5 m, depending on location and the state of the tide.

Access from land by vehicles was possible without too much difficulty.

Borings, standard penetrometer and vane tests showed that the soil consists of soft deposits extending to approximately 10 m below mudline (on average), underlain by layers of dense sand.

From seven boreholes, distributed fairly uniformly over the project area, with a boring depth from 26 to 30 m, the following average properties values of the soft clay were:

- 0.0 to 4.3 m c_u = 6.4 kPa; ϕ = 2°.
- 4.3 to 9.0 m c_u = 10.0 kPa; ϕ = 2°.
- 9.0 to 11.8 m c_u = 35.0 kPa; ϕ = 8°.
- 11.8 to 13.3 m c_u = 50.0 kPa; ϕ = 8°.

Consolidation tests carried out on the retrieved soil samples rendered values of consolidation coefficient ranging from 0.04 to 0.56 mm²/s with permeability coefficient ranging from 0.079 to 38 nm/s.

DESIGN

Slip circle analysis demonstrated that it would not be possible to dump sand fill (as required for the build-up of the bunds) directly on the undrained subsoil. Severe slip circle failure would lead to unacceptable subsidence and squeezing, in spite of the fact that the crest width of the bund would be 10 m with a gentle slope of the bund face, of the order of 5H:1V, as shown in typical design cross section of the bund (Figure 1).

The (verified) slip circle programme, which calculates total overturning moment of soil slices as compared to total resisting moment generated by soil friction along a potential failure plane, establishes the location of the centroid that renders the lowest safety factor (being the ratio of total resisting moment to total overturning moment).

The programme was run for three different situations:

- with a shallow failure plane (intersecting layer 1 only),
- with intermediate failure plane (intersecting layers 1 and 2), and
- deep failure plane (intersecting interface between layers 2 and 3 as well).

In consultation with the Client it was decided that the strength of the geotextile to be applied would have to be sufficient to render a minimum factor of safety of 1.2 for the worst case of the potential failure plane.

In order to arrive at this minimum factor of safety at the most critical moment (immediately after placement of full fill height) the calculations showed that the break strength of the geotextile in the principal stress direction had to be in the order of 80 kN/m.

This led to selection of Robusta woven polypropylene geotextile No. 500-Special. The properties of this geotextile, as tested to ISO Norm 5081, by Fibre Research Institute of T.N.O. Delft and Delft Hydraulics Laboratory, are as follows:

- tensile break strength in roll direction: 80 kN/m.
- elongation at break: 18%.
- permeability: 29 litres/m².s at 100 mm head.

Consolidation calculations indicated that the ultimate settlement would be in the order of 1.5 m which had to be taken into account in estimating the required total volume of fill.

The subsidence process will be slow, with 90% consolidation (U_{90}) being reached after roughly 3.5 years. For this type of structure, however, this was considered acceptable.

INSTALLATION

The geotextile was stitched together in lanes of 15 m width and laid with its roll direction at right angle to

Photo 1.   View of bund.

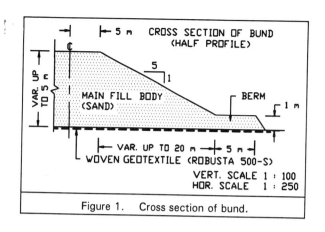

Figure 1.   Cross section of bund.

the axis of the bund. Overlap between lanes was at least 1 m.

In order to ensure proper anchoring of the geotextile after installation, a berm with a height of 1.0 m and a width of 5.0 m was installed first, at either side of the main bund profile, as shown in Figure 1.

The berms also act to counteract the subsidence of the central fill body.

In order to allow for subsoil strengthening as a result of the consolidation process, the main fill body was installed gradually. Each lift layer had a maximum thickness of 1 m and there was a minimum time interval between consecutive layers of not less than two weeks (as calculated).

The contractor accomplished this by shifting the filling work from bund to bund (and back, thus working in stages with minimum time loss).

REFERENCES

Koerner, R.M., "Designing with Geosynthetics", Prentice-Hall, Englewood Cliffs, NJ 07632, 1986, 424 p.

Veldhuijzen van Zanten, R., "Geotextiles and Geomembranes in Civil Engineering", Balkema, Rotterdam, Boston, 1986, 685 p.

Rankilor, P.R., "Membranes in Ground Engineering", John Wiley & Sons, New York, 1981, 377 p.

Bowles, J.E., "Foundation Analysis and Design", McGraw-Hill International, London, 3rd edition 1982, 816 p.

Kroezen, M., Vellinga, P., Lindenberg, J., and Burger, A.M., "Geotechnical and Hydraulic Aspects with regard to Seabed and Slope Stability", 1982, 13 p. (publication No. 272 of Delft Geotechnics, The Netherlands).

Ogink, H.J.M., "Investigations on the Hydraulic Characteristics of Synthetic Fabrics", 1975, 42 p. (publication No. 146 of Delft Hydraulics Laboratory, The Netherlands).

GEOGRID STABILIZATION FOR RAISING THE ELEVATION OF A TAILINGS DAM
BRITISH COLUMBIA, CANADA

W.J. Burwash and P.G. Arnall
Golder Associates (Western Canada) Ltd.
Calgary, Alberta, Canada

J.R. Kerr
The Tensar Corporation
Calgary, Alberta, Canada

Westar Mining Ltd., a coal mining company located in southeastern British Columbia, needed to increase the capacity of an existing tailings containment pond located at Sparwood, British Columbia. Because of downstream restrictions, raising the elevation of the existing dam necessitated upstream construction and placement of fill on top of the impounded tailings (Figure 1). In the vicinity of the pond, the tailings had a slurry consistency. Elsewhere the water table was well below the tailings level, and the tailings provided a good working surface for construction equipment. Use of a geogrid-reinforced fill over the slurry-like tailings was considered feasible and was proven by a test section. This technique was ultimately used on a full-scale basis.

DESCRIPTION

The tailings consisted of a saturated non-plastic silt with moisture contents ranging from 40 to 60%. Cone penetration resistance measured in the winter from the ice surface was essentially zero, and vane shear test results conducted after lowering of the pond surface indicated an average undrained strength of 4.6 kPa to a depth of 5 m. Based upon extensive triaxial testing, the angle of internal friction of the tailings (ϕ') was found to vary from 30° to 34° with zero cohesion (c').

The dam raising was constructed entirely of waste material which consisted of a coarse fraction (sand and gravel) with c' = 0 and ϕ' = 36° and a fine fraction (tailings predominately of silt sizes with some clay). The first stage of construction (Stage 1A), which was completed in 1987, called for a 3.6 m increase in the dam crest elevation using tailings wherever possible. The dam had been raised previously in 1978-79 from elevation 1105.5 to elevation 1111.5 m using upstream construction. The initial lift consisted of 1.5 to 1.8 m of coarse waste pushed onto the weak tailings surface. In the most severe areas, the initial lift resulted in displacement of the tailings in a 'mud wave'. Having established a relatively strong working platform, heavier equipment could then be used with an increased rate of construction.

During design of the 1987 raising, it was reasoned that if the thickness of the initial lift could be reduced by incorporating a geogrid to reinforce the base of the tailings, there would be a cost saving. This saving was possible because hauling and placement of the coarse waste was about twice as costly as that for the tailings.

DESIGN AND PERFORMANCE

The tensile reinforcement and fill thickness were selected using the method developed by Giroud et al.

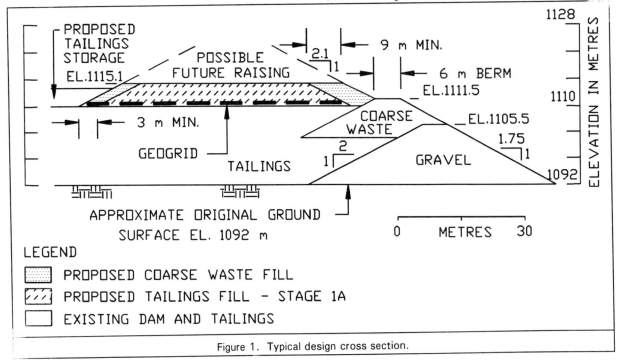

Figure 1. Typical design cross section.

Photo 1. Surface of tailings after drawdown of pond.

Photo 2. Placement of fill on geogrid.

[1984]. Tensar BX1000 (previously called SSO) geogrid was selected because of its high junction strength and high initial tangent modulus (219 kN/m roll direction, 367 kN/m cross-roll direction). A design thickness between 1.0 and 1.3 m was selected for the thickness of the first layer, which represented a thickness reduction of 40% over the unreinforced thickness. Design called for the initial lift to consist of coarse waste because of its high strength and excellent drainage capability. Subsequent lifts could consist of tailings.

The reinforced design thickness was verified with a field trial, and then construction proceeded using approximately 70,000 m² of geogrid. In order to facilitate construction, the pond level was drawn down to expose the tailings and allowed to dry for several weeks before placement of fill (Photo 1). The exposed surface dried sufficiently to allow workers to walk over the site and place the geogrid. The geogrid was then placed with a minimum overlap of 300 mm to ensure interlock between adjacent sheets; seaming or other methods of connection were not required. Fill was hauled using tandem dump trucks, and a D6 Caterpillar pushed the fill in place (Photo 2). The reduced thickness of fill enabled the first lift, or construction platform, to be finished more quickly and at

reduced cost. In some locations, displaced tailings (mud waves) were removed by backhoe before placing the fill in order to reduce differential settlement. Settlement plates, placed after the initial lift, showed a maximum settlement of 670 mm under a load of 9.1 m of fill. The settlement occurred immediately upon application of load, and no long-term settlement is expected. The reinforced alternative was successful and was shown to be more economic than unreinforced construction methods previously used.

ACKNOWLEDGMENTS

The authors would like to thank Messrs. Brian Schmidt, Dave Cunningham and Gil Brust of Westar Mining Ltd. for their cooperation and assistance during design and construction and for permission to publish this case history.

REFERENCE

Giroud, J.P., Ah-Line, C. and Bonaparte, R., "Design of Unpaved Roads and Trafficked Areas with Geogrids", Proc. Symposium on Polymer Grid Reinforcement in Civil Engineering, The Institute of Civil Engineering, London, 1984.

GEOTEXTILE REINFORCED EMBANKMENT OVER TIDAL MUD
DEEP BAY, NEW TERRITORIES, HONG KONG

P. Risseeuw and W. Voskamp
Akzo Industrial Systems bv.
Arnhem, The Netherlands

In April 1982, the construction of a 3.5 km long embankment through the tidal area of Deep Bay in the New Territories district of Hong Kong was awarded by the Public Works Department. The project was far from being one that could be considered conventional. The stability of the slopes of the 3.50 m high embankment was achieved by reinforcement of the base using a heavy duty polyester woven geotextile between the fill and the foundation mud.

DESCRIPTION

The Embankment

Early construction trials for the project experienced considerable problems when first undertaken a few years before actual construction. The instability of the slopes lead to a squeezing-out and sliding of the fill material. After evaluating the problems which had been encountered at these trials, the embankment was re-designed.

Soil Conditions

Undrained shear strengths were estimated to be as low as 5 to 10 kPa in the top 6 m of unconsolidated marine deposits, i.e., a very soft clay. It was decided not to increase the base area to reduce the pressure on the ground, because of the scarcity of land in Hong Kong.

Also, the embankment went along existing fish ponds. The dikes of these ponds were not to be damaged in any way during construction of the embankment. Additionally, the whole area was flooded twice a day, due to tides.

CONSTRUCTION

Construction work started by installing 5 m wide geotextile (Stabilenka 200, manufactured and supplied by Akzo Industrial Systems). The reinforcing geotextiles were sewn together on site utilizing local labour. As the illustrations show, the muddy conditions presented the labourers with some difficulties as they struggled to carry and pull the 30 m lengths of geotextile into position. Once the geotextiles were positioned and sewn together, however, access was not so difficult. It was possible for the contractor to move in immediately.

After a 1 m layer of fill was laid with the aid of light Komatsu dozers, the contractor was able to use heavily loaded 35 ton wheelbase trucks to dump the fill close to the front. Then, a fleet of large and small Komatsu swamp dozers was used to push the fill material into position. During the continued filling operation, the freshly deposited mud top layer (300 to 500 mm thick) squeezed out. The underlying stratum, however, was confined by the reinforcing geotextile.

The average work output to bring the 3.5 km long embankment up to its 3.50 m height was 150 m per week. This is considered a good rate of construction, taking into account the fact that installation of the geotextile and filling was restricted by the state of the tide. Initial work could only be accomplished at low tide. Completion was at the end of November 1982.

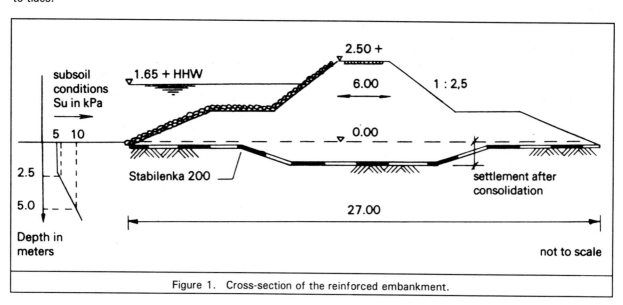

Figure 1. Cross-section of the reinforced embankment.

Photo 2. The task was relatively easy for the workers until they stepped off the end of already laid geotextiles and had to move over soft tidal mud.

Photo 1. The geotextile carried out into the bay.

Photo 3. After unrolling, the geotextile is pulled into position using the already placed geotextiles as a base to walk on.

PERFORMANCE

The primary benefit of the reinforcement was to contribute to the short term stability, whereas it was calculated that the embankment would be stable without the need for reinforcement after a prolonged period of subsoil consolidation.

The Reinforced Soil Group of the consultants, Binnie and Partners, decided to check the performance of the embankment by instrumented sections using piezometers, inclinometers and specially developed strain gauges glued to the geotextile. To date, no decrease of stability or excessive subsidence has been encountered.

REFERENCES

V. Van Zanten, R., "Geotextiles and Geomembranes in Civil Engineering", Balkema, Rotterdam, 1986.

Voskamp, W., "The construction of roads and dikes on low bearing soils", Proc. Symposium on Low Land Development in Indonesia, Jakarta, 1986.

CHAPTER 10

REINFORCED SOIL SLOPES

GEOGRID REINFORCED SLOPE OF SOIL EMBANKMENT
BRAMPTON, ONTARIO, CANADA

M. Devata and D. Dundas
Ministry of Transportation of Ontario
Downsview, Ontario, Canada

In 1983, the Ontario Ministry of Transportation constructed a 7 m high embankment with 1H:1V slopes reinforced with geogrids. This embankment was constructed at Highway 410 near Brampton, Ontario.

The decision to construct a steep embankment at this site was based on economic considerations and property constraints. Although alternatives such as retaining walls, 1.25H:1V rockfill slopes, and 2H:1V earthfill slopes were considered, the 1H:1V earthfill slope with geosynthetic reinforcement (geogrid) was the most economically advantageous option. Table 1 shows a comparison of the costs of the various alternatives considered (including property acquisition costs), for a total wall length of 1 km.

DESIGN CONSIDERATIONS

The purpose of the reinforcing geogrids at this site is to improve the internal and surficial stability of the 1H:1V slope. These elements were designed to provide additional resisting forces to a geometry that otherwise would have been unstable.

The design methodology was based on conventional soil mechanics techniques and required an evaluation of disturbing and restoring forces. The interaction between reinforcing elements and soil depends on the properties and distribution of the reinforcement, on the properties of the fill, and on the construction techniques employed. The limits of the zone of reinforcement were determined, assuming that this zone will behave monolithically, and the vertical spacing of the tensile elements was evaluated by two-part failure wedge theory.

CONSTRUCTION DETAILS

Three different tensile elements were incorporated in the construction of the reinforced embankment. Tensar SR2 geogrid was used in the fill to provide overall external stability. For internal strength, Tensar SS1 geogrid was utilized strictly in the granular frost protection zone (see Photo 1). To protect against surface erosion, Netlon CE111 geonet was placed directly on the embankment surface. The details of the reinforced earth embankment are illustrated in Figure 1.

Prior to the commencement of the embankment construction, the area beneath the reinforced fill was prepared. All organic and loose material was excavated by means of scrapers and removed from the site. The excavated area was then levelled transversely to the highway alignment to match the design elevation of the toe of the fill.

Table 1. Cost comparisons per km in 1983 Canadian million dollars.

Construction Method	Construction Costs	Property Costs	Total Costs
Reinforced conc. wall	1.52	Nil	1.52
Bin wall	1.42	Nil	1.42
Reinforced earth wall	1.38	Nil	1.38
Rockfill 1H:1.25V	0.93	0.30	1.23
Reinforced 1H:1V	0.48	Nil	0.48
Earthfill 2H:1V	0.30	0.90	1.20

Tensar SR2 geogrid was placed in 1.0 m abutting strips transversely in the fill. As indicated in the "Dimension Chart" in Figure 1, the geogrid extended horizontally from the face of the slope to a length varying with depth.

Tensar SS1 geogrid was placed horizontally between the SR2 elements at 250 mm vertical spacings. The geogrids were placed in such a way as to coincide with each second compacted lift. The 1.5 m SS1 tensile element was placed longitudinally in the granular zone. A small lip was formed of the SS1 geogrid at the face of the slope to provide direct contact with the overlying Netlon CE111 geonet.

Geogrid orientation and lapping requirements are shown in the "Plan Section" and "Detail B" in Figure 1.

Upon completion of the embankment fill, some difficulty was experienced in keeping the 50 mm loose topsoil cover on the 1H:1V slope. This resulted in having to compact the topsoil on the slope - an action which is not often practiced as it impedes the germination of grass seeds.

After the topsoil was applied, the Netlon CE111 geonet was placed on the slope surface in strips of 2.0 m overlapping 150 mm with adjacent strips. The Netlon geonet was anchored in place by using wooden pins at specified intervals. In addition, the geonet was anchored at the toe of the slope as illustrated in "Detail C" in Figure 1.

The slope was seeded utilizing a Ministry-owned hydroseeder and at the same time was covered with a

Photo 1. Installation of SS1 geogrid.

Photo 2. Monitoring slope performance.

hydraulic mulch and tackifier to hold all of the ingredients in place. Successful germination was observed three weeks after the initial application, and the area was totally covered with dense grass vegetation eight weeks after the initial seeding.

PERFORMANCE MONITORING

Upon completion of the embankment, deformities within the fill material were monitored by means of multipoint magnetic extensometers, and actual stresses developed in the reinforcing geogrids were measured by strain gauges. Slope performance is monitored as shown in Photo 2.

The results of this monitoring program have substantiated the excellent performance of the 1H:1V reinforced slope. Surficial erosion has occurred in some areas due to washout of topsoil. This is being repaired with a geomat (Tensar Erosion Mat) and reapplication of topsoil and seed.

REFERENCES

Devata, M., "Geogrid Reinforced Earth Embankments with Steep Slopes", Proc. Symposium on Polymer Grid Reinforcement in Civil Engineering, Institute of Civil Engineers, London, U.K., 1984.

Dubois, D., "The Variation in the Tensile Strength of Tensar SR When Subjected to Temperature over the Range 40°C to -20°C", Report #16, Netlon, Blackburn, UK, 1982.

Jones, C.J.E.P., "Practical Design Considerations", Proc. Symposium on Reinforced Earth, Report #451, T.R.R.L. and Heriot-Watt, Edinburgh, U.K., 1977.

Murray, R.T., "Fabric Reinforced Earth Walls: Developed of Design Equations", Supplementary Report #496, T.R.R.L., 1981.

Sarma, S.K., "Stability Analyses of Embankments and Slopes", Geotechnique, Vol. 23, 1973, pp. 423-433.

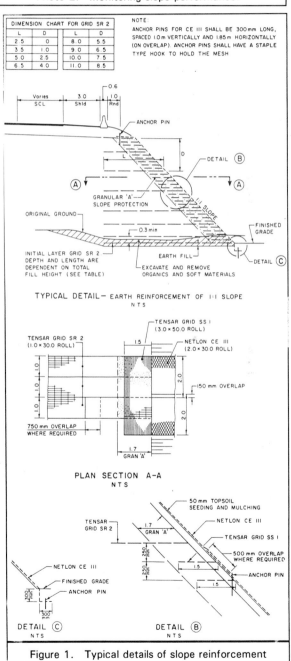

Figure 1. Typical details of slope reinforcement

GEOGRID REINFORCED SOIL REPAIR OF A SLOPE FAILURE IN CLAY
NORTH CIRCULAR ROAD, LONDON, UNITED KINGDOM

J.H. Dixon
Netlon Limited
Blackburn, United Kingdom

Slip failures had occurred over an extensive length of cutting formed in London clay on the London North Circular Road. A reinforced soil solution incorporating geogrids to reinforce the reinstated clay was selected on the basis of cost and ease of construction.

DESCRIPTION

In 1975, some seven years after construction, slip failures began to occur along a 500 m length of cutting on the A406, at Waterworks Corner where the North Circular Road runs through Epping Forest. The cutting was formed in London clay with the side slope of 2H:1V and a maximum height of 8 m. Slips became a recurrent problem, causing damage to fence lines and spillage onto the carriageway.

Several remedial measures were considered, including granular replacement, and toe retention with crib walling or sheet piling combined with flatter slopes. These options were prohibitively expensive. Lime stabilization was ruled out mainly due to doubts about the viability of achieving uniform mixing on site and uncertainty about long-term performance.

TECHNICAL CONSIDERATIONS

Design Philosophy

The extensive problem of shallow slope failures in highway embankments and cuttings with conventional side slopes formed from overconsolidated clay has been the subject of papers by the T.R.R.L. [1983] and Parsons et al. [1985].

Traditional repairs have involved excavation and off-site disposal of the slipped soil and replacement with granular fill, at a typical 1985 cost in southeast England of £25/m^3 [Greenwood et al., 1985].

Recently developed soil reinforcement techniques involving the re-use of the slipped clay, reinforced with geogrids, have enabled repairs to be carried out at a quarter of the traditional cost as reported by Oliver [1985] and with minimum traffic disruption and less public nuisance from construction traffic. This approach was adopted at Waterworks Corner.

Design charts have been developed by Murray [1984] to select the geogrid reinforcement requirements for a range of slope conditions. The reinforcement is designed to intersect potential failure planes. It must possess proven long-term tensile strength characteristics and sufficient interaction with the soil to resist direct shearing of soil over the reinforcement and also to provide pull out resistance using a relatively short anchorage length.

At Waterworks Corner, additional land was made available enabling the side slope to be flattened in places from the original 2H:1V to 3H:1V. As agent for the Department of Transport, the London Borough of Waltham Forest Department of Development incorporated in the design charts effective stress parameters for the remoulded clay of $c' = 0$ and $\phi' = 20°$ with $\gamma = 20$ kN/m^3 and pore pressure ratio $r_u = 0.25$.

Using "Tensar" SR2 geogrid, a vertical spacing of 1.5 m for the horizontal layers of primary reinforcement satisfied the design factor of safety. Short horizontal layers of "Tensar" SS1 geogrid were specified as secondary reinforcement at 500 mm spacing to stabilize the slope surface against potential sloughing between layers of primary reinforcement (Figure 1). Drainage was also included.

Construction

Main contractor, Fitzpatrick and Son, began work in September, 1985. The majority of the earthworks was carried out by sub-contractor, C.J. Pryor Ltd., using a Cat 215 tracked excavator, Volvo four-wheel drive dumptruck, Cat 951 dozer (four-in-one bucket) and a towed T182B Stotert and Pitt vibrating roller. Manual operations were carried out by two labourers.

Main earthworks began with the excavation and removal from site of a 35 m long strip of slipped soil. Excavation extended beyond the failure plane with benched steps cut into the undisturbed clay. To control any seepage, a 300 mm thick granular drainage layer was included over the excavated surface on the north side, where the forest slopes towards the cutting. The general sequence then adopted was to reinstate the first strip using fill excavated from an adjacent second strip, thereby minimizing double handling. The second strip was then reinstated using fill excavated from a third strip and so on.

Fill was tipped from the dumptruck, placed using the bulldozer (Photo 2) and compacted to a maximum layer depth of 200 mm using the vibrating roller towed by the bulldozer. The 2.0 m widths of "Tensar" SS1 secondary reinforcement were obtained by cutting the standard 4.0 m wide rolls in half on site with a disc cutter. "Tensar" SR2 rolls were cut to the required length and laid perpendicular to the slope alignment. Adjacent rolls were butt jointed (Photo 1). The slope face was over filled and trimmed in the conventional manner.

| Photo 1. Placing geogrids. | Photo 2. Placing cohesive soil over geogrids. |

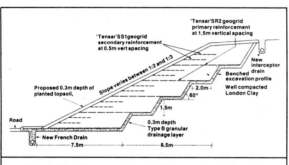

Figure 1. Cross-section of the repair of the slip failure.

Earthworks were completed in early February 1986. The approximate quantities of the main bill items were: excavation 23,000 m³, fill 12,800 m², gravel drain 5,400 m³, "Tensar" SR2 geogrid 17,000 m², "Tensar" SS1 geogrid 8,000 m². In March 1986 approximately 5,000 m³ of topsoil was placed over the reconstructed slopes for subsequent planting.

PERFORMANCE

No discernable movements have been noted and the grass cover on the slope is in a good condition with a pleasing appearance.

CONCLUSIONS

No special site equipment or expertise was required for the installation, which was carried out using conventional plant and labour.

The average construction time per 35 m long strip was about 3 days (typical strip quantities being: excavation 1,200 m³, fill 800 m³, gravel drain 350 m³, geogrids 2,000 m²).

Despite winter working, the natural moisture content of the excavated clay fill was suitable to allow good compaction.

REFERENCES

Greenwood, J.R., Holt D.A. and Herrick, G.W., "Shallow slips in highway embankments constructed of over consolidated clay", Proc. Symposium on Failures in Earthworks, London, 1985, pp. 79-92.

Murray, R.T., "Reinforcement techniques in repairing slope failures", Proc. Symposium on Polymer Grid Reinforcement, I.C.E., London, 1984, pp. 47-53.

Oliver, T.L.H., "Reinforced soil techniques for the reinstatement of failed slopes using geogrids", Proc. Symposium on Failures in Earthworks, London, 1985, pp. 417-419.

Parson, A.W. and Perry J., "Slope stability problems in ageing highway earthworks", Proc. Symposium on Failures in Earthworks, London, 1985, pp. 63-78.

Transport and Road Research Laboratory, "Studies of slope stability in highway engineering", T.R.R.L. Leaflet, 1985.

GEOGRID REINFORCEMENT FOR A SOIL SLOPE
LAWRENCE BERKELEY LABORATORY, CALIFORNIA, USA

P.C. Lucia
Woodward-Clyde Consultants
Oakland, California, USA

S.A. Blair
Lawrence Berkeley Laboratory
Berkeley, California, USA

The Lawrence Berkeley Laboratory (LBL) is located in the hills above the campus of the University of California, Berkeley. New construction designed to improve and realign roads resulted in excess soil due to excavations in the hill side. An economic solution to disposal of the excess soil was construction of a fill that would result in additional parking at the LBL facility. The steep topography of the hill side required that any new fill would need to be about 24 m high and with an overall slope no flatter than about 1H:1V.

DESCRIPTION

The LBL fill is a reinforced soil slope approximately 24 m high and with a length of about 90 m. Photographs of the finished slope and a view of an intermediate slope are shown in Photos 1 and 2 respectively. A cross section of the reinforced slope showing the vertical spacing and design lengths of the reinforcement is shown in figure 1.

Two geosynthetic materials were used for reinforcement. A high density polyethylene (HDPE) SR-2 geogrid and a polypropylene SS-2 geogrid. The SR-2 geogrid was designed to provide overall stability while the SS-2 geogrid is intended to provide near surface stability and minimize bulging at the face.

The project was constructed over the two construction seasons of 1985 and 1986. Construction was temporarily stopped in late 1985 due to the inability to compact fill during the winter rains. The portion of the fill with vegetation growing on the face was completed in 1985 and can be seen in Photo 1. The fill with the black geogrid exposed was constructed in the spring of 1986. The photograph was taken in the fall of 1986.

TECHNICAL CONSIDERATIONS

Soil Properties

The soils for the fill were to come from excavation of a new road alignment. The properties used for design were based on tests of representative soil samples performed by Harding Lawson Associates [1983]. Preliminary assumptions for design were that a cohesionless material with a friction angle of 34 degrees could be obtained from the excavation. The soil from the roadway excavation used as fill actually consisted of silty clays and clayey sandy gravels with variable amounts of volcanic rock fragments. The soil was compacted to 90% of the maximum density from ASTM D1557 (modified Proctor). The soil was more cohesive than had been assumed for analyses. Strength tests were not performed on the actual material in the fill.

Geosynthetic Properties

The geosynthetic reinforcement materials were the Tensar Corporation's HDPE SR-2 and polypropylene SS-2 geogrids. The SR-2 geogrid has an ultimate strength of approximately 80 kN/m and a recommended allowable strength of 29 kN/m.

Design

The design, including vertical spacing, embedment length, and required number of layers, was based on use of charts by Jewel [1984]. The slope was designed to be constructed with a series of benches and intermediate slopes of 0.75H:1V. The slope design considered overall stability, stability of the benched 0.75H:1V slopes and near surface stability. The spacing of the reinforcement placed more reinforcement near the bottom of the slope and had greater spacing between layers near the top of the slope. To maintain near surface stability and minimize bulging, spacing of reinforcement near the surface was kept at 900 mm or less. Where spacing of the SR-2 reinforcement exceeded 900 mm, intermediate layers of SS-2 were placed, as shown in Figure 1.

A reanalysis of the slope was performed after construction, assuming soil properties more consistent with the compacted low plasticity clays that were actually used for fill. The assumed soil properties were a cohesion of 15 kPa and a friction angle of 30°. The total amount of reinforcement placed in the slope resulted in an equivalent force per unit width of approximately 500 kN/m from the 17 layers of SR-2. The resultant of the reinforcement was slightly above the third point of the slope. The method of analysis was based on Duncan et al. [1985]. The calculated factor of safety, based on the slope geometry, reinforcement properties and assumed fill strength was about 1.25.

Further analysis was performed to evaluate the relationship between the calculated factor of safety and the amount of reinforcement in the slope. The results of the analysis are shown in Figure 2. The relationship shown in Figure 2 is primarily due to the friction angle of the soil and the geometry of the slope.

Based on the above analysis, an increase in the factor of safety of about 20%, from 1.25 to 1.5, would require about a 200% increase in the required number of reinforcement layers and greater length of reinforcement. For fills as high and steep as the LBL fill the choice of the allowable factor of safety has significant impact on the cost of construction.

ISSMFE., Committee TC9 - Geosynthetics Case Histories.

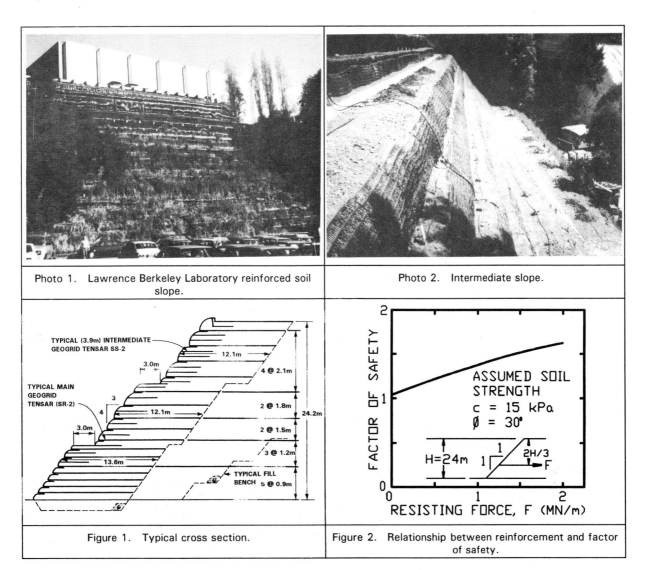

Photo 1. Lawrence Berkeley Laboratory reinforced soil slope.

Photo 2. Intermediate slope.

Figure 1. Typical cross section.

Figure 2. Relationship between reinforcement and factor of safety.

Performance

To date, the reinforced slope has performed as intended.

CONCLUSIONS

The application of soil reinforcement can substantially increase the stability of slopes. For cohesive soils, the stability of slopes 24 m high or greater can only be marginally improved by incorporation of reinforcement as demonstrated by the LBL fill.

REFERENCES

Duncan, J.M., Low, B.K., and Schaefer, V.R., STABGM: "A Computer Program for Slope Stability Analysis of Reinforced Embankments and Slopes", Virginia Polytechnic Institute and State University, Department of Civil Engineering, September 1985.

Harding Lawson Associates, "Geotechnical Investigation Building 17 to 25A Road Realignment", Lawrence Berkeley Laboratory, Berkeley, California, 1983.

Jewell, R.A., Paine, N., and Woods, R.I., "Design Methods for Steep Reinforced Embankments", Proc. Symposium on Polymer Grid Reinforcement in Civil Engineering, The Institute of Civil Engineers, London, 1984.

GEOSYNTHETICS FOR LANDSLIP STABILIZATION
NORTH COUNTRY, UNITED KINGDOM

P.R. Rankilor
Manstock Geotechnical Consultancy Services, Ltd.
Manchester, United Kingdom

In 1987, for the first time, Directionally Structural Fabric linear inlay geotextiles were used to construct steep reinforced soil retaining walls for the stabilization and reconstruction of a major landslip. Geotextile wrapped ground drains and geocomosite fin drains were used to intercept and remove groundwater. Geojute[R] was used for erosion control.

DESCRIPTION

The Problem

A major landslip in Quaternary sands and clays had occurred, removing the crest of several domestic gardens and the upper two-thirds of a steep, wooded hillside. Stabilization options were limited by:

a)   the need to restore the gardens to their original position, therefore the slope could not be cut back to a flatter angle; and

b)   the slip "daylighted" two-thirds of the way down the hillside, thus precluding the use of a "toe weight" solution.

TECHNICAL CONSIDERATIONS

Groundwater

A number of longitudinal downslope drains were constructed to a depth of 5 m. They were placed at 5 m intervals and each drain was wrapped in geotextile (Bidim U34) [Manstock Geotechnical, Ltd. 1986] and backfilled with a carrier pipe and coarse granular drainage stone. These were constructed as the first phase of the work in order to remove excess groundwater and to raise the safety factor back to just above 1.

The Lower Bank

The cross-section of the slip was as shown schematically in Figure 1. The slip was continuously moving out along the lower part of the 4 m thick clay seam. This presented a most difficult stabilization problem which was solved by cutting out slices of the clay and replacing it with reinforced soil granular embankment wedges. In order to maintain reasonable control of the overall slope, only narrow sections of the clay could be excavated at any time and replaced by reinforced soil banks. This was done on a sequence basis as shown in Figure 2. The weight, granularity and permeability of the lower reinforced soil bank prevented further slippage of the slope outwards and stabilized the slip, raising the safety factor to 1.35.

The reinforced soil bank was constructed sideways in 2 m wide modules. The pre-constructed ground drains were cut out as the bank reached each one. Each severed ground drain was reconnected beneath the bank and drains from the bank itself were connected into these lower ground drains. The use of a geotextile wrap facilitated the cutting out of the drains and the reconnection of the drains whilst keeping the stone clean and re-wrapped upon final completion.

MATERIALS USED

Geotextile Filter for Drainage Works

A heavier than normal grade of geotextile filter was chosen, because difficult laying conditions were expected to be encountered in the execution of 5 m deep drains being cut at a 2H:1V or sometimes steeper hill side. The nonwoven needlepunched geotextile behaved well and was placed with 5 m of gravel cover, without tearing. The subsequent re-excavation of the banks gave a useful opportunity to examine the geotextile and the way it had behaved during placing. It was found that it had not been damaged at all, and its good extensibility had permitted excellent geotextile-to-ground contact.

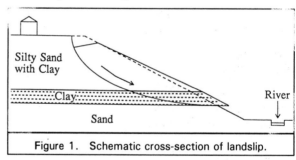

Figure 1.   Schematic cross-section of landslip.

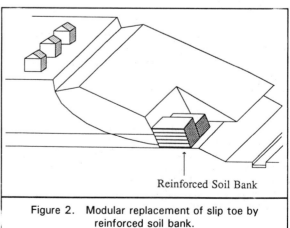

Figure 2.   Modular replacement of slip toe by reinforced soil bank.

| Photo 1. Reinforced soil bank being constructed using directionally structural fabric geotextile. | Photo 2. Reinforced soil layers contoured back at top of bank to aid landscaping. |

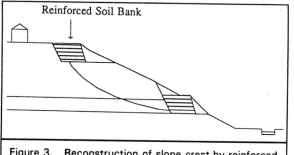

Figure 3. Reconstruction of slope crest by reinforced soil bank.

Geocomposite Fin Drains

A small T:PC:T type [Rankilor, 1985] geocomposite fin drain was laid behind the soil bank across the direction of maximum soil thrust. Due to the high forces involved, the strongest a crush-resistant geocomposite fin drain (Hydraway) was selected.

Reinforcing Geotextile

The newly-developed directionally structural fabric geotextiles were chosen for the soil reinforcement function because of their high strength and relatively low cost; also because they are made of polyester which is highly creep resistant. The product chosen was a Fryma mid-size reinforcing mesh, suitable for use with medium-to-coarse granular materials. This geotextile has an strength of 120 kN/m and an effective mesh size of 15 mm x 15 mm. Due to the high safety factors required for the reconstruction, in view of the proximity of domestic residences, a working stress of <30 kN/m was adopted.

Geojute[R]

Geojute[R] erosion control textile was used on the crests and 1.8H:1V steep surfaces, to prevent soil wash.

RECONSTRUCTION OF SLOPE CREST AND GARDENS

Construction of Crest

As shown in Figure 3, a second steep reinforced soil bank was constructed at the top of the slope to bridge the original slip circle plane and to re-establish the crest in its original position. The same reinforcing geotextile was used as for a lower bank, and the same granular specification of $\phi > 30°$ was adopted.

Reinstatement of Slope

Once the banks had re-stabilized and the slope re-established its structural geometry, granular fill and topsoil were placed to achieve a final profile. After grass seeding Geojute[R] was pegged out to prevent soil wash.

PERFORMANCE

Geotextile Filter Drains

The filter drains performed well in terms of both ease of installation and ground filtration. Clear water runs continuously from all the drain outlet points at the base of the slope.

Reinforced Soil

The reinforcing geotextile performed excellently, permitting the construction of each layer without the need for externally-propped shuttering or facing units.

CONCLUSION

This is the first known reinforced soil bank to use directionally structural fabric geotextiles. The construction and placement of a major embankment by means of excavating the toe of a landslip is a design technique which uniquely utilizes the instant support power of reinforced soil banks.

The technique of cutting the longitudinal drains to lower the water table and then inserting the reinforced soil bank, connecting the drains beneath the bank, was successful and is a useful development in the stabilization techniques for landslips.

The relatively undemanding design parameters chosen, allowed the use of mixed local sand from the site and imported granular materials.

REFERENCES

Manstock Geotechnical Consultancy Services Ltd., "International Directory of Geotextiles and Related Products", Manchester, 1986.

P.R. Rankilor, "The Specification and Use of Geotextile Fin Drains", Geotextiles and Geomembranes, Elsevier Applied Science Publishers Ltd., 1985.

GEOGRID REINFORCEMENT FOR A STEEP ROAD EMBANKMENT SLOPE
KYUSHU ISLAND, JAPAN

T. Yamanouchi
Kyushu Sangyo University
Fukuoka, Japan

N. Fukuda
Fukken Co., Ltd. Yokohama Branch Office
Yokohama, Japan

M. Ikegami
Mitsui Petrochemical Industries, Ltd.
Tokyo, Japan

In 1984, for the first time in Japan, a polymer geogrid was used as reinforcing material in a steep road embankment built with an extremely erosive pumice soil, called "Shirasu". The road was located at the south end of Kyushu Island. To check the design parameters against those of the actual construction, the geogrid strains and slope displacements were measured at the site.

DESCRIPTION

The Embankment

In the course of construction it became necessary to construct 3 to 7 m high embankments in a 60 m valley section. A steep slope of 1H:5V was adopted with a view to increase the available area of the site.

Polymer Geogrid

- Type: uniaxial polymer geogrid (Tensar SR-2).
- Properties: design tensile strength: 31 kN/m (that is 40% of actual tensile strength) based on creep test results.
- Mass per unit area: 850 g/m².
- Peak strain: 10%.
- Modulus (tensile stiffness): J = 700 kN/m at 1% strain based on tensile tests at a strain rate of 2%/min.

It should be noted the geogrid displays a visco-elastic behaviour.

DESIGN

The design for the steep reinforced embankment was based on the method proposed by Jewell et al. [1984]. Strength parameters in the design were taken as follows: c = 0 kPa; $\phi = \tan^{-1}(2/3) \tan\phi' = 30°$ ($\phi' = 41°$). The bulk unit weight (γ) considered for the soil was 17.7 kN/m³. The design geogrid length was taken as 4.5 m as derived from the external stability analysis. The vertical reinforcement spacing at the lowest part of the embankment was 970 mm as derived from the internal stability analysis. Based on this computation the geogrid spacing was taken to be 1 m throughout the whole height of the embankment.

CONSTRUCTION

Sand and bags were piled up, each 1 m height, to retain the compacted earth fill, before the whole layer was wrapped up by the polymer grid. The slope is in the form of steps 1 m high and 200 mm wide. On the top of each compacted soil layer, the geogrid is wrapped back by 1.5 m. The wrapped-back portion of the geogrid is connected to the overlying geogrid by steel pipes (Photo 1) intertwined within the geogrid strands. In order to eliminate relaxation of the geogrid during construction, tension was added to the free end of the geogrid and temporarily retained through a wooden pile, until earth-filling was done. This technique of construction does not require working from the front side of the embankment and it is found to be speedier than an ordinary conventional work, e.g. the concrete retaining wall.

PERFORMANCE

Embankment Deformation

The vertical and horizontal displacements of the slope after completion of construction were 180 mm and 120 mm, respectively. Afterwards, those values increased to 240 mm and 170 mm respectively as the embankment was affected by rain during the following 8 month period. This proves that the embankment is durable in severe weather conditions. In other words, it can be concluded that the embankment of such a type, even though it has displacements, tends to move towards a stable condition as a result of geogrid reinforcement.

Strain Distribution in Geogrids

The geogrids' strain distribution was measured by foil strain gauges attached to the geogrids (Figure 1). Maximum strain (ε_{max}) was found to be as low as 0.15 to 0.3%. The changes of geogrid strains after completion of the embankment were insignificant.

COMPARISON BETWEEN DESIGN AND PRACTICE

A comparison between design and field data was done with a view to verify the validity of the design. Geogrid tensions were derived from measured strains using the following equation:

$$T^{*}_{max} = J \cdot \varepsilon_{max}$$

where J is the tensile stiffness and ε_{max} is the maximum strain of the geogrid.

Using this equation, maximum tensions of 1.1 to 2.1 kN/m were calculated for geogrids located at elevations 1 to 4 m in the actual embankment.

On the other hand, tension at each geogrid was computed in accordance with the basic design equation:

$$T^{*}_{max} = K \left(\gamma \cdot h_i + q_s \right) S_v$$

Photo 1.   Geogrid placement.

Photo 2.   View of the reinforced embankment slope.

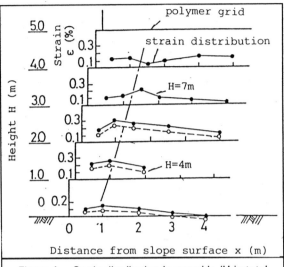

Figure 1.   Strain distribution in geogrids (H is total embankment height).

REFERENCES

Fukuda, N., Yamanouchi, T. and Miura, N., "Comparative Studies of Design and Construction of a Steep Reinforced Embankment", Geotextiles and Geomembranes, Vol. 4, Nos. 3 & 4, 1986, pp. 269-284.

Jewell, R.A., Paine, N. and Woods, R.I., "Design Methods for Steep Reinforced Embankments", Proc. Symposium Polymer Grid Reinforcement in Civil Engineering, London, March 1984, Paper No. 3.1, pp. 70-81.

Yamanouchi, T., Fukuda, N. and Sutoh, Y., "Tests for Estimating of Design Strength of Polymer Grid", Proc. 30th. Symposium JSSMFE, Nov. 1985, pp. 23-26, (in Japanese).

Yamanouchi, T., Omagari, D., Fukuda, N. and Ikegami, M., "Design and Practice of Steep Reinforced Embankments by using Polymer Grids", Proc. 30th. Symposium JSSMFE, Nov. 1985, pp. 13-18 (in Japanese).

Yamanouchi, T., Fukuda, N. and Ikegami, M., "Design and Techniques of Steep Reinforced Embankments Without Edge Supportings", Proc. 3rd. Int. Conf. on Geotextiles, Vienna, Vol. 1, April 1986, pp. 199-204.

where h_i is the distance between the grid in the i-th layer and the top of the embankment, K is the earth pressure coefficient, q_s is the surcharge load, S_v is the vertical grid spacing, in this case equal to 1.0 m. Maximum tensions between 14.7 and 29.4 kN/m were computed using the design soil properties in comparison with 9.7 kN/m where the calculations use more realistic soil properties. Ratios between tensions obtained from field data and tensions calculated using the design equation (with realistic soil properties) was found to be in the 9 to 26% range at elevations 1 to 4 m in the embankment. This indicates a higher order of reinforcing effect than that proposed in the present design method.

CONCLUSION

The main lessons from this case history were:

- Construction of steep slopes is economical and feasible. Accordingly, similar reinforced embankments with maximum heights of 15 m have been constructed at more than 20 places in Japan.

- From the geogrid strains measured in the field, it was found that the actual tensions in the geogrid are much lower than that computed using the design method by Jewell et al. [1984]. This is due to the fact that soil and geogrid are integrated into a rigid body. Hence such additional integration effects should be incorporated in future designs.

GEOTEXTILE REINFORCED SOIL STRUCTURE FOR LANDSLIDE REPAIRS TROUVILLE SUR MER AND LIXING, FRANCE

Y. Matichard[1], J.C. Blivet[2], H. Perrier[3] and Ph. Delmas[4]

[1] Laboratoire Régional des Ponts et Chaussées de Nancy, France
[2] Laboratoire Régional des Ponts et Chaussées de Rouen, France
[3] Centre d'Expérimentations Routières de Rouen, France
[4] Laboratoire Central des Ponts et Chaussées de Paris, France

Landslide stabilization is one of the most challenging problems the geotechnical engineer has to solve. Standardization is not possible due to the variety of cases. Often drainage and an associated earth abutment are an economic solution. Use of geotextile-reinforced soil structure allows for a reduction of earth work by changing the geometry and allows the use of soils with average mechanical properties. When the structure is built, geotextiles enable the repaired soil to withstand the forces imposed by an unstable uphill mass. Two cases are presented:

- replacement of unstable soils and drainage on a slope
- abutment of a landslide.

The first case is located at Trouville sur Mer (France) and described by Blivet et al. [1985]. A landslide occurred during the winter of 1982-83 on the coastal road. Stabilization was ensured with drainage and soil reinforcement. The base of the reinforced soil structure was placed below the observed failure surface. Use of geotextiles allowed for an economical repair using fill material locally available at no cost (sand from a nearby dredging work). This very fine sand was deemed unsuitable for use with steel reinforcement because of its lack of dilatancy. The geotextile reinforced soil structure is 5.0 m high and was built with six reinforcement layers spaced at 800 mm, each 4 m long (Figure 1). Their function is one of reinforcement only. It was built in a few days during June 1984. The originality of this work was the use of geotextile cubic containers as formwork.

The second case is located at Lixing near Sarreguemines (France). A new departmental road was built in 1977 near the town of Lixing. The road was formed by a cutting of total height 18 m at the foot of a natural hill side with a slope of 17°. After a few years, landslides affecting both the cutting and the hill side occurred. Two geotextile reinforced soil structures were built, one at mid-height and the other at the toe of the cutting (Figure 2). The structures have vertical faces protected by light concrete chips.

Only the second case, the Lixing reinforced soil structure, is discussed below.

DESCRIPTION

The uphill structure is 80 m long and 4.5 m high maximum with six reinforcement layers spaced at 750 mm and 5 m long. The downhill structure is 40 m long and 3.0 m high with four reinforcements spaced at 750 mm and 3.0 m long. In these structures, the geotextiles have only a reinforcement function.

Locally available sand (from weathered Vosgian sandstone) was used in the reinforced soil structures. This sand contained too many fine particles to be used with steel reinforcement. Its characteristics are: (1) natural water content, 9 to 12%; (2) normal Proctor optimum water content, 12%; (3) normal Proctor unit weight, 17.7 kN/m³; (4) internal friction, 36.5°.

DESIGN

The stability analysis and design work followed the methodology described by Delmas and Matichard [1986]. Three points were examined:

- Stabilization of Landslide: The design requirement was to increase by 20% the factor of safety along the observed failure surface. This led to the geometry of the uphill structure with reinforcement layers longer than usual. The geometry of the downhill structure resulted from the requirement of a safety factor of 1.50 along the potential failure surfaces 2 and 3 (Figure 2).

- External Stability of the Structures: Stability of the uphill structure was evaluated with respect to overturning, foundation bearing and shear failures under the loads calculated (90 kN/m on the back side). For the downhill structure, classical analyses for retaining structures were used.

- Internal Design of the Structures: Calculations were performed using the displacement method [Delmas et al., 1985] to ensure internal stability considering various potential failure surfaces and to satisfy the criterion of less than 25 mm displacement. This design step led to minimum requirements for geotextile characteristics.

In the design calculations a 0.9 ratio was used between the geotextile/soil interface shear strength and the soil shear strength (tanφ).

GEOTEXTILE REINFORCEMENT

The polypropylene woven geotextile No. 44614 produced by UCO was selected. Its properties, measured by the Laboratoire Régional des Ponts et Chaussées de Nancy according to the French standards are:

- mass per unit area: 560 g/m²
- force per unit width at failure: 100.5 kN/m
- strain at failure: 18.7%
- tensile stiffness at 5% strain: 400 kN/m

Photo 1. Uphill and downhill geotextile reinforced soil structures at Lixing.

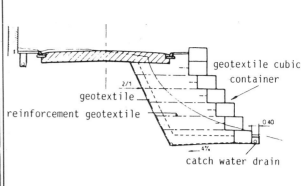

geotextile cubic container

geotextile
reinforcement geotextile

catch water drain

Figure 1. Geotextile reinforced embankment with geotextile cubic container facing at Trouville.

Table 1. Strain measured in the geotextile for Lixing uphill structure		
Layer no.* Distance from face	2	4
1 m	2.6%	2.0%
2 m	1.3%	2.5%
3 m	0.85%	0.94%
4 m	0.55%	0.82%
* The layers are numbered from the bottom up.		

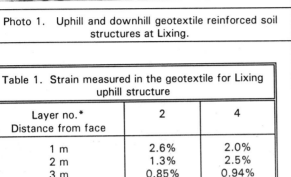

A - ALTERNATE LAYERS OF SHALE AND LIMESTONE
B - FOLIATED SHALE
C - FRACTURED LIMESTONE WITH SHALE AND EMBEDDED LAYERS OF BLACK SHALE
D - SUBLITHOGRAPHIC LIMESTONE
E - STIFF SHALE WITH SOME LIMESTONE LAYERS

Figure 2. Use of geotextile reinforced soil structure as abutment of landslide at Lixing.

CONSTRUCTION

Construction took place in a two-month period at the end of 1984. The uphill structure was built in two parts to ensure optimum stability of unstable soils during construction. A special procedure was developed for joining these two parts.

Formwork and facing patented by the Laboratoires des Ponts et Chaussées were used. Each layer was sustained by formwork that slide on a vertical fixed frame.

PERFORMANCE

The uphill structure was instrumented to confirm the design assumptions as it was a rather unusual application of geotextile-reinforced soil structure at mid-height of a slope for landslide repair. Strain gauges were placed in two layers on the same cross section. Values measured during construction are given Table 1. Strain gauges did not show any significant variation in the measured strains after construction. They allowed the determination of a locus of maximal strains which was not very different from the locus considered in design.

Inclinometers in the uphill structure have indicated some movement at the soil-geotextile interface, corresponding to the failure surface observed in the soil. Displacements, which stopped after two years, are less than 3 mm. Inclinometers in the downhill structure only showed a horizontal displacement of the top. This was less than 1 mm.

CONCLUSION

The Lixing and Trouville reinforced soil structures have shown that geotextile reinforced soil abutments can perform well as a landslide repair. The method yields substantial cost saving by allowing and optimizing the use of an inexpensive fill material. Also, measurements on the structures confirmed the validity of the design method.

REFERENCES

Blivet, J.C., Douillot, H., Perrier, H., "Stabilisation d'un glissement de terrain par renforcement tout textile - Route de la corniche à Trouville", Revue Générale des Routes et Aérodromes, No. 617, Mar 1985, pp. 11-15.

Delmas, P., Matichard, Y., "Landslides confortation with geotextile reinforced earth work", Proc. 3rd. Int. Conf. on Geotextiles, Vol. 4, Vienna, Austria, Apr 1986, pp. 1091-1095.

GEOSYNTHETIC YARN-SOIL MIXTURE FOR SLOPE RETAINING STRUCTURES
A7 MOTORWAY, NORTHERN FRANCE, FRANCE

E. Leflaive
Consulting Engineer
Paris, France

M. Audouin
Société d'Application du Texsol
Orsay, France

The A7 Motorway is the link between Northern France and Northern Europe at one end and the French Mediterranean coast and Spain, at the other end. Built a number of years ago with 4 (2 x 2) lanes, this motorway needed to be widened to accommodate the increasing traffic of this major route. This is why, each year, the "Société des Autoroutes du Sud de la France" has been calling bids for works to add one lane to a 10 to 15 km stretch of this motorway.

THE PROBLEM

In the hilly region between Lyon and Valence, the existing motorway has many cut sections. In order to avoid buying new land, which is costly and time consuming, widening required increasing the angle of the slopes. Long term soil properties, however were such that retaining structures became necessary.

Initial tender documents called for conventional L-shaped concrete walls, but alternate solutions could be proposed, provided they would fulfil the following conditions:

- short construction time,
- good incorporation in natural environment,
- possibility of construction next to existing traffic,
- cost.

A Texsol solution was proposed and finally chosen by Scetauroute, the engineers, as shown on Figure 1.

GEOSYNTHETIC SOLUTION

The Texsol technique has been described in various publications [Leflaive, 1985; Leflaive and Liausu, 1986]. It is the intimate mixing of soil particles and polymer yarn. Patents are owned by the French Government. The mixture is obtained by projecting the soil through a pneumatic or mechanical (conveyor belt) system and simultaneously projecting a number of continuous yarns. Soil and yarn mix together as they fall down. Appropriate relative movements must be given to the soil and to the yarns in order to obtain a proper mixture; thus a specific equipment must be used.

The proportion in weight of yarn, with respect to soil, is typically in the 0.15 to 0.18 percent range. The equipment used on the A7 Motorway has a long conveyor belt to raise the soil high enough to build 10 m high retaining structures and a short, fast moving conveyor belt to project the soil. Photos 3 and 4 show the equipment used on this job, which has replaced a previous machine working on the same principle.

The yarn used on the A7 Motorway retaining structure is 167 decitex polyester yarn. This yarn is appropriate for the soil used on this job, which is a fine natural sand coming from the site itself. The amount of fines must not exceed 10% for the hopper and conveyer belt system not to clog.

DESIGN AND CONSTRUCTION

In order to create the space required to construct the

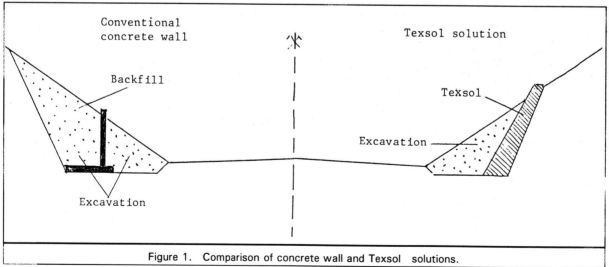

Conventional concrete wall

Backfill

Excavation

Texsol solution

Texsol

Excavation

Figure 1. Comparison of concrete wall and Texsol solutions.

ISSMFE., Committee TC9 - Geosynthetics Case Histories.

Photo 1. View of Texsol retaining structures.

Photo 2. View of Texsol retaining structures.

Photo 3. View of construction equipment.

Photo 4. View of construction equipment.

extra lane, it was proposed to build a Texsol inclined wall against the cut slope, with the following characteristics:

- 60° angle between outer face of wall and horizontal,
- foundation of wall 0.50 to 0.80 m deep,
- height between 3 and 7 m according to location,
- Texsol thickness at the top: 0.55 m,
- Texsol thickness at the base: 0.80 to 1.80 m according to height and stability analysis, so as to ensure the required factor of safety.

As construction of the wall progressed, the Texsol material was compacted using a small hand-driven vibratory roller or a vibrating plate.

Calculation of internal stability takes into account the anisotropic cohesion of the Texsol produced with the equipment shown. External stability is calculated as usually. Full size tests of 3 m high Texsol walls loaded up to failure have shown failure by overturning.

PERFORMANCE AND CONCLUSIONS

On the A7 job, short term stability was ensured. The slopes were therefore cut to the required profile, then the Texsol was installed. The output of the equipment was about 100 m³ per day in 1984-85 and is now 250 m³ per day. After installation the Texsol has been grass seeded.

Photos 1 and 2 show typical views of the Texsol retaining structures; on Photo 2 the left side shows the slope after one year when the grass cover had developed, while the right side shows the Texsol material immediately after completion. No protection against rain and wind erosion is needed.

Seven years after construction, the Texsol wall still performs well. Only the vegetation requires some maintenance.

On that site approximately 50,000 m² of wall have been built. Two features must be outlined: The appearance, which mixes with the environment more than any other technique and the cost, since this technique has been the cheapest of all proposed solutions.

REFERENCES

Leflaive, E., "Soil reinforced with continuous yarns: the Texsol", Proc. 11th. ICSMFE, San Francisco, U.S.A., 1985, Vol 3, pp. 1787-1790.

Leflaive, E., Liausu, Ph., "The reinforcement of soils by continuous threads", Proc. 3rd. Int. Conf. Geotextiles, Vienna, Austria, 1986, Vol 2. pp. 523-528.

GEOTEXTILE-REINFORCED SOIL FACING FOR NAILED SLOPE
ZURICH, SWITZERLAND

R. Rüegger and B. Borrer
Rüegger AG, Consulting Engineers
St. Gallen, Switzerland

In 1987 a cutting with a height of up to 12 m was constructed in a slope of 30 to 40° in order to straighten a section of the Zürich Regional Railway SZU (Sihltal-Zürich-Uetliberg Railway). Because of the loamy, gravelly subgrade with an angle of friction of approx. 35° (angle of total shear strength), the project could only be realized with a retaining construction.

PROJECT OBJECTIVES

The project was required to take into account the natural surroundings (a river landscape with sparsely wooded water-meadows and tree-lined slopes). This objective was achieved with a combination of two new construction techniques (Figure 1):

a) injection nailing to form a soil mass with permanently stressed reinforcement (system according to Ribbert AG, Switzerland)

b) a slim frontal facing construction of geotextile-reinforced soil using the Textomur system which can be completely grassed (using hydroseed) and planted with shrubs and small bushes.

PROJECT DESCRIPTION

The injection nailing using the Ribbert-system is a means of stabilising soil using the "lances or nails" which are grouted in two stages using silica gel and cement mortar. The technique is used here both as permanent soil reinforcement and to secure temporary works.

Textomur is a geotextile-reinforced soil retaining construction system which can be completely grassed over. It was used here purely as a facing wall, as the injection nailing took care of the soil pressures. The system consists of three basic elements (Figure 2):

1) A nonwoven reinforcement geotextile acts as a tension member in the soil and, therefore, must possess high tensile strength at low extensions. It is installed in horizontal layers. The advantage of a nonwoven as opposed to a woven geotextile lies in its transmissivity (permeability in the plane of the fabric). Each reinforcement layer thus acts as a drainage layer.

Properties:	Mass/ unit area	350 g/m^2
	Tensile strength	40 kN/m
	Working tension	13 kN/m

2) A nonwoven vegetation geotextile is installed at the face and serves as a protection against erosion and as a base layer for the hydroseed since it is capable of being penetrated by roots.

Properties:	Mass per unit area	160 g/m^2
	Tensile strength	18 kN/m

The geotextiles used in the Textomur system are produced by F. Landolt AG, Switzerland, and were specially developed for this system.

3) A steel mesh shuttering placed on the slope is simply a construction expedient. It enables a regular surface to be achieved, which in turn allows the use of machines in the maintenance of the slope. The mesh has no long-term load bearing function, so corrosion may be permitted.

The Textomur system has the following advantages:

● the system blends into the surrounding scenery
● in-situ subgrade materials can be used in the construction
● the construction is simple and requires no special machinery
● a steep slope with a regular, even surface can be achieved
● bushes and shrubs can be incorporated

REINFORCEMENT LENGTHS

The reinforcement length is dependent on the following factors:

● the height of the construction
● the quality of the foundation and fill materials
● the overall stability of the slope
● the angle of the slope above and below the construction

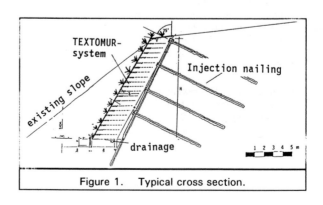

Figure 1.   Typical cross section.

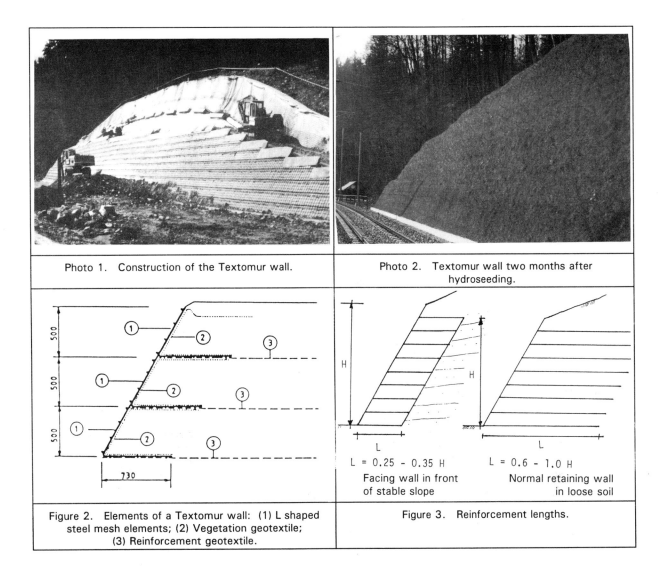

| Photo 1. Construction of the Textomur wall. | Photo 2. Textomur wall two months after hydroseeding. |

Figure 2. Elements of a Textomur wall: (1) L shaped steel mesh elements; (2) Vegetation geotextile; (3) Reinforcement geotextile.

L = 0.25 - 0.35 H
Facing wall in front of stable slope

L = 0.6 - 1.0 H
Normal retaining wall in loose soil

Figure 3. Reinforcement lengths.

For facing walls, the reinforcement length is about 25 to 30% of the wall height, for normal geotextile-reinforced retaining walls between 60 and 100% of the height (Figure 3).

VEGETATION

Grassing of the face of the Textomur system is accomplished using a two-layer special hydroseed. Shrub layers are planted subsequently. The vegetation must be appropriate to the site and the surrounding vegetation. Particular attention must be paid to the insolation and moisture conditions.

Careful grassing and vegetation is an important aspect of the whole structure. It must provide good surface protection and ensure optimum harmonisation with the surrounding landscape.

REFERENCES

Rüegger R., "Geotextile-Reinforced Soil Structures on which Vegetation can be Established", Proc. 3rd. Int. Conf. on Geotextiles, Vol. 2, Vienna, Austria, 1986, pp. 453-458.

GEOGRID BASAL REINFORCEMENT FOR EMBANKMENT ON SLICKENSIDED CLAY CHELMSFORD BY-PASS, UNITED KINGDOM

J.H. Dixon
Netlon Limited
Blackburn, United Kingdom

The Chelmsford By-Pass includes an 8.5 m high embankment traversing a London clay formation containing relatively weak pre-sheared surfaces within the upper 2.0 m.

In 1984 'Tensar' geogrid reinforcement was installed within the base of the embankment fill in order to provide stability without the need for excavation.

DESCRIPTION

The A12 is a Department of Transport trunk road forming a major radial connection with London. At Chelmsford a By-Pass was constructed to alleviate traffic congestion.

The By-Pass crosses the A130 at Howe Green, on an 8.5 m high embankment formed from London Clay with 2.5H:1V side slopes. Locally the formation comprises London clay, which as a result of periglacial activity contains extensive slickensides within the upper 2.0 m. These polished shear planes, which are orientated approximately parallel with the ground surface, are not uncommon features of the overconsolidated London and Gault clays of south east England.

When constructing high embankments over this type of formation the two traditional methods involve excavation below the pre-sheared zone adjacent to the toes of the embankment, followed by either

1. Disposal of the clay and backfilling with imported granular material. This method is awkward if working below the water table. It is expensive in areas where granular fill is not locally available, such as south east England, and also generates considerable haulage traffic.

or

2. Replacement of the clay in compacted layers to re-orientate the fissures [Garrett et al., 1985]. Handling and compaction can be difficult if the clay is wet. In addition remoulding is likely to reduce the permeability relative to the unexcavated clay below the body of the embankment. This could create a high build up of pore pressure below the embankment and cause serious instability, particularly if a drainage blanket is not installed.

Both these traditional methods entail some uncertainty about the excavation depth necessary to remove all pre-sheared material. Work may be further complicated by the presence of existing buried services.

DESIGN

The consulting engineers, G. Maunsell & Partners chose a design for the embankment using basal reinforcement without any excavation. 'Tensar' geogrid reinforcement was specified on the basis of well documented characteristics including soil interaction particularly with clays [Jewell, 1980] and proven performance. The integral grid structure enables the maximum tensile capacity of the reinforcement to be mobilised, minimises anchorage lengths and resists direct shearing of the soil over the reinforcement [Jewell et al., 1984].

A series of 3 part wedge slip surfaces were analyzed at various sections across the embankment width and the reinforcing force necessary to achieve overall stability was calculated. The design factor of safety was > 1.2 and effective stress strength parameters for the pre-sheared clay taken as $c' = 1.5$ kPa and $\phi' = 14°$ with pore

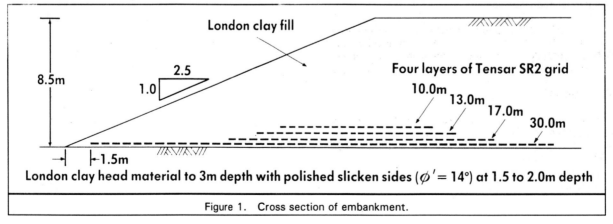

London clay fill

8.5m

2.5
1.0

Four layers of Tensar SR2 grid

10.0m
13.0m
17.0m
30.0m

1.5m

London clay head material to 3m depth with polished slicken sides ($\phi' = 14°$) at 1.5 to 2.0m depth

Figure 1. Cross section of embankment.

Photo 1.   Basal reinforcement in place.

pressure ratio (r_u) = 0.5. The maximum reinforcing force was approximately 110 kN/m which was required over only a limited width of the embankment. Very little reinforcement was found to be required outside a 15 m zone centred below each crest.

'Tensar' SR2 geogrid provided the design flexibility to select the minimum number of layers of reinforcement required at any location. Below the crest, four layers at 250 mm vertical spacing were used; this reduced to only one layer for a significant width of the shoulder (Figure 1).

CONSTRUCTION

Main contractor, Cementation Construction Ltd began installation of 31,000 m² of 'Tensar' SR2 reinforcement in late 1984 using a non-specialist workforce (Photo 1). Earthworks were completed the following spring using conventional equipment. To save time and wastage on site the reinforcement rolls were factory cut to four non-standard lengths to suit the design layer lengths.

PERFORMANCE

There have been no discernible movements since construction and the performance has been entirely satisfactory.

REFERENCES

Garrett, C. and Wale, J.H., "Performance of Embankments and Cuttings in Gault Clay in Kent", Failures in Earthworks Conference, London, 1985, pp. 106-7.

Jewell, R.A., "Some Effects of Reinforcement on the mechanical Behaviour of Soils", PhD Thesis, University of Cambridge, 1980.

Jewell, R.A., Milligan, G.W.E., Sarsby, R.W. and DuBois, D., "Interaction between Soil and Geogrids", Proc. Symposium on Polymer Grid Reinforcement, Thomas Telford, London, 1984: pp. 18-30.

CHAPTER 11

REINFORCED SOIL WALLS

GEOGRID REINFORCED CANTILEVER WALL TO RETAIN SLOPE
LIGHT RAIL TRANSIT PROJECT, CALGARY, CANADA

W.J. Burwash
Golder Associates (Western Canada) Ltd.
Calgary, Alberta, Canada

D. Lunder
Geo-Crete Products Ltd.
Calgary, Alberta, Canada

Expansion of the City of Calgary's Light Rail Transit (L.R.T.) system into northwest Calgary encroached into a hill side necessitating a retaining wall. After review of several systems, the City's Transportation Department, L.R.T. Construction Division selected a precast concrete wall system developed and distributed by Geo-Crete Products Ltd. of Calgary. The wall is reinforced with geogrid UX 1200 (SR2) distributed by the Tensar Corporation. Golder Associates was retained by Geo-Crete to act as their geotechnical consultant.

SOIL CONDITIONS

The hill side which has an overall height of about 30 m at a 15° inclination consists of lacustrine sands and silts overlying glacial till with the water table lying near the interface. The hill side overlooks the Bow River valley which is infilled with a shallow layer of silt overlying an extensive deposit of very dense sands and gravels. The 10 m deep excavation extended through the lacustrine deposit and into the glacial till and was supported by a sloping shored excavation consisting of steel piles, timber lagging and tiebacks (see Figure 1).

GEOGRID WALL SYSTEM

The wall was constructed in tiers with a maximum height of 10 m and four tiers (see Figure 1) with an overall slope of about 50°. Each tier consisted of full height precast panels 2.4 m in width. The panels were reinforced with up to 4 layers of Tensar SR2 geogrid. The length of the geogrids varied and, at some locations, the geogrids were tied into the shored excavation as shown on Figure 1. The number of geogrid panels, their length and vertical distribution were determined using the method suggested by Bonaparte et al. [1985]. Backfill consisted of a well graded free draining gravel compacted to a minimum of 95% standard Proctor dry density. A drainage system consisting of a perforated pipe was provided behind the wall. A geodrain was provided at the joint between panels for additional drainage.

CONSTRUCTION AND PERFORMANCE

The wall has an overall length of 155 m and a total area of 1,280 m². Each panel was placed on concrete levelling pads and supported by inclined rakers on the outside face (see Photo 2). The full length geogrid strip was then attached to the geogrid stub embedded in the concrete panel using a polymer bar threaded through the fingers of the connecting pieces. The geogrid was pretensioned to a predetermined value of 15-20% of design load using stretchers as shown on Photo 1. The granular fill was then placed and compacted and the process repeated at each geogrid layer. To meet the landscape requirements the exterior face has alternating layers of exposed aggregate with deep reveals between the bands. The project was constructed during the period April to June, 1986 and the L.R.T. line was put into service several months later. Follow-up inspection has shown no noticeable movement and the wall is functioning fully as intended.

ACKNOWLEDGEMENTS

The authors would like to thank Mr. Ed. Dobson, P. Eng., Chief Construction Engineer, L.R.T. Construction Division of the City of Calgary's Transportation Department for permission to publish this case history.

REFERENCES

Bonaparte, R., Holtz, R.D., and Giroud, J.P. "Soil Reinforcement Design Using Geotextiles and Geogrids", ASTM Special Technical Publication No. 952 "Geotextile Testing and the Design Engineer", 1985.

Photo 1. Compaction of granular backfill. Note stretchers for pretensioning geogrid.

Photo 2. Wall nearing completion. Note struts on top tier used for temporary support.

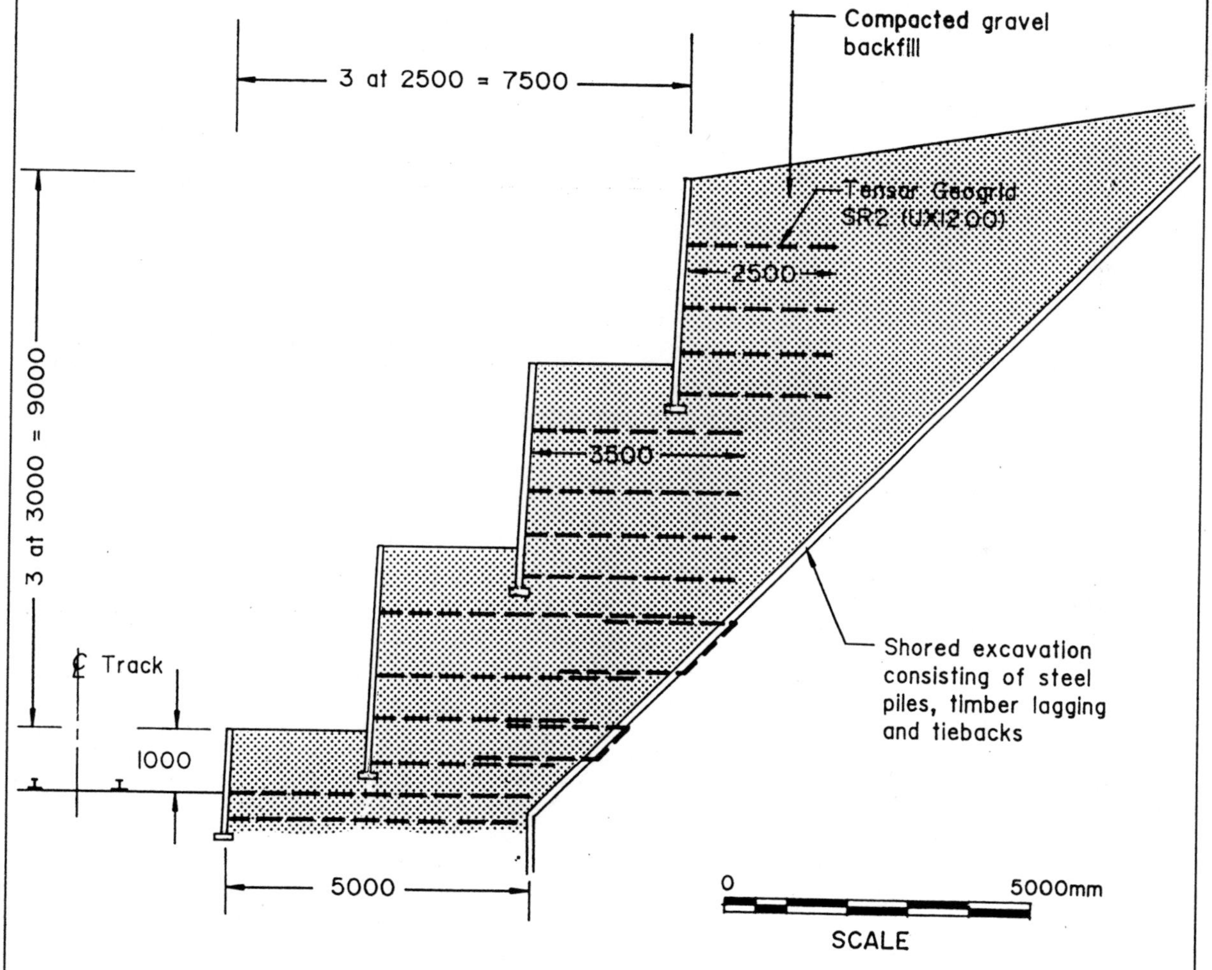

Compacted gravel backfill

3 at 2500 = 7500

Tensar Geogrid SR2 (UXI200)

2500

3500

3 at 3000 = 9000

₵ Track

1000

Shored excavation consisting of steel piles, timber lagging and tiebacks

5000

0   5000mm

SCALE

Figure 1.   Typical four tier section of geogrid reinforced retaining wall for Calgary Northwest L.R.T. Project.

GEOGRID REINFORCED SOIL AGAINST PRECAST CONCRETE BUILDING WALL
BRITISH COLUMBIA, CANADA

H.G. Wilson
Gordon Wilson Associates Inc.
Vernon, British Columbia, Canada

The Gorman Brothers Lumber Ltd. is located in Westbank, British Columbia, Canada, on Highway 97, a four-lane major north/south highway. This site has very little extra space to accommodate expansion of the mill facilities. The highway precludes expansion to the east while to the west are rock bluffs. To the south, the highway meets the rock bluff with more rock to the north.

In order to use the available space to its full capacity, the precast concrete rear wall of a new kiln building was used as the face of a reinforced soil mass supporting a haul road. Alternative solutions rejected by the owner included a cast-in-place wall and relocation of the building.

DESCRIPTION

A new dry-kiln building was to be built with a log haul road on a ramp behind the building. After discussions, it was deemed feasible to locate the log haul road immediately behind the kiln building by filling and reinforcing the soil against the rear wall of the building.

A geogrid-reinforced soil mass was constructed along the 43.9 m long rear wall of the kiln building. The height of this reinforced soil mass varies from 1.8 to 4.9 m.

The rear wall of the kiln building was built using 18 Waffle-Crete panels. These precast concrete panels are 2.44 m wide and, in this particular project, are 6.10 m high. These panels are smooth on one side and, on the other side, have a waffle looking pattern, 1.22 m (H) x 0.61 m (V), resulting from the horizontal and vertical structural ribs. Total panel thickness is 200 mm, including the 50 mm thick face. The waffle looking side was inside the kiln building and, therefore, the smooth side was against the reinforced soil mass. The kiln building has no internal bracing by partitions, only the two side walls.

DESIGN

The design of this structure is based on conventional design for reinforced soil structures including analyses for internal and external stability and overall site stability. The minimum factors of safety used in the external stability analyses were:

- Sliding   2.0
- Overturning   1.5
- Bearing   2.0

Internal stability analyses were used for:

- Tension analysis (checking the geogrid for the maximum tension at each level).

- Wedge analysis (checking the wedge sliding at each geogrid level).
- Embedment length (checking the geogrid anchorage length required behind the slip plane and adding to the length from wall face to slip plane).

The factor of safety on the geogrid mechanical properties was 1.5.

The design surcharge load was zero on the reinforced fill (not accessible to trucks) and 5 kPa on the adjacent backfill strip. Beyond this is a 1.5H:1V slope.

Soils used for this wall were obtained on site and were sandy gravels with cobbles and the occasional boulder. Soil properties used in design were: cohesion 0 kPa, friction angle 35°, and unit weight 20 kN/m³.

The vertical spacing between geogrids was 0.61 m, as imposed by the spacing between horizontal ribs in the Waffle-Crete panels. The geogrid length obtained from the design was 60% of the height of the wall. For example, where the wall is 4.9 m high, geogrid length was 2.9 m.

GEOSYNTHETIC REINFORCEMENT

The SR2 uniaxial geogrid manufactured by The Tensar Corporation was used in this project. There was no consideration made of other geosynthetics for this project.

This geogrid, manufactured of high-density polyethylene, has a peak tensile strength of 79 kN/m and a tensile strength at 2% strain of 22 kN/m. The rolls are 1 m wide, which works well with the 1.22 m waffle structure. Two geogrids were used per panel width (2.44 m), which gives an 82% geogrid coverage. The author had no specific tests made for this project and relied on the manufacturer's test results and the author's previous experience. At that time, it was the fourth reinforced soil wall project where the author has been involved in both the design and the construction. These projects totalled six individual walls.

SPECIFICATIONS AND CONSTRUCTION

The specifications included the following noteworthy points: (1) tensioning of the geogrids to remove mechanical slack prior to fill placement (the author uses a tensioner which he has developed); (2) compaction to a uniform compaction density of 95% of ASTM D-698 (standard Proctor); (3) face panel erection batter of 2% of wall height; and (4) presence of the designer or other approved person during wall erection to ensure compliance with specifications.

Photo 1. Rear wall of the kiln building.

Photo 2. Construction of wall.

Photo 3. Geogrid tab built into wall.

The first construction step was the prefabrication of special Waffle-Crete panels with geogrid tabs sticking out from the smooth side of the panels at appropriate levels. These tabs were embedded in concrete, at rib levels, when the panels were cast. It should be noted that these panels are different from the Waffle-Crete panels typically used with the Tensa-Crete reinforced soil wall system. In that system, geogrid tabs stick out from the panel ribs as the waffle-looking side of the panel is against the soil while the smooth side of the panel remain visible. The concrete panels being part of the kiln building were erected by the building contractor.

Construction of the reinforced soil mass took place in April 1986. Geogrids were attached to the geogrid tabs embedded in the face panels and were tensioned using a stretcher developed by the author. The reinforced soil mass construction was completed in two working days using three labourers, a supervisor, a large rubber-tired loader, and a vibratory compactor.

PERFORMANCE AND CONCLUSIONS

Small movement during construction caused up to 20 mm bow in the panels, which did not pose any problems. Performance of the reinforced soil mass, the wall panels, and the log haul road has been good. As of the end of 1992, no cracking or movement of the panels have been observed.

The benefits of using the geogrids in this project is that they, in combination with the lightweight, precast concrete face panels enabled Gorman Brothers Lumber to create a larger and safer log storage yard by moving the log

haul road closer to the kiln building. More generally, reinforced soil structures provide a fast, economical retaining wall system with an attractive appearance that can be used as soon as completed.

REFERENCES

Non supplied.

GEOGRID REINFORCED CANTILEVER WALL FOR HIGHWAY INTERCHANGE
TRANS CANADA HIGHWAY, KAMLOOPS, BRITISH COLUMBIA, CANADA

H.T. Stamper and A.J. Rushforth
Graeme and Murray Consultants Ltd.
Victoria, British Columbia, Canada.

As part of the 200 km Coquihalla Highway, which is a six lane freeway constructed through British Columbia, upgrading of the Trans Canada Highway No. 1 was required at Kamloops, British Columbia, at the Pacific Way interchange between the two highways.

The Ministry of Transportation and Highways of British Columbia commissioned Graeme and Murray Consultants Ltd. to carry out the detailed design of this highway section to the west side of Kamloops.

This urban section of freeway consisted of three major interchanges and frontage roads through an already developed area consisting of major shopping centres, major retail outlets and service commercial areas.

PACIFIC WAY INTERCHANGE - THE PROBLEM

The interchange at Pacific Way was limited by a major retail store on the north side and service commercial outlets on the south side of the existing Highway No. 1.

A retaining wall was necessary to accommodate the north west ramp of the diamond interchange. The wall was to be 170 m long with a maximum height of 7.2 m. The wall runs parallel to the highway ramp alignment with a minimum radius of 200 m.

The main line and ramp grades were such that the retaining wall had to be founded on original ground at one end and on fill material at the other. Consolidation of the ground and fill material was therefore anticipated under the foundation and the design had to accommodate the resulting movements.

Finally the wall was openly visible to users of the freeway and to the restaurants on the south side of the highway and required to be aesthetically attractive.

SOLUTION

A reinforced soil retaining wall design using "Tensar" SR-2 geogrid was selected. This method uses the geogrid to reinforce and stabilize the soil backfill behind the retaining wall facing.

The wall facing is designed to carry the local bending effects from the back fill pressure spanning between the geogrid anchor points plus an allowance for global bending of the panel. The concrete panels were designed to be made in one piece for the full height of the wall and bear on a strip footing.

A stub geogrid sheet is anchored into the panel when cast and a field connection is made to the soil reinforcing layers as backfill construction proceeds (see Figure 1).

A vertical groove feature was incorporated in the face of the precast concrete panels and an exposed aggregate concrete finish given to the paved slope below the wall.

The backfill was a granular material with a maximum particle size of 75 mm, with less than 10% by weight of particles smaller than 75 μm. Vertical spacing between geogrid layers varies: for the highest portion of the wall (7.2 m), the vertical spacing varies from 400 mm at the base to 900 mm at the top. Reinforcement length is 5.2 m for the 7.2 m high portion of the wall and 2.5 m for the 3.2 m high portion of the wall (with the exception of the top geogrid layer, which is 3.3 m long).

CONSTRUCTION

Construction took place in 1986.

The contractor precast the panels off site. Although he had no previous experience in geogrid wall panels of this type, he was most satisfied with his production rates and costs.

The panels were stepped on a strip footing for end bearing and braced in position with a small back slope (approximately 1%) to allow for elongation of geogrids as construction proceeds. The geogrids are spliced to the wall stubs and receive some pretensioning before being backfilled over.

CONCLUSION

This wall system proved to be a cost effective and aesthetically pleasing solution to the geotechnical and alignment problems of the site.

The client, the Ministry of Transportation and Highway of British Columbia, is pleased with the finished product and its appearance. To date performance has been good, with no signs of settlement or cracking.

REFERENCES

Non supplied.

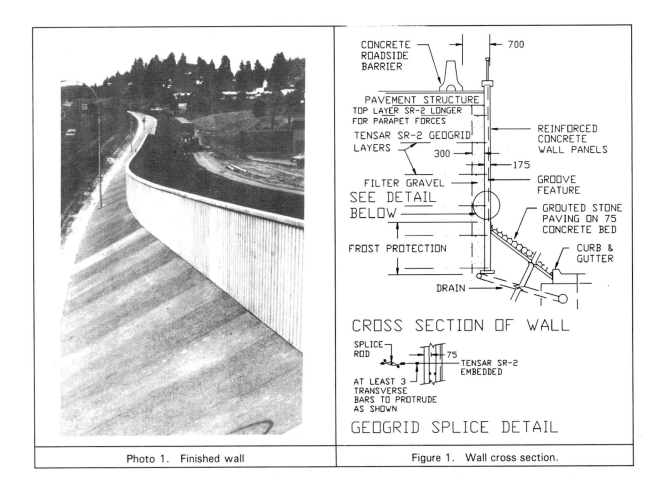

| Photo 1. Finished wall | Figure 1. Wall cross section. |

The following labels appear in Figure 1:

CONCRETE ROADSIDE BARRIER

700

PAVEMENT STRUCTURE
TOP LAYER SR-2 LONGER
FOR PARAPET FORCES

TENSAR SR-2 GEOGRID
LAYERS

300

FILTER GRAVEL
SEE DETAIL BELOW

REINFORCED CONCRETE WALL PANELS

175

GROOVE FEATURE

GROUTED STONE PAVING ON 75 CONCRETE BED

CURB & GUTTER

FROST PROTECTION

DRAIN

CROSS SECTION OF WALL

SPLICE ROD

75

TENSAR SR-2 EMBEDDED

AT LEAST 3 TRANSVERSE BARS TO PROTRUDE AS SHOWN

GEOGRID SPLICE DETAIL

GEOGRID REINFORCED PRECAST CONCRETE PANEL FACE WALL TO CREATE TENNIS COURT SITE KELOWNA, BRITISH COLUMBIA, CANADA

H.G. Wilson
Gordon Wilson Associates Inc.,
Vernon, British Columbia, Canada

At a residence located in Kelowna, British Columbia, Canada, a 30 m by 20 m tennis court was built on a platform located at mid height of a 20 m high escarpment. To create the platform, several geogrid reinforced retaining walls were constructed (Figure 1). There was no consideration of other geosynthetics made for this project, however, the owner had considered cast-in-place reinforced concrete walls and rejected them due to cost.

DESCRIPTION

The walls were constructed with the Tensa-Crete reinforced soil retaining system which uses Tensar uniaxial geogrids and Waffle-Crete precast concrete face panels. The panels are 2.44 m wide and up to 7.32 m high.

The walls on Cross Sections B-B and C-C are 7.32 m high. The stepped wall in the lower portion of Cross Section A-A is 8.53 m high, using two 4.27 m panels with the upper panel set back 1.83 m from the lower one to create a planter. The stepped wall in the upper portion of Cross Section A-A is 7.32 m high using a 2.44 m lower panel and a 4.88 m upper panel, set back to create a planter.

DESIGN

The design of these walls follows conventional design for reinforced soil structures. Three analyses were conducted: external stability, internal stability, and overall site stability.

External stability was checked for sliding, overturning and bearing. Factors of safety were found to be respectively 1.53, 2.45 and 2.

Internal stability analyses were used to design and check geogrid type, vertical spacing, and length. Factors of safety used were 1.5 minimum.

Loads used for design included 1.5H:1V surcharge slopes from the face of the upper walls, 5 kPa surcharge on the 8.53 m wall, a 4.27 m soil surcharge on the lower 4.27 m wall, and a 15 kPa surcharge on the lower 7.32 m wall.

The geogrid vertical spacing was governed by the position of the panel structural ribs in which the geogrid tabs were embedded. The spacing was typically 0.61 m and, sometimes, 1.22 m. The geogrid lengths resulting from design vary significantly depending on panel height and surcharge load. Typically, the length was between 50% and 75% of the panel height, except for low walls where the relative length could be greater.

GEOGRID REINFORCEMENT

Tensar uniaxial geogrids SR2 and SR3, manufactured by The Tensar Corporation, were used for this project at the locations shown in Figure 1. The author had no specific tests made for this project but relied on those made by the manufacturer and his previous experience with the design and construction of 22 walls.

CONSTRUCTION

The walls were constructed in 15 days in June of 1987 with a three-man labour crew, a large, rubber tired front-end loader, and a compactor.

The Waffle-Crete face panels were placed on a cast-in-place levelling pad, using a light crane. The panels were temporarily braced at a slight inward batter (2% of height). While prefabricating the panels, short tabs of geogrid had been cast into the panels. The tabs were chipped out and the main geogrid sheets attached to them using a slip connection and a piece of PVC pipe. The geogrids were then pretensioned.

On-site soils were placed between the geogrid layers and compacted. These soils are tills (silty sand with some gravels and cobbles). They were easy to compact at 95% density (ASTM D 698).

Additional features of the structure include: (1) stepped bases for panels in the direction perpendicular to the panels cross-sectioned in Figure 1; and (2) panels with tops sloped to the adjoining ground angle. A light brush/rake drag finish was applied to all face panels.

PERFORMANCE

Approximately one year after construction, four panels of the stepped wall shown in the upper part of Cross Section A-A started showing distress. Unknown to the designer, a septic disposal system had been built behind these four panels. It was also discovered that a row of geogrids was missing in that area. The panels were removed, a geocomposite drain was placed against the soil, and the panels were reinstalled. A year later, distress was noted in panels located below the tennis court. This was attributed to excess water in the ground due to a leaking pipe. Repairs done in this area were similar to the ones done a year before. During these repairs, it appeared easy to remove panels and replace them. The reinforced soil on each side of the panels being replaced remained virtually intact with only some minor ravelling.

Since then, the walls have performed well.

Photo 1. Wall under construction.

Photo 2. Finished wall with tennis court in background.

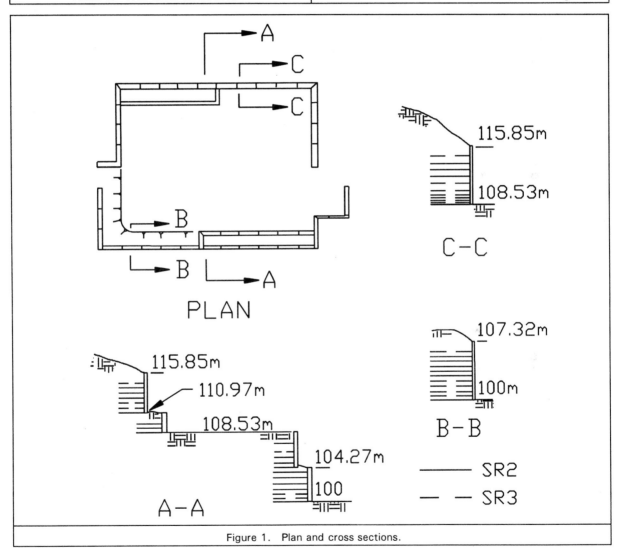

Figure 1. Plan and cross sections.

CONCLUSIONS

This case history illustrates the importance of drainage and construction quality assurance. It also shows that repairs can easily be done.

The benefits of using geogrids in these walls and others are that they, in combination with the light concrete face panels, provide a fast, economical wall system with a pleasing appearance.

REFERENCES

Non supplied

GEOGRID REINFORCED WALLS FOR GRADE SEPARATION
TANQUE VERDE ROAD, TUCSON, USA

R.R. Berg
Ryan R. Berg and Associates, Inc.
Woodbury, Minnesota, USA

V.E. Chouery-Curtis
The Tensar Corporation
Morrow, Georgia, USA

The Tanque Verde Project was the first major reinforced soil retaining wall project in North America that utilized planar sheets of polymer geogrids as the soil reinforcing elements. Forty-six individual walls, equal to a length of approximately 1,600 m, were constructed as part of an intersection grade separation. The geogrid reinforcing elements were mechanically connected to full-height precast concrete facing panels.

DESCRIPTION

The Tanque Verde Road retaining wall project is located at the intersections of Tanque Verde and Pantano Roads in Tucson, Arizona, U.S.A. The vertical retaining walls support the roadway approaches to and retain soil adjacent to the roadways beneath two bridge structures. The walls vary in height from 1 to 6 m. Approximately 1,600 linear m of wall were constructed between December 1984 and September 1985.

The wall facing elements are 150 mm thick, 3 m wide, full-height precast concrete panels, as illustrated in Figure 1. Two 4.7 m high, 3 m wide panels sections were instrumented to monitor performance. The instrumentation program was conducted under the direction of the owner, Pina County Department of Transportation and Flood Control District and subject to approval of the U.S. Federal Highway Administration (FHWA).

Connection flexibility and strength, and panel deflection tolerances were considered when designing the geogrid to panel connection. Looped connections, as illustrated in Figure 2, were used on these walls. This connection detail was specifically designed for this project to achieve maximum flexibility. This type of looped connection has not been routinely used since the Tanque Verde project. The loop portion of the connection was created by casting the ends of a short length of geogrid into the concrete panel. The main geogrid was then inserted into the geogrid loop and pinned in place with a 25 mm diameter, Schedule 40 PVC (polyvinyl chloride) connector pin. Handling and erection stresses, and not in-service stresses, controlled structural design of the concrete panels. The panels were sand blasted to achieve a desired exposed aggregate finish after wall erection was completed.

TECHNICAL CONSIDERATIONS

Design

The retaining wall structures were designed utilizing a tie-back wedge method of analysis and assuming an active Rankine state of pressure and a trapezoidal distribution of stresses from the retained backfill as described by Berg et al. [1986]. The analysis methods are further described by [Netlon; Jones, 1982; and Tensar, 1986].

Economic Benefit

The use of a geosynthetic soil reinforcement on this project was introduced as a value engineering proposal. The proposal was more economical than the use of steel strip reinforced soil retaining walls as originally designed. Costs savings were realized by the use of a geosynthetic in lieu of steel reinforcement because: (1) the contractor cast his own facing panels instead of purchasing concrete panels from the steel reinforcement supplier; (2) 3 m wide full-height precast panels in lieu of incremental height precast panels were utilized and were more quickly erected; and (3) structural details associated with the traffic barrier on top of the wall were changed to reduce forming and casting costs.

Geogrid Reinforcement

The reinforcement used in the construction of these walls was Tensar SR2 (UX1200) geogrid. This material is a high density polyethylene grid structure with a mass per unit area of approximately 970 g/m^2 and a roll width of 1 m. The peak tensile resistance of Tensar SR2 geogrid has been found to be approximately 70 kN/m (tensile strain rate of 2% per minute at 20°C). Extrapolated long-term constant load creep tests on this material have been used to derive a tensile force of 29 kN/m for a 10% strain limit and 120 year creep loading [McGown et al., 1984].

Performance

From a qualitative standpoint, the retaining wall structures have been performing well since December, 1984 when the first walls were installed. The walls are also performing well from a quantitative standpoint based upon instrumentation results from the wall sections installed in October, 1985. Performance was monitored by: (1) surveying wall face movements; (2) measuring strains in the geogrid reinforcement with resistance strain gages and inductance coils; (3) measuring strain in the connection with resistance strain gages attached to the geogrid cast into the concrete facing panel; (4) measuring horizontal and vertical displacements (strains) in the wall fill with inductance coils; (5) measuring pressure on the wall face and vertical stresses in the soil fill with pressure cells; and (6) monitoring effects of seasonal temperature variations in the wall fill and on the outside of the wall with resistance thermometers.

Photo 1. Series of walls around west bridge abutment.

Photo 2. East abutment, instrumented panels in right centre of photo with data collection boxes in front.

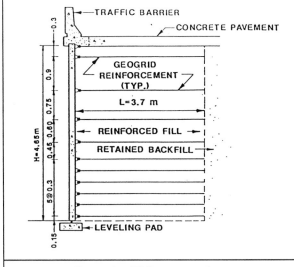

Figure 1. Wall cross section.

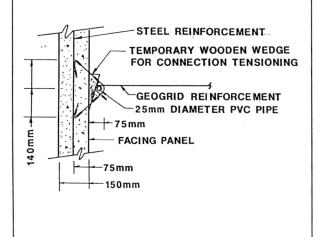

Figure 2. Connection detail.

Results of the instrumentation program have been presented by FHWA [1989] and Fishman et al.[1991], and include the following observations. The top of the two 4.7 m high walls rotated out approximately 65 mm during construction. Peak tensile strains in the geogrid reinforcement occurred adjacent to the face near the bottom of the wall. The strains measured in the geogrid were all less than 1%. No discernible creep effects were observed. Horizontal soil strains were highest adjacent to the face and attenuated with distance from the wall face. Temperature fluctuations within the soil mass appeared to be the result of seasonal variations in atmospheric temperature, and not the results of daily temperature fluctuations.

CONCLUSIONS

The conclusions drawn from this case history are:

(1) the full-height facing panel, geogrid reinforced soil system used on the Tucson project performed within acceptable tolerances;

(2) for full-height facing panel walls with mechanical loop type connections, such as that used on the Tucson Project, and granular wall fill a minimum batter of 1 to 60 appears to be appropriate;

(3) measurements of wall performances to date are not fully consistent with behaviour predicted with the tie-back wedge method of analysis; and

(4) geogrid strains and vertical soil stresses near the wall facing are substantially smaller than predicted by design calculations.

REFERENCES

Berg, R.R., Bonaparte, R., Anderson, R.P., and Chouery, V.E., "Design, Construction, and Performance of Two Geogrid Reinforced Soil Retaining Walls", Proc. 3rd. Int. Conf. on Geotextiles, Vol. II, Vienna, Austria, 1986, pp. 401-406.

Berg, R.R., Bonaparte, R., Anderson, R.P., and Chouery, V.E., "Tensar Geogrid Reinforced Soil Wall", Experimental Project 1, Ground Modification Techniques, FHWA-EP-90-001-005, FWHA, U.S. Department of Tranportation, January 1989.

Fishman, K.L., Desai, C.S., and Berg, R.R., "Geosynthetic-Reinforced Soil Wall: 4-Year History", Transportation Research Record No. 1330, January 1991.

Jones, C.J.F.P., "Earth Reinforcement and Soil Structures", Butterworth and Co., Ltd., London, 1982, 183 p.

Netlon, "Guidelines for the Design and Construction of Reinforced Soil Retaining Walls Using 'Tensar' Geo-grids", Netlon, Ltd., Blackburn, England, no date, 39 p.

Tensar, "Guidelines for the Design of TENSAR Geogrid Reinforced Soil Retaining Walls", TTN:RW1, The Tensar Corporation, Morrow, Georgia, August 1986, 25 p.

McGown, A., Andrawes, K.Z., Yeo, K.C., and DuBois, D., "The Load-Strain-Time Behaviour of Tensar Geogrids", Proc. Polymer Grid Reinforcement Conf., London, 1984, pp. 11-17.

GEOGRID REINFORCED SOIL WALL ON DAM CREST
CASCADE DAM HYDROELECTRIC FACILITY, KENT COUNTY, MICHIGAN, USA

B.R. Christopher
Polyfelt Inc.
Atlanta, Georgia, USA

S.B. Steinberg
Froehling and Robertson Inc.
Sterling, Virginia, USA

For the reconstruction of the Cascade Dam Hydroelectric facility, a wall was needed to allow widening of the access road for construction equipment. Complicating the design was the necessity to support heavy service cranes, as well as required construction of the wall within a limited working area. With these considerations, STS Consultants Ltd., owners of the dam, designed and constructed a geogrid-reinforced soil wall. The wall was fully instrumented to monitor internal and external lateral movement, as well as strain levels in the geogrid elements. The wall was constructed in the summer of 1986 and was monitored throughout reconstruction of the hydroelectric facility. The dam is located in Kent County, Michigan, and has an installed capacity of 1.6 MW.

DESCRIPTION

The hydroelectric facility is located at the centre portion of a concrete wall earthen fill dam. Prior to construction of the new reinforced soil wall, access to the facility was by a service road along the crest of the dam. It was determined that reconstruction of the hydroelectric facility would require access by construction equipment, including a 6 axle, 840 kN crane for placing the turbine and generator. The surcharge stress at the base of the timber mats supporting the crane during lifting was estimated to be approximately 96 kPa. The crane, with its outriggers extended fully, would require a manoeuvring and operating space of approximately 9 m. Since the crest of the dam was only 6.4 m wide, a wall was required to be constructed on the side slope of the embankment to expand the crest.

The decision to use a reinforced soil wall was based on the ease of construction of such a wall in a limited work area, as well as the anticipated lower cost as compared to a traditional reinforced concrete wall. In addition, a wall built with a geosynthetic reinforcement would provide a flexible face and allow for anticipated lateral displacement under temporary, very high surcharge loading. After reconstruction of the hydroelectric facility, a wood facing could be attached to the wall, and the surface above the wall could be used for parking.

DESIGN CONSIDERATIONS

The primary design considerations were the major surcharge loading resulting from the wheel loads of the crane while moving it into position, as well as the dead load of the crane as applied through outrigger jacks.

Design of the wall included analysis of the external and internal stability of the system. The external stability was evaluated by treating the reinforced soil section as a gravity retaining wall and by analysing its potential for failure by sliding, bearing capacity, overturning and overall deep-seated slope failure. The internal stability analysis involved selecting a geosynthetic layer spacing to fit the construction sequence and facing requirements. The reinforcement tensile strength required to resist horizontal stresses from the retained soil mass and surcharge loads and the length of reinforcement to resist pullout at the stress levels were then determined.

GEOTEXTILE SELECTION

For ease of construction, a 300 mm vertical spacing between geosynthetic layers was chosen. To provide a factor of safety of 1.5 against rupture during the crane loading, the required design strength was approximately 14 kN/m and a maximum tolerable strain of 5%. The ultimate strength required using a factor of safety of 3 was 42 kN/m. The geogrid selected was comprised of orthogonal strands of highly oriented polyester that were welded together at the crossover points. The strands were approximately 12 mm wide by 1 mm thick with nodes placed approximately 76 mm on centre in both directions.

CONSTRUCTION CONSIDERATIONS

The wall was built using conventional construction equipment. The original embankment was excavated back to a 1H:1V side slope to key the reinforced soil wall into the embankment. The embankment consisted of a medium dense fine sand with some clay. It was supported on alternating layers of natural, very stiff fine sandy clay and extremely dense fine sand. The sandy gravel fill was manually spread and levelled to approximately 300 mm lift thicknesses and hand compacted, using a vibratory compactor, to the specified density. The geogrid was placed at each lift level with the longitudinal direction perpendicular to the face of the wall. Adjacent rolls of geogrid were overlapped a minimum of 2 grid spaces. At the base of the wall, the geogrid was folded at the back of the reinforced soil section to maximize pullout resistance. The facing support system consisted of overlapping and tying adjacent layers of geogrids. This system resulted in a savings of approximately 1.4 m of material per grid level. The wall construction took 3 days.

PERFORMANCE

Both the instrumentation data and observations of the actual wall performance indicated that the wall performed its intended function with no apparent overstress of the reinforcement. Negligible settlement of the crane platforms was observed during the lifting of the generator. The stationary position of the levelling bar in

Photo 1. Heavy live loads being applied to newly constructed wall.	Photo 2. Finished wall with wood facing.

the crane was also an indication of adequate performance.

Long term data were gathered approximately 16 months after completion of the wall that indicate performance well within the anticipated limits. The data indicate that the applied surcharge stress set up a residual stress in the structure which was not relaxed after unloading. A slight increase in strain was also observed and was attributed to gauge and polymer creep.

CONCLUSIONS

The use of the geogrid-reinforced soil wall allowed the efficient and rapid construction of the wall in a restricted area and provided the flexibility during application of the significant surcharge loads. Unlike a reinforced concrete wall, the reinforced soil wall allowed movement during placement of the live loads, thus providing stress relief to the system. The construction time was cut to less than 1 week compared to a 2 to 3 week construction time anticipated for a reinforced concrete wall. The wall system also allowed the opportunity to choose a facing material to appropriately match the aesthetics of the wall with the aesthetics of the dam. Furthermore, it was easy to work the corner points of the wall into the existing embankment so that the system blended well with the landscape. The total cost of the wall was approximately $19,000, compared to an estimated cost for the reinforced concrete wall of $21,000.

REFERENCES

Christopher, B.R., "Geogrid Reinforced Soil Retaining Wall to Widen Earth Dam and Support High Live Loads", Proc. Geosynthetics '87 Conf., New Orleans, LA, 1987.

Christopher, B.R. and Holtz, R.D., Geotextile Engineering Manual, Report No. FHWA-TS-86/203, Federal Highway Administration, 1985.

Yako, M.A. and Christopher, B.R., "Polymerically Reinforced Retaining Walls and Slopes in North America", NATO Advanced Workshop, Kingston, Ontario, June 1987.

GEOSYNTHETIC CELLULAR CONFINEMENT CELLS FOR GRAVITY RETAINING WALL RICHMOND HILL, ONTARIO, CANADA

R.J. Bathurst
Royal Military College of Canada
Kingston, Ontario, Canada

E. Crowe
Associated Geotechnical Systems Inc.
Milton, Ontario, Canada

A.C. Zehaluk
M.M. Dillon Limited,
Willowdale, Ontario, Canada

The concept of cellular confinement of soils and construction fills to improve their structural performance was pioneered by the U.S. Army Corps of Engineers during the late 1970s. The soil-confinement concept was realized commercially with the introduction of a product called Geoweb, manufactured by Presto Products Inc. [1985]. Geoweb is constructed from 200 mm or 100 mm wide, non-perforated high-density polyethylene strips welded together to give a durable cellular mattress when expanded (Figure 1). The Geoweb material shown in the figure has expanded cells approximately 200 mm by 200 mm in plan view. Typical applications of the material include: road base and track support reinforcement, structural slab support, erosion control and the construction of multi-layered retaining walls and protective barriers.

This paper describes the design and construction of a 3 m high Geoweb retaining wall comprising 520 m^2 of face area. The wall extends along 200 m of property line between the Canadian National Railway mainline right-of-way and a residential development in the Town of Richmond Hill, Ontario, Canada. The retaining wall was constructed to support a sloped backfill which in turn was required to mount a 1.8 m high acoustic barrier between the track and the residential properties.

The Geoweb construction method for this retaining wall was chosen because it offered a relatively quick construction technique on a property with restricted access. The finished structure was also required to be aesthetically pleasing since it is visible from a road leading into residential properties. A typical cross-section of the retaining wall is shown in Figure 2.

TECHNICAL CONSIDERATIONS

The subsoils at the site comprised approximately 4 m of silty clay fill overlying natural subsoils. Over approximately one-half the length of the wall, the subsoils comprised a firm silty clay till and, along the remaining length, a soft compressible organic clay. The structure was founded at the elevation of the natural soils.

DESIGN

The structure was designed as a gravity retaining wall. The dimensions of the Geoweb layers comprising the wall were determined on the basis of stability analyses using conventional active earth pressure theory. Horizontal earth pressures were assumed to be developed behind the wall due to an active Coulomb wedge extending from the heel of each layer through the sand backfill. Resistance to sliding was assumed to be due to friction developed at the interface between Geoweb layers. Large-scale, direct shear box tests carried out at the Royal Military College have shown that interlayer friction angles are controlled by the density of the compacted granular infill [Bathurst, 1987a]. Hence, the friction angle from the results of direct shear box tests carried out on samples of the sand infill at representative densities and normal stress levels was used in horizontal stability calculations. Resistance to overturning was evaluated with respect to the toe of each Geoweb layer. The geometry of the wall was optimized by sizing the Geoweb layers to give a minimum factor of safety of 1.5 against layer sliding and a minimum factor of safety of 2 against overturning. The Geoweb layer widths were chosen based on a range of widths that can be pre-ordered from the manufacturer. The cellular mattresses can be manufactured to any number of cell widths, and

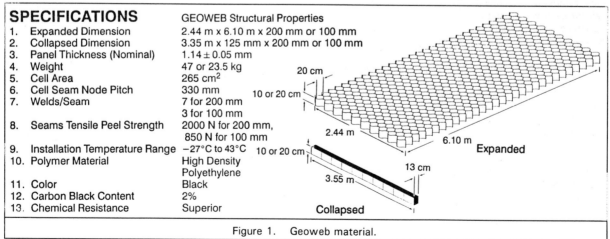

SPECIFICATIONS		GEOWEB Structural Properties
1.	Expanded Dimension	2.44 m x 6.10 m x 200 mm or 100 mm
2.	Collapsed Dimension	3.35 m x 125 mm x 200 mm or 100 mm
3.	Panel Thickness (Nominal)	1.14 ± 0.05 mm
4.	Weight	47 or 23.5 kg
5.	Cell Area	265 cm^2
6.	Cell Seam Node Pitch	330 mm
7.	Welds/Seam	7 for 200 mm
		3 for 100 mm
8.	Seams Tensile Peel Strength	2000 N for 200 mm,
		850 N for 100 mm
9.	Installation Temperature Range	−27°C to 43°C
10.	Polymer Material	High Density Polyethylene
11.	Color	Black
12.	Carbon Black Content	2%
13.	Chemical Resistance	Superior

Figure 1. Geoweb material.

| Photo 1. Richmond Hill wall under construction (spreader frames in foreground). | Figure 2. Typical cross section. |

thus wastage at the site due to trimming is avoided. The wall was initially designed and costed using a crushed limestone infill with an assumed friction angle $\phi = 40°$. Ultimately it was found that a cheaper sand material was more economical even though the friction angle of $\phi = 35°$ assumed for this material resulted in a larger volume of Geoweb. The same sand material was used for the backfill immediately behind the wall to ensure that the backslope was free-draining and easy to compact. The sand was a medium pit-run sand with a top size of 2 mm and a coefficient of uniformity of 2.8.

CONSTRUCTION

Following excavation of the wall base, a minimum 100 mm depth of good quality, free-draining granular fill (Granular A) was placed and compacted to 95% of Modified Proctor to provide an initial working surface. Soft subsoils were excavated to a depth of 1 m and replaced with Granular A. A total of 1,200 prefabricated (numbered) sections of collapsed Geoweb sections was shipped to the site on 3.3 m by 1 m pallets. As construction proceeded, each section was expanded onto a 5 m long adjustable wooden stretcher (2 sections per stretcher) and the assembly flipped into position for infilling. The edges of adjacent sections of Geoweb were interleaved and stapled together to give a continuous composite layer. After each 15 m long section was positioned, sand infill was placed and levelled with a smooth-edged 1.5 m³ bucket. The sand was struck approximately 50 mm above the cells and the stretcher frames removed and advanced along the wall. Any remaining cells were hand-filled and the sand compacted using a hand-held, gasoline-powered vibrating plate tamper. Each subsequent layer of the wall was indented 35 mm from the face of the wall to achieve a 1H:6V front batter. The bulk density of the compacted fill was typically 1,680 kg/m³. The same sand material was placed immediately behind the wall for drainage. In addition, a geotextile-wrapped, 150 mm diameter perforated drain was included at the base of the backfill with the pipes extending below the base of the wall on 60 m centres.

The wall was built in winter and is shown under construction in Photo 1. Despite adverse winter conditions over the duration of the project and restricted site access, the wall was completed in 18 working days using a backhoe, a tracked loader and 5 men. The contractor had no previous experience with this type of construction but

nevertheless had no difficulty training unskilled labour to construct the wall in the manner described above.

MONITORING

A total of 8 settlement plates was installed during construction in order to monitor settlements due to compression of the soft subsoils at the site and compression of the Geoweb/soil composite wall. The plates were installed at the base of the wall and at elevations 800 mm, 1.4 m and 2.0 m above the base.

PERFORMANCE

Readings taken shortly after wall construction was completed showed that the settlement at the base of the wall was about 50 mm at the location of the soft subsoils and that the wall had compressed about 25 mm. These deformations were not visually apparent, and no structural distress of the Geoweb material including the welds was observed. The ability of this structure to tolerate large settlements was anticipated based on the results of laboratory tests carried out to evaluate the compressibility and strength of Geoweb/soil composites [Bathurst, 1987b]. This investigation involved large-scale, unconfined compression tests carried out on samples of sand infilled Geoweb. The specimens were constructed 1.44 m high and 1 m square in plan view. They were then subjected to a series of monotonically increasing vertical loads equivalent to a maximum surcharge pressure of 155 kPa (i.e., 10 m of soil). Under this loading, the 1.44 m high columns compressed by about 25 mm. Nevertheless, no rupture of the Geoweb material was observed even after elevated load levels were sustained for many days.

REFERENCES

Bathurst, R.J., "Results of Large-Scale Shear Box Testing of Geoweb/Sand Composites", Report to Presto Products Inc., Jan. 1987a.

Bathurst, R.J., "Large-Scale Unconfined Compression Tests on Geoweb/Granular Fill Composites", Report to Presto Products Inc., Oct 1987b.

Presto Products Inc., "GEOWEB Grid Confinement System", Technical Data, 1985.

GEOTEXTILE TIED BACK, GREEN, OPEN CONCRETE BLOCK ELEMENT WALL NEAR ULM, GERMANY

H.H. Schmidt
FHT Stuttgart and Baugrundinstitut Smoltczyk and Partner
Stuttgart, Germany

H. Reinschütz and H. Stützle
Betonwerke Munderkingen GmbH,
Munderkingen, Germany

A few soil structures reinforced with metal strips were built in Germany, but there are still concerns with regard to the corrosion of the metal. Therefore, a new type of reinforced retaining wall was developed: geotextile straps tie back the face-elements and reinforce the backfill of the wall. The open precast concrete facing elements allow vegetation to grow in and upon the wall.

DESCRIPTION

Near Ulm, South Germany, a retaining wall was built in 1986. The brand name of the wall is "Remu-Tex-Wand". Single precast concrete elements are stacked on a strip footing in a special order (see Figure 1 and Photo 1). Each element is tied back in the backfill by a geotextile strap (width = 600 mm; length ≈ 2 x 4 m + 0.4 m = 8.4 m). Thus the straps work as anchors. In addition, the geotextile reinforces the backfill and therefore increases the shear resistance of the backfill. Hence the lateral earth pressure will be smaller than with a non-reinforced backfill.

The dimensions of the concrete elements are 1.1 x 1.0 x 0.4 m. The weight of one element is 4.5 kN (i.e., a mass of 460 kg). The length of the wall is 40 m, the height is 4 m. The wall has an inclination of 70°.

The structure was built to provide space for an access road (see Figure 1). The toe of a 100-year old deposit of gravelly and sandy silt, which had a slope of approximately 30°, had to be removed to provide free space for the wall. On top of the slope was a house, which had been built earlier.

DESIGN

The German design procedure for reinforced soil structures is divided into two parts: an external and an internal stability analysis.

In the external stability analysis, the facing and the reinforced soil mass are considered together as a block wall. The analysis includes forward sliding, bearing failure, slip failure, and tilting (with no tension between each layer of the reinforced soil mass). At the back of the block wall only the active lateral earth pressure has to be taken into account.

The internal stability analysis consists of wedge stability analysis with one or more slip planes or a slip circle. The tensile resistance of the straps provide external anchor forces, which prevent sliding on the failure planes or circles. Comparisons of the results related to slip planes or circles have shown that for structures supporting heavy traffic loads, the slip circle method yields the smaller safety

factors and is therefore the safer method.

Further, the tensile force in each strap and the pullout resistance must be considered. For the pullout resistance a coefficient of friction of $\delta = 0.4$ was applied, which is approximately $\tan (2/3 \; \varphi')$.

The facing concrete elements are designed to resist active lateral earth pressure. The active lateral earth pressure was calculated without considering the greater shear resistance due to reinforcement of the backfill with the straps. Therefore, there are hidden reserves in the facing system.

GEOTEXTILE SELECTION

For the anchor straps a woven geotextile (Stabilenka 400) was selected for the Remu-Tex-Wand wall construction.

The mass per unit area of the geotextile is 800 g/m². The chemical composition is polyester and polyamid. The tensile strength in the roll direction is 413 kN/m. The strain at failure is approximately 11%. The strain in a 500-hour creep test at 25% of the rupture force is 4.5%. The allowable tensile force per unit width was chosen at 100 kN/m (with a strap width of 600 mm: 60 kN per strap).

CONSTRUCTION

The wall was constructed in 2.5 days. The main construction steps are as follows:

- Excavation of the temporary slope. Stockpiling of soil for backfill behind the wall.
- Construction of a concrete strip foundation.
- Preparation and compaction of the soil base.
- Setting the first row of concrete elements and looping the geosynthetic straps through the eyelets of the concrete elements.
- Placement of the first backfill layer (400 mm) and compaction with light equipment (Proctor density = 97% of maximum).
- Wrapping the second half of the strap around the fill layer.
- Filling the concrete elements with garden mulch.
- Preparation of the next fill layer and next concrete element row.
- Planting bushes or flowers after completion of the whole wall (Photo 2). In Ulm no planting was done but, as one can see on Photo 3, weeds started growing shortly after erection of the wall.

Photo 1. Construction of the wall.	Photo 2. Completed wall.

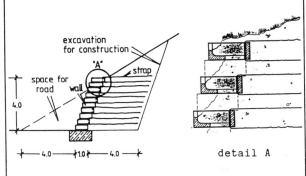

Photo 3. Vegetation in concrete facing.	Figure 1. Cross section of the wall. (Dimensions are in meters).

BENEFITS

This particular case history illustrates the benefits of the technique which may be summarized as follows:

- Very short construction time.
- Versatility with regard to various heights and curvatures.
- Relatively flexible structure, therefore design of block wall (external stability) and facing elements (internal stability) only with active earth pressure.
- No danger due to vandalism.
- No problem with UV-resistance of the geotextile.
- Nice appearance of the light and open structure, especially with vegetation, generally considered preferable, in terms of ecology to conventional structures like closed concrete walls or even stone walls.

PERFORMANCE

Performance up to the time of writing has been excellent.

REFERENCES

"Anwendung und Prüfung von Kunststoffen im Erd- und Wasserbau", DVWK-Schriften, heft 76, Verlag Paul Parey, Hamburg-Berlin, 1986.

"Bedlingungen für die Anwendung des Bauverfahrens "Bewehrte Erde", Allgemeines Rundschreiben StraBenbau Nr. 4, Bundensanstalt für StraBenwesen, Köln, 1985.

"Das Geotextilhandbuch", Schweizerischer Verband der Geotextilfachleute, Verlag Vogt-Schild AG, Solothurn, Schweiz, 1985.

Gudehus, G. and Schwing, E., "Standsicherheit kunststoffbewehrter Erdbauwerke an Geländesprüngen", Proceedings Deutsche Gesellschaft für Erd- und Grundbau, Essen, Germany, 1986.

GEOTEXTILE AND YARN REINFORCEMENT FOR PRELOADING SOIL MASS
A 86 MOTORWAY, NEAR PARIS, FRANCE

P.J. Gigan and A. Hirschauer
Laboratoire Régional de l'Est Parisien
Le Bourget, France

Ph. Delmas
Laboratoire Central des Ponts de Chaussées
Paris, France

A. Hossard
Direction de l'Equipement du Val de Marne
France

Confronted with the difficult problem of construction of a bridge abutment on a compressible foundation soil, the design engineer had to propose innovative solutions due to the cost of traditional techniques. For the A 86 Motorway embankment which is the subject of this case history, the use of horizontal layers of geotextile reinforcement and yarn-reinforced sand facing turned out to be technically and economically sound.

DESCRIPTION

Between the viaduct across the Seine and the approach to the Thiais grade south of Paris, the A 86 Motorway crosses an alluvial valley on an embankment about 10 m high. In that area, an underpass had to be constructed where the foundation soils consist of rather compressible silts to a depth of about 12 m. Geotechnical studies and monitoring of nearby experimental embankments indicated that settlement under the embankment would probably be as much as 100 to 150 mm, which ruled out building the underpass bridge abutment on shallow foundations without improving the soil. Other types of foundations such as piles or rafts were deemed too expensive.

Compressible soils can be improved by accelerating soil consolidation. This can be achieved by preloading. A usual preloading technique consists of constructing a conventional embankment on top of the soil to be consolidated. This technique could not be used for the A 86 Motorway underpass because the wide footprint of a conventional embankment would not meet two essential requirements of the project: (1) the underpassing road had to be kept open and (2) the location where the underpass bridge abutment was to be built had to remain clear. The project supervisor proposed an original approach which consisted of constructing a geotextile-reinforced preloading soil mass with a subvertical face, just adjacent to the soil to be consolidated, taking advantage of the fact that stresses induced in the adjacent soil by a vertically faced embankment are greater than those induced by a sloping embankment.

DESIGN

The geotextile-reinforced preloading soil mass was designed by the Laboratoire Régional de l'Est Parisien with the help of the Laboratoire Central des Ponts et Chaussées, using the Cartage computer program [Gourc et al., 1986]. A factor of safety of 2 on the geotextile tensile strength was used.

The design included 19 layers of geotextile with 600 mm vertical spacings (Figure 1). Each layer was 12 m long: 9 m of reinforcement length and 3 m to construct the wrap-around face. To obtain a face having a batter of no more than 1H:10V, it was planned to use a sliding formwork bearing against the ground.

The selected contractor proposed an alternate solution which consisted of constructing the preloading soil mass without formwork, using instead the yarn-reinforced sand system known as Texsol [Leflaive, 1985]. At each reinforcement level, a Texsol beam was to be constructed and the geotextile wrapped around it (Figure 2).

The same Texsol material was substituted for the natural ground supporting the facing, thereby eliminating the bottom three layers of geotextile and the corresponding earthworks.

Optimization of the reinforced mass design led to the decision to use variable layer spacings - from 600 mm to 1.20 m - and retain the reinforcement length of 9 m.

The geotextile selected for the reinforcement layers was a Stabilenka 150 woven polyester having a mass per unit area of about 260 g/m^2 and a tensile strength of 160 kN/m. The deformation at failure of this geotextile is 16%.

CONSTRUCTION

The work began in August 1986 with the substitution of Texsol for part of the natural ground as a foundation for the facing. A trench 2.4 m deep and 1 m wide was filled with a mixture of Fontainebleau sand with 0.14 to 0.2% yarn, produced by the Texsolair equipment, in which the sand is sprayed using compressed air. The sand-yarn mixture was placed in layers and compacted.

The geotextile, delivered in rolls 100 m long and 5 m wide, was cut into strips 12 m long (approximately 8 m to be covered with compacted silt, approximately 1 m to be covered with Texsol, and 3 m to be wrapped around the Texsol beams). The geotextile strips were laid on the ground with a 300-mm overlap. A first layer of silt 300 mm thick was laid down to protect the geotextile from damage. The construction equipment was driven only on the silt.

The Texsol was produced by the Texsoleuse plant, in which the sand is sprayed by mechanical means. The Texsol, containing 0.12% yarn, was laid down in thin layers, shaped to form a subvertical face, and compacted by a vibrating plate tamper. When the thickness corresponding to the reinforcement layer spacing was reached, the excess yarns were cut off. Then, the geotextile strips were wrapped around the just completed

ISSMFE., Committee TC9 - Geosynthetics Case Histories.

| Photo 1. View of the construction. | Photo 2. General view of the site. |

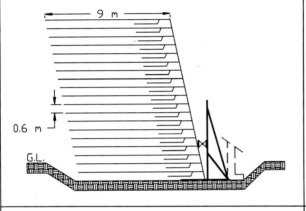

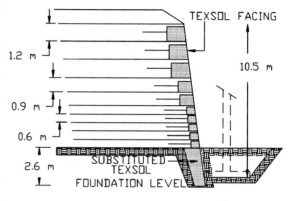

| Figure 1. Cross section of planned geotextile-reinforced preloading soil mass and formwork. | Figure 2. Cross section of the as-built geotextile-reinforced preloading soil mass. |

Texsol beam. The next layer of silt was placed, and a small vibratory compactor was used for compaction near the face, and so on.

Two similar preloading masses were built. The construction of the first mass took 18 working days. The other preloading mass, located on the other side of the road, was completed in 12 days. Total quantities for the two preloading masses are as follows: 1,350 m² of face, 31,000 m² of geotextile, 15,000 m³ of reinforced fill, and 1,500 m³ of Texsol (including 500 m³ used to substitute for the natural soil at the toe of the facing). The verticality tolerances were met, and the resulting structure was very attractive for a work of this type (Photo 2).

BEHAVIOUR OF THE PRELOADING MASS

After two months of preloading, settlement of the foundation soil reached 150 mm under the preloading mass, 100 mm at the face, and more than 50 mm in the centreline of the future underpass bridge abutment foundation. At that point, consolidation of the soil was deemed sufficient and construction of the bridge abutment was started.

Deformations of the face were monitored for more than a year following construction. The horizontal displacements measured after excavation work for the underpass foundation were less than 40 mm.

After construction of the underpass bridge abutment, the space between the bridge abutment and the preloading mass was filled with sand.

CONCLUSION

This case history shows an application that is original because of the concept (preloading next to, not on top of, the soil to be consolidated) and because of the combination of two geosynthetic techniques, horizontal geotextile reinforcement and yarn-reinforced sand. Also, the rapidity of construction deserves to be mentioned. Therefore, from a technical standpoint, this solution can be considered to have been a good choice for crossing this compressible area. The selected solution was also a good choice from an economical standpoint because it was 35% cheaper than the usual technique of building the bridge on piles.

REFERENCES

Gourc, J.P., Ratel, A., and Delmas, P., "Design of fabric retaining walls: the 'displacement method'", Proc. 3rd. Int. Conf. on Geotextiles, Vienna, Austria, 1986, Vol. 4, pp. 1067-1072.

Leflaive, E., "Soil reinforced with continuous yarns: the Texsol", Proc. 11th. ICSMFE, San Francisco, U.S.A. 1985, Vol. 3, pp. 1787-1790.

GEOTEXTILE REINFORCED WRAP AROUND FACED WALL
PRAPOUTEL, FRANCE

J.P. Gourc
Irigm-UJF
Grenoble, France

P. Risseeuw
Akzo Industrial Systems bv.
Arnheim, The Netherlands

The technique of geotextile reinforced soil embankments for retaining purposes, has been widely developed over the last few years. In 1982, however, the type of structure presented in this paper was exceptional in terms of its total height, the slope of the facing, and the spacing between the reinforcement sheets.

DESCRIPTION

General Context

The structure is located in the French Prapoutel-Les Sept Laux ski resort. The objective was to widen one of the roads serving the resort, passing along an existing embankment, so as to improve accessibility to a series of new buildings and increase the number of parking spaces.

The geotextile solution was preferred to a reinforced concrete retaining wall or Reinforced Earth solution, essentially for cost reasons (the Reinforced Earth solution was estimated to be 40% more expensive).

Presentation of the Geotextile-Reinforced Embankment

The design is based on an extremely steep embankment (76% relative to the horizontal). Its length is 170 m and its height ranges between 2 m and 9.6 m.

The embankment material available at the site was graded in layers 1.20 m thick, with successive layers being separated by a geotextile sheet.

The structure was built in late 1982.

DESIGN

The development of calculation methods specific to geotextile reinforced soil structures did not take place until after 1982. At that time, methods available for other techniques had to be extrapolated for a geotextile-reinforced structure. It was thus possible to use the "Reinforced Earth" calculation method or the anchor-tied wall design method proposed by Broms [1980]. The design calculations presented hereafter were derived from the second method. Gourc et al. [1988] have shown that the method used for the Prapoutel wall leads generally to a factor of safety less than those obtained with other design methods, which indicates that the method used was more conservative than others.

The geotextile manufacturing company Akzo Industrial Systems bv. took a direct part in the design and in monitoring of the structure.

Spacing ΔH between the Geotextile Sheets

The design principle is to assume a uniform active earth pressure over the entire height H of the embankment:

$$\sigma = 0.65 \, K_a \, (\gamma H + 1.5q),$$

where: K_a = coefficient for active earth pressure,
γ = soil unit weight
q = uniform working load on top of the embankment.

Regarding the soils forming the embankment, the following characteristics are considered:

$$\gamma = 18 \text{ kN/m}^3 \qquad \phi = 30° \qquad c' = 33 \text{ kPa}$$

It should be noted that the calculation considers the embankment as if it were a vertical wall, which is conservative.

Balancing the earth pressure and the geotextile working strength gives the maximum spacing between sheets, ΔH.

The selected geotextile was Stabilenka 200, a woven polyester product, with a mass per unit area of 450 g/m^2 and a tensile strength of σ_t = 200 kN/m and a strain at failure of ϵ_f = 8% (roll direction). A geotextile working strength of 25% of the tensile strength is used to limit the initial strain of the fibres and creep under load. This gives an allowable working force of σ = 50 kN/m. for an embankment height H = 9.6 m and a uniform working load at the top of the embankment q = 10 kPa, this gives a spacing of ΔH = 1.20 m.

Length L of the Geotextile Sheets

Although the soil-geotextile friction ϕ_g measured in the laboratory is equivalent to the soil-soil friction, it was considered preferable to adopt the value

$$\phi_g = 0.8 \, \phi'$$

in order to take into account the modifications in water content at the site.

The allowable anchor force σ_a is taken as equal to the maximum anchor force with the following safety coefficient applied:

$$\sigma_a^{allow} = \frac{\sigma_a^{max}}{1.3}$$

Photo 1. The Prapoutel reinforced embankment under construction.

Photo 2. Overall view of the completed reinforced embankment at Prapoutel.

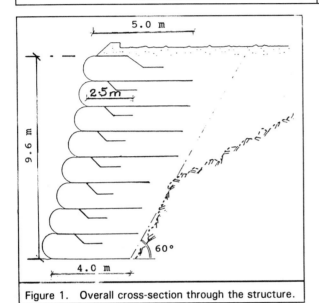

Figure 1. Overall cross-section through the structure.

The geotextile reinforcement lengths adopted on the basis of the above calculations, were 5 m in the upper layers and 4 m in the lower layers.

PERFORMANCE

Ten years after completion, the structure has given no cause for criticism, regarding its overall stability. It is therefore of interest to compare the design assumptions with the actual site conditions. In fact, the public works contractor awarded the contract had not previously used this technique, and encountered a number of difficulties.

Firstly, the soil, taken in situ, was compacted with too high a water content. Two core samples taken during construction, when the embankment height was 5 m, showed a very high water content in the lowest layer of reinforced soil, W = 22.7%, which is close to the liquid limit W_L = 27.5%. This was confirmed by the seepage of water observed on the embankment facing, at the level of the geotextile sheets.

Secondly, specially made angle forms were used for placing the successive 1.20 m thick layers. The work rate was approximately 50 linear m on each layer per day. In view of the steepness and height of the embankment, scaffolding was erected beneath each form, for security reasons. It was thus not possible to compact the soils

correctly close to the embankment facing (impossible to use a vibrating roller).

Thirdly, the measured mechanical properties of the soils

$$\gamma = 20.5 \text{ kN/m}^3 \quad \varphi' = 36° \quad c' = 4 \text{ kPa}$$

differed significantly from the values assumed for design purposes.

All these factors lead to a substantial reduction in the safety compared to that estimated at the preliminary design stage. It is to be observed, however, that this difference had no serious consequences regarding performance of the structure.

The only reservation to be made concerns the facing of this embankment. Because of the steep slope, plant growth after hydraulic seeding proved to be difficult, and a bituminous protection with mulch was subsequently provided. It appears, however that some geotextile deterioration has occurred.

At a few locations on the face, large stones have punctured the geotextile, with no significant soil loss. A slight loss of soil from the facing occurred at certain joints between adjacent sheets. Joints were made simply by overlapping, probably over an insufficient width.

CONCLUSION

This geotextile reinforced embankment is a remarkable example on account of its age and its height, and also because it demonstrates the possibility of using soils of poor mechanical characteristics with an ample safety margin (as is proven by the discrepancy between the characteristics assumed at the design stage and the characteristics actually measured on site).

REFERENCES

Broms, B.B., "Design of Fabric Reinforced Retaining Structures", Proc. the Symposium on Earth Reinforcement, Pittsburg, 1980, ASCE.

Gourc, J.P., Ratel, A., and Gotteland, Ph., "Comparison of Existing Design Methods and Proposal of a New Approach", The Application of Polymeric Reinforcement in Soil Retaining Structures, edited by P. Jarrett and A. McGown, NATO ASI series, Applied Sciences, Vol. 147, 1988.

GEOTEXTILE REINFORCED WRAP-AROUND FACED WALL FOR HAUL ROAD
BATON ROUGE, LOUISIANA, USA

J.N. Paulson
Exxon Chemical Company
Atlanta, Georgia, USA

A 4.5 m high, internally reinforced soil wall was constructed in the Greater Baton Rouge area of Louisiana in 1987. This near-vertical retaining structure constructed across a ravine supports a haul road for a large hazardous waste landfill operation. It is believed to be one of the first applications of a geotextile reinforced earth structure in the South Louisiana area.

DESCRIPTION

On-site soils are described as soft to medium stiff clays indigenous to the lower Mississippi region. The geotextile reinforced soil wall was a total of about 25 m long and crossed a 5 m deep ravine. This depression served as a major drainage swale, which required the installation of large storm water piping through the structure. Because the wall was going to be in use for several years, it was decided to shotcrete the exposed wall face to prevent ultraviolet exposure and potential geotextile degradation.

DESIGN

Design Requirements

The soft to firm subgrade conditions in the ravine area dictated a retaining structure that was both flexible and also keyed into the foundation materials. A geotextile reinforced wall is an inherently flexible structure, allowing for potential post construction settlements. To prevent lateral movement a soil key was constructed at the bottom, below the first layer of geotextile reinforcement.

Design Method

This design was based on the procedures presented in the Federal Highway Engineering Manual [Christopher et al., 1985] and procedures described by Koerner [1986]. Lateral earth pressures were calculated assuming at-rest (K_o) conditions, uniformly distributed below final grade levels. Resultant lateral earth forces were then used to determine the amount of reinforcement required, the reinforcement tensile strength, and the required reinforcement spacing. External stability was checked, and a key was specified, preventing lateral sliding of the entire reinforced structure.

Geotextile Selection

The primary geotextile requirements consisted of:

(a) grab tensile strength (ASTM D4632)   1,200 N
(b) wide width tensile strength (ASTM D4595)   38 kN/m
(c) wide width seam strength (ASTM D4595)   28 kN/m

The original specification called for either a woven or nonwoven geotextile. A woven flat tape polypropylene geotextile, Exxon GTF300, was used.

Geotextile spacing was at 305 mm intervals. The front face was not quite vertical but was stepped back between 50 mm and 75 mm for each lift. This facilitated forming of the front face. The end result was a near vertical wall at an angle of approximately 80°. Embedment lengths were a minimum of 6 m. The wrap-around portion was extended approximately 2.1 m into the fill.

CONSTRUCTION

Construction began by stripping of the vegetation and excavation of soft sediments at the bottom of the ravine. The key trench was then dug and the first layer of geotextile extended down into the key trench. High quality crushed limestone (unit weight of 22 kN/m^3, angle of internal friction of 35°) was used as a backfill material.

The contractor elected to form the wall face using a flat, smooth steel plate, in a horizontal position, onto which a 300 mm high vertical steel plate was welded. Steps that followed were:

- forms were placed on a previous layer,
- the geotextile was laid against and over the form,
- stone was placed and compacted, thereby pushing the geotextile against the form,
- geotextile was wrapped around a stone windrow created by the contractor to tighten the face of the geotextile

This process was repeated for each successive lift. Forms were pulled out perpendicularly to the face and reused at a higher elevation. This construction procedure caused the wall face to remain tight and straight, facilitating the subsequent shotcrete treatment.

Storm Water Drainage

This swale is a major drainage feature for the site area. As such, the retaining structure required piping conduits installed in it to allow for storm water runoff. This was performed using culvert pipes at two separate elevations. Special care was taken during pipe installation and geotextile wrapping to eliminate the possibility of backfill wash out. 50 mm diameter polyvinyl chloride drain pipes were installed in selected locations along the wall face to provide drainage of ground water from the stone backfill.

Photo 1. Key trench to prevent lateral sliding.	Photo 2. Steel forms used to shape face.
Photo 3. Drainage culverts to carry storm water runoff.	Photo 4. Shotcrete applied to the complete structure.

Shotcrete Facing

The exposed face of the geotextile wall required protection from ultraviolet light degradation. A 50 mm x 50 mm wire mesh was draped across the face and anchored into the wall with rebar anchors. The face was subsequently shotcreted and trowelled smooth.

CONCLUSIONS

A geotextile reinforced soil structure was designed and constructed using recognized geotechnical procedures. Both internal and external stability considerations were satisfied.

The haul road has been in operation after 1987 with the geotextile reinforced soil retaining structure performing well. No cracking or displacement of the roadway or the facing has been evident. The use of the geotextile resulted in an inexpensively constructed retaining wall to support the heavy vehicle loads induced by the hauling equipment.

REFERENCES

Christopher, B.R., Holtz, R.D. and Dimaggio, J.A., "Geotextile Engineering Manual", U.S. Department of Transportation, FHWA Contract DTFH 61-80-C-00094, 1984.

Koerner, R.M., Designing with Geosynthetics, Prentice Hall, 1986.

AUTHOR INDEX